A Handbook Series on Electromagnetic Interference and Compatibility

Volume 4

Filters and Power Conditioning

D1496884

Interference Control Technologies, Inc.
Gainesville, Virginia

Interference Control Technologies, Inc.
Route 625, Gainesville, VA 22065
TEL: (703) 347-0030   FAX: (703) 347-5813

© 1988 by Interference Control Technologies, Inc.
All rights reserved.
Published 1988
Printed in the United States of America
95 94 93 92 91 90 89 88   5 4 3 2 1

Library of Congress Catalog Card Number: 88-81460
ISBN: 0-944916-04-X

Editor's Note

During the conceptual stage of this volume, it was recognized that problems usually arise when several authors work independently on the same project. There were, of course, aesthetic considerations of consistency and literary style, plus the usual difficulties in coordination and timing. But the grand anxiety centered around organization and presentation of the subject matter: how to avoid excessive overlap, technical inconsistencies and obvious informational gaps. Whether by design or fortune, we seem to have avoided most of the pitfalls and produced a cohesive product.

In a larger sense, however, the sin of omission is an inevitability whenever one attempts to cover such a broad subject in a single volume. Each of the main chapters (2 through 8) easily could be expanded into one or more separate volumes. Indeed, hundreds of related books, articles and symposium papers are now in print. For this reason, the authors have provided extensive bibliographies which will aid those who require more detailed information.

Because this and other books in the EMC handbook series will be revised and updated from time to time, the reader is invited to address his comments and suggestions to the editor. If a widely perceived need to expand the scope of this book is demonstrated, it may be accommodated in later editions. Your observations will be appreciated and considered carefully.

Jeffrey K. Eckert
Editor

Other Books in the 12-Volume Series

Contents

Chapter 3   Signal Line EMI Suppression
Steven F. Srebranig
Leonard F. Crane

Common Terms
and Abbreviations
in EMC Literature

Prefixes for Decimal Multiples

10^{12}	tera	T
10^9	giga	G
10^6	mega	M
10^3	kilo	k
10^2	hecto	h
10	deka	da
10^{-1}	deci	d
10^{-2}	centi	c
10^{-3}	milli	m
10^{-6}	micro	μ
10^{-9}	nano	n
10^{-12}	pico	p

Technical Terms

absolute	abs
alternating current	ac
American wire gage	AWG
ampere	A
ampere per meter	A/m
ampere-hour	Ah
amplitude modulation	AM
amplitude probability distribution	APD
analog to digital	A/D
analog-to-digital converter	ADC or A/D converter
anti-jamming	AJ
arithmetic logic unit	ALU
audio frequency	AF
automatic data processing	ADP
automatic frequency control	AFC
automatic gain control	AGC

average	avg
bandwidth	BW
binary coded decimal	BCD
bit	b
bit-error rate	BER
bits per second	bps
British thermal unit	Btu
broadband	BB
byte	B
bytes per second	Bps
centimeter-gram-second	cgs
central processing unit	CPU
characters per second	cps
common-mode coupling	CMC
common-mode rejection ratio	CMRR
complementary metal-oxide semiconductor	CMOS
continuous wave	CW
coulomb	C
cubic centimeter	cm^3
decibel	dB
decibel above 1 milliwatt	dBm
decibel above 1 volt	dBV
decibel above 1 watt	dBW
degree Celsius	°C
degree Fahrenheit	°F
degree Kelvin	°K
diameter	dia
differential-mode coupling	DMC
digital multimeter	DMM
digital to analog	D/A
digital voltmeter	DVM
digital-to-analog converter	DAC or D/A conv.

diode-transistor logic .... DTL
direct current .... dc
double pole double throw . DPDT
double sideband .... DSB
double sideband suppressed
  carrier........................... DSB-SC
dual in-line package.......... DIP
electric field .... E-field
electromagnetic
  compatibility .... EMC
electromagnetic
  interference................... EMI
electromagnetic pulse....... EMP
electromotive force .... EMF
electron volt..................... eV
electronic countermeasures ECM
electrostatic discharge ...... ESD
emitter-coupled logic .... ECL
extremely high frequency . EHF
extremely low frequency... ELF
farad............................... F
fast Fourier transform ...... FFT
field intensity.................. FI
field intensity meter .... FIM
field-effect transistor......... FET
foot................................ ft or
frequency......................... freq
frequency division multiplex FDM
frequency modulation .... FM
frequency shift keying ...... FSK
gauss .... G
gram............................... g
ground .... gnd
ground loop coupling........ GLC
ground support equipment GSE
hazards of electromagnetic
  radiation to ordnance..... HERO
henry.............................. H
hertz (cycles per second)... Hz
high frequency .... HF
high-power transistor-
  to-transistor logic .... HTTL
high-speed complementary
  metal-oxide
  semiconductor .... HCMOS
high-threshold logic .... HTL
hour................................ hr
inch................................ in or "
inch per second............... ips
industrial, scientific and
  medical .... ISM
infrared........................... IR
input/output .... I/O
inside dimension.............. ID

instantaneous automatic
  gain control................... IAGC
insulated-gate field-effect
  transistor...................... IGFET
integrated circuit IC
interference-to-noise ratio . I/N
intermediate frequency ..... IF
joule .... J
junction field-effect
  transistor...................... JFET
kilogram .... kg
kilohertz.......................... kH
kilovolt............................ kV
kilowatt........................... kW
kilowatt-hour .... kWh
lambert L
large-scale integration....... LSI
least significant bit........... LSB
length l
length (of cable) .... l_c
line impedance stabilization
  network......................... LISN
line of sight..................... LOS
liter................................ l
local oscillator .... LO
low frequency.................. LF
lower sideband .... LSB
lumen.............................. lm
lux.................................. lx
magnetic field .... H-field
master oscillator power
  amplifier....................... MOPA
maximum.......................... max
maxwell .... Mx
mean time between failure MTBF
mean time to failure.......... MTTF
mean time to repair .... MTTR
medium frequency
  (300 kHz to 3 MHz)...... MF
metal-oxide semiconductor MOS
metal-oxide semiconductor
  field-effect transistor...... MOSFET
metal-oxide varistor.......... MOV
meter............................... m
microfarad........................ μF
microhenry....................... μH
micron (10^{-6} meter)......... μ
micro-ohm........................ $\mu\Omega$
microwave .... MW
mile................................ mi
military specification .... MIL-SPEC
military standard.............. MIL-STD
milliamp........................... mA

million instructions per second	MIPS
millisecond	ms
millivolt	mV
milliwatt	mW
minimum	min
minimum discernable signal	MDS
minute	min
modulator-demodulator	modem
most significant bit	MSB
multilayer board	MLB
multiplex, multiplexer	mux
nanofarad	nF
nanohenry	nH
nanosecond	ns
narrowband	NB
negative	neg
negative-positive-negative (transistor)	npn
negative-to-positive (junction)	n-p
newton	N
noise equivalent power	NEP or P_n
non-return to zero	NRZ
N-type metal-oxide semiconductor	NMOS
nuclear electromagnetic pulse	NEMP
oersted	Oe
ohm	Ω
ohm-centimeter	Ωcm
ohms per square	Ω/sq
ounce	oz
outside dimension	OD
peak	pk
peak-to-peak	p-p
phase lock loop	PLL
phase modulation	PM
positive	pos
positive-negative-positive (transistor)	pnp
positive-to-negative (junction)	p-n
pound (sterling)	£
pound per square centimeter	p/cm^2
pound per square inch	psi
power factor	PF
printed circuit board	PCB
private branch exchange	PBX
P-type metal-oxide semiconductor	PMOS
pulse per second	pps

pulse position modulation	PPM
pulse repetition frequency	PRF
pulse-amplitude modulation	PAM
pulse-code modulation	PCM
pulse-duration modulation	PDM
pulse-width modulation	PWM
quasipeak	QP
radiation hazard	RADHAZ
radio frequency	RF
radio interference and field intensity	RI-FI
radio-frequency interference	RFI
random access memory	RAM
receiver	RX
reference	ref
relative humidity	RH
resistance-inductance-capacitance	RLC
return to zero	RTZ
revolutions per minute	rpm
roentgen	R
root-mean-square	rms
second	s
sensitivity time control	STC
shielding effectiveness	SE
sideband	SB
siemens	S
signal-to-interference (ratio)	S/I
signal-to-noise (ratio)	S/N
silicon controlled rectifier	SCR
single sideband	SSB
square meter	m^2
standing-wave ratio	SWR
super high frequency	SHF
super low frequency	SLF
surface acoustic wave	SAW
surface-mount technology	SMT
surface-mounted component	SMC
surface-mounted device	SMD
television	TV
temperature coefficient	TC
tesla	T
time division multiplex	TDM
transistor-to-transistor logic	TTL
ultra high frequency (360 MHz to 3 GHz)	UHF
ultraviolet	UV
very high frequency (30 MHz to 300 MHz)	VHF
very high-speed integrated circuit	VHSIC
very large-scale integration	VLSI
very low frequency (3 kHz to 30 kHz)	VLF

List of Abbreviations

volt V
volt meter .... VM
voltage standing wave ratio VSWR
voltage-to-frequency
   converter .... VFC
voltampere .... VA
volt-ohm meter .... VOM
watt .... W
waveguide beyond cuttoff . WGBCO
weber.............................. Wb
words per minute .... wpm
yard .... yd

Mathematical Functions and Operators

absolute value .... abs
approximately equal .... $\approx$
argument .... arg
cosine.............................. cos
cosine (hyperbolic)............ cosh
cotangent .... cot
cotangent (hyperbolic)....... coth
determinant...................... det
dimension .... dim
exponential....................... exp
imaginary......................... im
inferior............................. inf
limit.................................. lim
logarithm, common (base$_{10}$) log
logarithm,
   Napierian (base$_e$)........... ln
sine.................................. sin
tangent............................. tan
tangent (hyperbolic).......... tanh

Common Variables in EMC Equations

attenuation constant,
   absorption factor .... α
Boltzmann's constant........ K
capacitance (in farads) C
charge.............................. Q
coefficient of self-inductance L
conductance in mho.......... G
conductivity, propagation
   constant, leakage
   coefficient, deviation...... σ
current I
dielectric constant,
   permittivity.................. ϵ
frequency (in Hz) .... f
impedance........................ Z
induced voltage .... E
inductance (in henrys)....... L
infinity .... ∞

length (coil turn, ground
   loop, etc.) l
length in millimeters .... l_{mm}
magnetic susceptibility ..... χ
magnetizing force.............. H
parasitic capacitance......... C_p
permeability of free space μ_o
permeability of medium
   relative to μ_o .... μ_r
phase constant .... β
radius............................... r
relative permittivity.......... ϵ_r
resistance (in ohms).......... R
rise time .... τ_r
shield thickness................ d
time.................................. t
time constant, transmission
   factor .... τ
velocity, volume................ V
wavelength....................... λ

About the Authors

Leonard F. Crane

Leonard Crane received a BSEE from the University of Illinois at Champaign in 1979 and a Masters of Engineering Management from Northwestern University in Evanston, Illinois, in 1988. He currently serves as engineering manager for Coilcraft, Inc., in Cary, Illinois, specializing in switching power supply and data communication transformers. Mr. Crane presented "Applying Statistical Techniques to the Design of Custom Magnetic Components" to the Power Electronics Conference in Anaheim, California, in February 1988. He also participated in a series of switching power supply design seminars in Taiwan, Hong Kong and South Korea. For Coilcraft, Mr. Crane has also participated in authoring notes regarding local area network transformer applications and transformer design for international safety requirements.

Jeffrey K. Eckert

Jeff Eckert is a graduate of Ohio University, Athens, Ohio, where he received a BFA. He has also done substantial graduate work in computer science. From 1975 to 1980, Mr. Eckert was media director for the University of South Florida at Sarasota. In this capacity, he supervised all non-print media operations, including the campus radio station and recording studio, and produced radio programs for WUSF and National Public Radio.

From 1980 until 1986, Mr. Eckert was features editor for *Evaluation Engineering*, a test and measurement magazine, and an associate editor with *Modern Applications News*, a metalworking journal. During these years, he authored and published over 300 technical articles and contributed book reviews to the *Tampa Tribune*. He presently is director of publications for Interference Control Technologies, Inc., with project management responsibility for technical handbooks and *EMC Technology* magazine. Mr. Eckert is author of Volume 9 in this handbook series and is a member of the IEEE Electromagnetic Compatibility Society, the EOS/ESD Association, the National Speleological Society and the Aircraft Owners and Pilots Association.

Daryl Gerke

Daryl Gerke, PE, is a principal in the engineering consulting firm of Kimmel, Gerke & Associates, Ltd. A technical specialty of the firm is Electromagnetic Compatibility (EMC), an area of electrical engineering that deals with electronic interference, or "noise." The firm was founded in 1978 and is located in St. Paul, Minnesota.

Mr. Gerke received his BSEE from the University of Nebraska in 1968. He has been actively involved in computer technology throughout his career. Mr. Gerke is a registered professional engineer and also holds an FCC Commercial License and a Minnesota Master Electrician's License. Mr. Gerke can be reached in St. Paul, MN, at (612) 330-3728.

Warren H. Lewis

Since 1958, Warren Lewis has held various engineering jobs with Fortune 100 companies such as IBM, Burroughs, NCR and Xerox. During his employment with Xerox, he was a senior member of the technical staff and later was the chief facilities engineer for one division.

In 1976 Mr. Lewis co-founded Computer Powered Systems (CPS) Corporation where he was both the developer of the product line and vice president of engineering and later of technology. The CPS product line was exclusively in the area of computer power conditioning and ac distribution and grounding equipment.

Mr. Lewis retired from CPS in 1984 after the firm was sold to Emerson Electric. He then successfully entered the consulting field and has served such clients as IBM, Sperry UNIVAC, JPL, TRW, Ford Aerospace and many others. Mr. Lewis is the co-author of the FIPS-94 guideline and serves on the IEEE working group as the chapter chairman on the effort to produce the new color book, called the "Emerald Book," which is about electronic systems power and grounding requirements. He has authored several IEEE papers on the subject, most of which have been reprinted in *IEEE Transactions.*

Mr. Lewis also served on the NFPA Code Making Panel #12, Sub-committee for the rewrite of the NEC Article 645 on Data Processing Systems for the 1990 edition. He has also authored several changes to the NEC over the years.

William H. Parker

Bill Parker holds a BSEE from North Carolina State University and is a registered electrical engineer in California. He has managed the EMC Engineering Services Department at Genisco Technology Corporation since 1976. His experience includes designing EMI filters, providing EMC consulting to military and aerospace customers and supervising EMI test operations. Mr. Parker has been active in the SAE and IEEE and is a past national vice president of the IEEE EMC society. He has been teaching Interference Control Technologies seminars since 1972. In his spare time, Mr. Parker is a private pilot and ham radio operator.

Robert Rynkiewicz

Bob Rynkiewicz was born in Milwaukee, Wisconsin, where he earned Electronics Technology and Electrical Engineering degrees at the Milwaukee School of Engineering and Marquette University. His interest in power electronics began in his teens with the design of theatrical stage lighting and controls. He now makes his home in Minneapolis, Minnesota, where he has been involved in the design and development of power conversion and servo control equipment, in the areas of aircraft navigation and flight control, computers, industrial control and consumer products. Other interests include singing with local chamber choral groups and bicycle touring. He feels that technologists should be aware of the historical, social and economic context of their work, as well as the purely technical.

Lon M. Schneider

Lon Schneider is in his eighth year at Corcom Inc., where he is director of engineering and development. In this role he is responsible for design engineering within Corcom's North American division as well as manufacturing engineering, test equipment and the development production line. All of these functions are located at the Libertyville, Illinois, facility.

The author's major technical contributions include the development of analytical methods for designing catalog emissions filters for simplified message processing simulation (SMPS) to specific agency emission limits. This capability led to the development of a large family of SMPS emissions filters which are rated for their performance to FCC Class A and B and VDE A and/or B.

Mr. Schneider's prior work experience includes 11 years in the commercial mobile two-way radio field. He holds an MSEE from Northwestern University and a BSEE from Illinois Institute of Technology. Mr. Schneider is a Senior Member of the IEEE. His family consists of wife, Sandra, and children, Kimberly and Mark. His outside interests include tennis and classical music.

Steven F. Srebranig

Steve Srebranig received a BSEE from the University of Wisconsin, Madison, in 1984. He currently serves as a research and development engineer for Coilcraft, Inc., specializing in RF magnetics, filters and EMI control. He also serves as software systems engineer in the design and development of automatic and automated testing equipment and consumer software. Mr. Srebranig presented his paper, "Automatic Testing with Correlation," at NEPCON 88 in Anaheim, California, and his paper, "Data Line Filtering," can be found in the *Interference Technology Engineer's Master, 1988* (ITEM 88).

Mr. Srebranig and Mr. Crane co-authored, "Common-Mode Filter Inductor Analysis," which was presented to the Power Electronics Conference in October 1985. Together they have published and presented application notes on passive filter design, passive component design and testing methodology.

Edward E. Wetherhold

Ed Wetherhold graduated in 1956 from Tri-State College, Angola, Indiana, where he received a BS degree in radio engineering. Before college, he spent four years in the U.S. Air Force as a radio mechanic and instructor. While in the service, he obtained an amateur radio license, W3 NQN, and since 1979 has served as a technical advisor to the American Radio Relay League (ARRL).

Between 1956 and 1962, Mr. Wetherhold worked for RCA and the Allen Organ Company, before moving to Annapolis, Maryland. Since 1962, he has been employed at the Signal Analysis Center of Honeywell Inc., where he tests communication systems. Because the test procedures require many different detection system bandwidths, Mr. Wetherhold has become experienced in designing and constructing passive LC filters for this purpose. He has had many articles published on LC filters in the electronics trade magazines and in several amateur radio journals and handbooks. He is a member of the IEEE Electromagnetic Compatibility and Professional Communication societies.

Donald R.J. White

Don White, chairman of Interference Control Technologies, holds BSEE and MSEE degrees from the University of Maryland. He lectures and consults in the United States and abroad on various EMC topics and is the author of several definitive books on the subject, including *Electrical Filters: Synthesis, Design and Applications.* He co-authored Volumes 3 and 8 of this handbook series and has published many EMC-related papers.

Mr. White has held positions in government and industry and is a past national chairman of the IEEE Professional Group on EMC. In addition, he is a past chairman of EMC Expo.

Chapter 1

Introduction

by Donald R.J. White and Jeffrey K. Eckert
Interference Control Technologies, Inc.
Gainesville, VA 22065

Although electrical noise reduction practices often appear hopelessly intricate, the EMC engineer's caldron bubbles with only three primary ingredients: grounding, shielding and filtering. The first two subjects are covered in Volumes 2 and 3, respectively, in this handbook series. The third is the topic of this volume.

1.1 Definitions

It is expected that most readers of this book will have a basic knowledge of filter types and applications. However, some may benefit from a brief explanation of terms.

A classic definition of an **electrical filter** is a device which "may be placed between the terminals of an electrical network, electronic circuit, black box or equipment to emphasize, deemphasize or control the frequency components of either a desired or undesired signal which would otherwise be present." For present purposes, both passive and active devices are included, for both telecommunication and power engineering applications. The concept has been extended to include devices which compensate for an extended loss of power, i.e., uninterruptible power supplies (UPSs).

1.2 Passive Filters

The four classes of passive filters described in this book are defined below and illustrated in Fig. 1.1.

Lowpass Filters

A **lowpass filter** is one which allows electrical energy having frequency components from dc up to the **cutoff frequency** to pass with little or no attenuation. Above the cutoff frequency, attenuation increases by 20 dB per decade (6 dB per octave) multiplied by the number of passive elements (inductors plus capacitors).

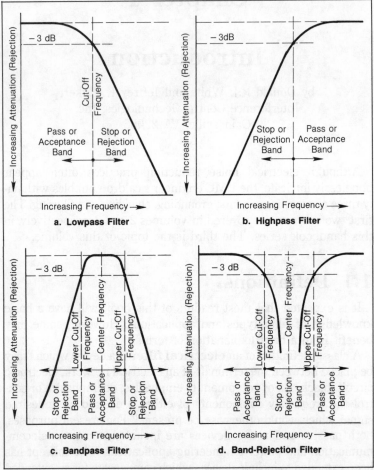

Figure 1.1—Typical Frequency Responses of the Four Filter Types

Highpass Filters

A **highpass filter** is the converse of the lowpass filter; i.e., it allows relatively unattenuated passage of energy above the cutoff frequency. Attenuation in the stopband changes by 20 dB per decade multiplied by the number of passive elements.

Bandpass Filters

A **bandpass filter** accepts energy within a specified frequency band and rejects it outside that band. Thus, it acts as both a highpass and a lowpass filter, with a **passband** in between.

Band-Rejection Filters

A **band-rejection filter**, also commonly known as a **bandstop filter**, is the converse of the bandpass filter. It rejects energy within a specified frequency band and accepts it outside that band.

1.3 Filter Specifications

Electrical filter specifications are commonly based on the performance characteristics outlined below and illustrated in Fig. 1.2.

Insertion loss is a measure of the attenuation provided by the filter in the passband (desired response frequencies). It is the ratio, expressed in decibels, of the unfiltered, desired signal amplitude to the amplitude of the same signal after the filter is inserted into the circuit. Insertion loss is an inevitable effect. The smaller this value, the better, provided there is no penalty in terms of physical realizability.

Band rejection is the mathematical equivalent of insertion loss, but it refers to attenuation in the stopband (unwanted frequencies). Therefore, one may generalize that the higher the band rejection, the more effective the filter, again provided there is no penalty in terms of physical realizability. Attenuation will not be uniform over the stopband range; and it may disappear completely at higher frequencies, due to spurious responses.

Cutoff frequency refers to the dividing line between the acceptance and rejection bands. It corresponds to an attenuation of 3 dB below the insertion loss. Bandpass and bandstop filters have two cutoff frequencies.

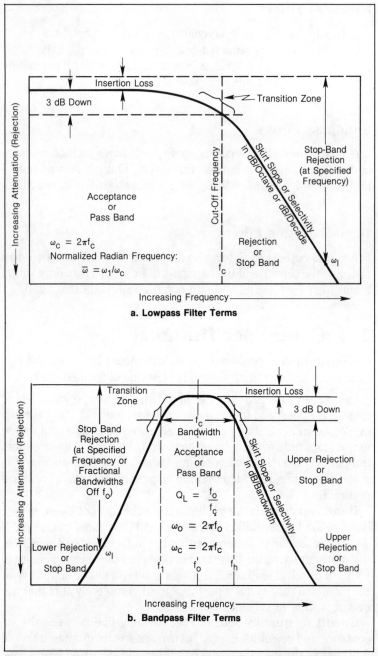

Figure 1.2—Terminology Used to Describe Filter Characteristics

1.4

Bandwidth is the frequency range of the 3 dB passband. In a bandpass filter, this corresponds to the area between the upper and lower stopbands. In a lowpass filter, it refers to the area between dc and the cutoff frequency.

Center frequency is the **geometric mean** (square root of the product) frequency between the 3 dB cutoff frequencies in a bandpass filter.

Q factor is the ratio of the center frequency to the bandwidth in describing bandpass filters. For determining Q factor, the center frequency may be approximated by the **arithmetic mean** between the 3 dB cutoff frequencies when the Q factor is higher than approximately 10:

$$Q = \frac{f_o}{f_c} = \frac{\sqrt{f_h f_L}}{f_h - f_L} \qquad (1.1)$$

$$\approx \frac{0.5(f_h + f_L)}{f_h - f_L} = 0.5 + \frac{f_L}{f_c}, \text{ for } Q \geqslant 10$$

$$\approx \frac{0.5 (f_h + f_L)}{f_h - f_L} \qquad (1.2)$$

where,

f_o = center frequency
f_c = bandwidth (see Fig. 1.1)
f_h = upper cutoff frequency
f_L = lower cutoff frequency

Note that Q factor in this case is the **loaded** Q factor in the sense that the driving and terminating impedance loads are connected to the filter when it is inserted in a network. This is to be distinguished from the **unloaded** Q factor, which is a measure of component performance as used for filter design and fabrication.

Impedance level is the value, in ohms, of both the filter source and termination impedances. Typically, the input and output impedance levels are the same, especially for communication filters in transmission lines. On the other hand, power mains filters, especially those used in 50/60 and 400 Hz generator lines for harmonic rejection, rarely have equal input and output impedances. This is because the internal voltage drop at the generator should be small. Also, where filters are driven or terminated by a transistor, the input and output impedances generally differ.

Power handling capacity is the rated average power in watts above which filter performance may degrade or the component may burn out. **Peak power** is occasionally used to specify power handling capacity, especially where a breakdown of components or a gas inside a hollow transmission line is involved. Peak power is generally more important in filters handling more than a watt.

Another specification one encounters is **shape factor**. For bandpass filters, this is the ratio of the bandwidth at the 60 dB points below insertion loss to the bandwidth at the 6 dB points below insertion loss. The shape factor is often used to describe IF amplifier and surface acoustic wave (SAW) filters. SAW filters having ideal shape factors approaching one are achievable today.

This book also describes active devices for reducing power line conducted noise, including isolation transformers, line voltage regulators, motor-alternator sets, uninterruptible power supplies, etc. Section 8.3 provides the appropriate definitions and descriptions.

1.4 Organization of This Book

As defined in Section 1.1, all filters and signal-conditioning devices perform essentially the same function. However, they cover a wide range of sizes, shapes, types and purposes, and few if any engineers claim to be masters of all filtering techniques. Therefore, the approach of this book is to combine the efforts of several authors, each of whom has particular expertise in a specific field. The book begins with simple, low-power LC components and progresses to more complex, high-power devices.

Chapter 2 covers "Electric Wave Filters for Communication Systems." It is limited to a discussion of odd-degree, equally-terminated Chebyshev and elliptic (Cauer) filters because these provide practical solutions to most commonly encountered communication system filtering problems. Here the reader will find not only useful definitions, application data and performance specifications but several computer programs in BASIC language that help to automate filter design.

Chapter 3 continues with an essay on "Signal Line EMI Suppression," including an overview of typical electrical noise specification limits (FCC, VDE, etc.), local area network (LAN) performance standards and signal line filtering applications including cable and connector selection. Circuit layout, grounding techniques and equipment enclosures are also examined, so the chapter serves as a general "how-to" guide.

Chapter 4 shifts to the power line side of electrical noise control with an examination of "Power Line Electromagnetic Interference." It presents background information on common power line disturbances and their effects, plus explanations of the various coupling modes. It includes both man-made and natural (lightning) noise sources.

The types of interference discussed in Chapter 4 flow directly into equipment power supplies, which are both susceptible to and generators of EMI. Therefore, Chapter 5, "EMC in Power Supplies," is included to cover this specialized area. It details both linear and switch-mode devices, noise coupling paths and various EMI control techniques. Radiated sources are also examined.

Moving from the component to equipment level, the reader comes to Chapter 6, "Equipment Power Line EMI Filters." Installed at the power mains input, these components are essentially lowpass filters which protect computers and other equipment from high-frequency (i.e., higher than line frequency) conducted EMI. The author describes the elements and unique qualities of power line filters and required performance levels for both commercial and military applications. Finally, advice is provided on how to select and install appropriate off-the-shelf filters. A directory of filter manufacturers is included.

The next step up in the hierarchy is addressed by Chapter 7, "Facility Power Line Filters." Used to provide RF isolation between a dedicated power distribution service and the local power distribution system, these are commonly rated for currents as high as 250 A or higher for single-filter units. Common examples of such facilities are shielded architectural structures and unshielded computer rooms. Here the author provides some introductory material, dissertations on filter design and specification, plus a discussion of considerations for filter acquisition and installation.

The final chapter in this book, "Power Line Conditioning," takes on the often controversial subject, which includes not only simple passive surge suppression devices (metal-oxide varistors and the like) but an array of active signal conditioning devices (ferroresonant and tap-switching voltage regulators, rotary power systems, etc.). It also covers power line analysis equipment and techniques.

Chapter 2
Electric Wave Filters
for Communication Systems

by Edward E. Wetherhold
Honeywell Inc.
Annapolis, MD 21401

2.1 Introduction

2.1.1 Purpose

The purpose of the material presented in this chapter is to assist the electronics engineer and technician not acquainted with filter theory to design simple passive LC filters suitable for use in communication systems. **Communication systems** are defined as systems designed for the transmission of sinusoidal-type signals on a line having a specific impedance level. A 50 Ω transmission line connecting a 50 Ω RF amplifier to a 50 Ω load is an example of a communication system for which the filter design procedures are applicable. Consequently, the design applications are limited to passive LC filters having equal source and load impedances where the magnitude response of sinusoidal signals is of primary interest.

2.1.2 Scope

Only the modern design odd-degree, equally-terminated Chebyshev and elliptic (Cauer) responses are discussed because they have optimum magnitude (attenuation) performance and are usually adequate to solve the majority of common filtering problems encountered by the average electronics engineer and technician. These filters produce attenuation over the desired frequency band by causing a mismatch between the source and load. That is, in the passband, the filter appears like a window between the source and load, and virtually all the signal passes through the filter and is absorbed by the load. In the stopband, the filter appears like a mirror, and virtually all of the signal is reflected to the source. Linear phase and other filter types are beyond the scope of this discussion, but suitable references for these other types are listed in Section 2.4 of this chapter.

The normalized filter design tables usually found in the typical filter design handbook are absent in this chapter. Instead, two general procedures of passive LC filter design are considered in the sections that follow. The first and simplest procedure uses tables of computer-calculated 50 Ω lowpass and highpass designs spanning the 1 to 10 MHz decade in which standard-value capacitors (SVCs) are featured. Tables of fifth and seventh-degree lowpass and highpass Chebyshev SVC filters and tables of fifth-degree lowpass and highpass elliptic SVC filters are used when it is desired to minimize calculations and to simplify the realization of the design by using standard-value capacitors. Although the SVC tables are based on 50 Ω terminations and cutoff frequencies within the 1 to 10 MHz decade, SVC designs for any impedance level and virtually any cutoff frequency can be obtained using a simple scaling procedure. In addition, procedures are explained for designing bandpass and bandstop filters based on prototype SVC lowpass and highpass filters.

The second procedure of passive LC filter design requires access to a personal computer (PC). A decade ago, this requirement probably would not have been convenient for most readers, but today (and for years to come), practically every engineer and technician either owns a PC or has access to one at work. It therefore is more convenient to generate the more common normalized filter design tables with a BASIC-programmed PC rather than trying to find a reference containing the normalized tables. Also, the user may specify the exact design parameters desired instead of being forced to use the published values.

A BASIC program for generating normalized lowpass tables of odd-degree Chebyshev designs is presented with procedures for transforming the lowpass designs into highpass, bandpass and bandstop filters. Other BASIC programs generate other Chebyshev data such as attenuation versus normalized frequency and passband attenuation versus reflection coefficient, voltage standing wave ratio (VSWR) and return loss. The BASIC programs conclude with a listing for odd-degree 50 Ω elliptic designs scaled to any cutoff frequency (in hertz) specified by the user. Each BASIC program is short enough to be copied directly from the book and put to use within an hour. The program statements associated with the design parameters are easy to understand and change so tables with different parameters may be generated. For example, although the elliptic design program is written to calculate 50 Ω designs, the program may be listed and the impedance variable changed to any value desired.

Chapter 2 concludes with a listing of references and magazine articles on filter design and related subjects. Those special filter types not discussed in this chapter may be found in one or more of the listed references.

2.2 Magnitude Response Filters

Where the magnitude response is of primary interest, the two optimum filter responses most frequently used are the **Chebyshev** and the **elliptic** (also known as **Cauer**). The following discussion relates only to equally terminated filter networks having an odd number of branches, that is, only odd-degree designs (N = 3, 5, 7, etc.). These filters are suitable for solving the majority of non-stringent filtering problems where it is not essential to use an absolute minimum number of components.

2.2.1 Chebyshev Filters

This filter is named after the Russian mathematician who developed the polynomials upon which the response is based. The Chebyshev response is characterized by peaks of equi-ripple passband attenuation (A_p) that can be selected to be between a minimum of zero (where the response degenerates into a Butterworth response) and a maximum of 3 dB. Very low amplitudes of passband ripple are preferred to minimize filter input VSWR and reflection coefficient which are both directly related to passband attenuation. For example, designs with maximum ripple amplitudes of 0.010, 0.043 and 0.177 dB have VSWRs of 1.1, 1.22 and 1.5, respectively. Generally, the ripple amplitudes are so small that they are swamped by the losses in the filter components. Consequently, passband ripples are not shown in the plots of attenuation versus frequency presented in this chapter. The Chebyshev passband ends when the passband attenuation first exceeds the maximum ripple amplitude, A_p. This frequency is called the "ripple cutoff frequency" and has a normalized value of unity. All Chebyshev designs are based on the ripple cutoff frequency instead of the familiar 3 dB frequency of the Butterworth response.

The Chebyshev stopband response is monotonic; that is, it continually increases with increasing frequency, and its slope is directly related to the number of elements (N) and the maximum passband attenuation (A_p). Lowpass configurations and response curves for N = 5 and N = 7 are shown in Figs. 2.1 and 2.2. Highpass con-

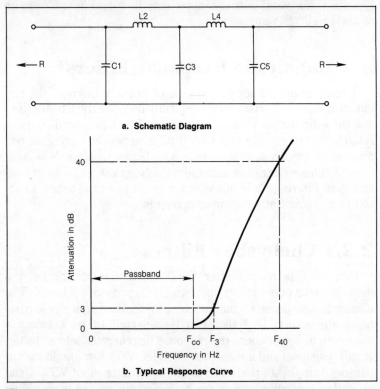

a. Schematic Diagram

b. Typical Response Curve

Figure 2.1—Five-Element Chebyshev Lowpass Filter, C-in/out

figurations and response curves are shown in Figs. 2.3 and 2.4. Only the capacitor input/output configurations are shown as this type is preferred to minimize the number of inductors. Inductors are generally more bulky, more costly and more lossy than capacitors.

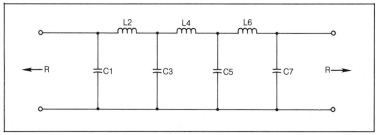

Figure 2.2—Schematic Diagram of Seven-Element Chebyshev Lowpass Filter, C-in/out (See Fig. 2.1b for typical response curve.)

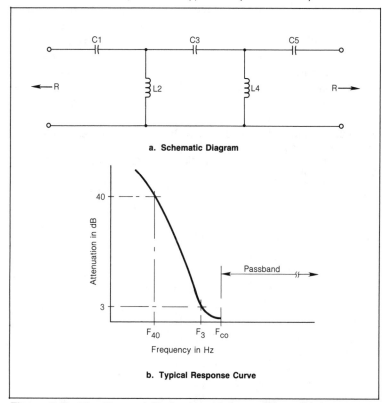

Figure 2.3—Five-Element Chebyshev Highpass Filter, C-in/out

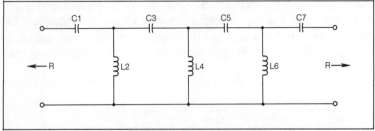

Figure 2.4—Schematic Diagram of Seven-Element Chebyshev Highpass Filter, C-in/out (See Fig. 2.3b for typical response curve.)

2.2.1.1 Table of Chebyshev Normalized Component Values

Chebyshev filters are designed by selecting a particular number of elements and a particular level of maximum passband attenuation that will give the desired stopband response. From a table of normalized element values, the actual component values required for the filter are calculated by scaling the normalized element values to the desired impedance level and cutoff frequency. To use this design procedure, the reader must have a suitable reference con-

Table 2.1—Element Values of Chebyshev Lowpass Filters Normalized for a Ripple Cutoff Frequency of 1 rad/s and 1 Ω Terminations. Use top column headings for C-in/out filter and bottom column headings for L-in/out filter.

N	A_p (dB)	RC (%)	$F_3/F\text{-}A_p$ Ratio	C1 (F)	L2 (H)	C3 (F)	L4 (H)	C5 (F)	L6 (H)	C7 (F)
3	0.0100	4.80	1.8772	0.6292	0.9703	0.6292				
3	0.0437	10.00	1.5385	0.8535	1.104	0.8535				
3	0.1000	15.09	1.3890	1.032	1.147	1.032				
3	0.1773	20.00	1.3006	1.189	1.154	1.189				
5	0.0100	4.80	1.2912	0.7563	1.305	1.577	1.305	0.7563		
5	0.0437	10.00	1.1840	0.9732	1.372	1.803	1.372	0.9732		
5	0.1000	15.09	1.1347	1.147	1.371	1.975	1.371	1.147		
5	0.1773	20.00	1.1050	1.302	1.346	2.129	1.346	1.302		
7	0.0100	4.80	1.1453	0.7969	1.392	1.748	1.633	1.748	1.392	0.7969
7	0.0437	10.00	1.0925	1.010	1.437	1.941	1.622	1.941	1.437	1.010
7	0.1000	15.09	1.0680	1.181	1.423	2.097	1.573	2.097	1.423	1.181
7	0.1773	20.00	1.0531	1.335	1.389	2.240	1.515	2.240	1.389	1.335
N	A_p (dB)	RC %	$F_3 1F\text{-}A_p$ Ratio	L1 (H)	C2 (F)	L3 (H)	C4 (F)	L5 (H)	C6 (F)	L7 (H)

taining the desired normalized table. Another method is to use a BASIC-programmed computer to calculate normalized tables for a given number of elements and levels of passband attenuation. Table 2.1 shows a listing of Chebyshev normalized component values for three, five and seven elements for four different levels of passband ripple. In addition to the normalized element values, data are shown for the associated reflection coefficients and the ratios of the 3 dB to the ripple cutoff frequencies.

Program 2.1 lists the BASIC program used to generate Table 2.1. By changing the DATA in line 10, the user may specify any level of passband attenuation (A_p) that may be desired. If $N > 7$ is desired, the FOR/TO loop in line 90 should be changed to the maximum odd degree of N desired; however, the component designations at the top and bottom of the columns should be ex-

```
10 DATA  .01, .04365, .1, .1773, 10 : REM MAX PASSBAND RIPPLE (Ap) in dB.
20 CLS  : PI=3.14159265#           : REM  RC = % REFLECTION COEFFICIENT.
30 PRINT "Table 2-1. Element values of Chebyshev lowpass filters normalized for a"
40 PRINT "ripple cutoff frequency of one rad/sec and 1-ohm terminations. Use top column"
50 PRINT "headings for C-in/out filter and bottom column headings for L-in/out filter."
60 PRINT
70 PRINT " N    Ap    R C   F3/F-Ap  C 1   L 2   C 3   L 4   C 5   L 6   C 7"
80 PRINT "     (dB)   (%)    Ratio   (F)   (H)   (F)   (H)   (F)   (H)   (F)"
90 FOR N=3 TO 7 STEP 2 : REM CALCULATES ONLY FILTERS WITH AN ODD NUMBER OF ELEMENTS.
100 READ AP : RC = 100*SQR(1-.1^(AP/10)) : IF AP>5 THEN 260
110 E = SQR(10^(AP/10)-1) : V = 1/N*LOG(1/E+SQR(1/E^2-1))   : F3=(EXP(V)+EXP(-V))/2
120 A = AP/(17.3718)     : B = LOG((EXP(A)+EXP(-A))/(EXP(A)-EXP(-A)))
130 D = (EXP(B/(2*N))-EXP(-B/(2*N)))/2
140 FOR K=1 TO N        : A(K)=SIN((((2*K)-1)*PI)/(2*N))
150 B(K) = ((D)^2)+(1-COS((2*K*PI)/N))/2 : NEXT K
160 G(1) = 2*A(1)/D     : REM G(1) = NORMALIZED VALUE OF FIRST ELEMENT.
170 FOR K=2 TO N        : G(K)=4*A(K-1)*A(K)/(B(K-1)*G(K-1)) : NEXT K
180 PRINT N; : PRINT USING " .#### ";AP;  : PRINT USING " ##.## ";RC;
190 PRINT USING "#.#### ";F3;            : REM  PRINTS F3/F-Ap RATIO.
200 FOR K=1 TO N STEP 1
210 IF G(K)>1 THEN 230
220 PRINT USING " .#### "; G(K); : GOTO 240 : REM PRINTS G(K) TO FOUR PLACES.
230 PRINT USING " #.### "; G(K);
240 NEXT K
250 PRINT  : GOTO 100   : REM READS NEXT VALUE OF Ap.
260 PRINT  : RESTORE    : NEXT N : REM RESTORES ALL Ap VALUES AND READS NEXT N.
270 PRINT "N    Ap    R C   F3/F-Ap  L 1   C 2   L 3   C 4   L 5   C 6   L 7"
280 PRINT "     (dB)   (%)    Ratio   (H)   (F)   (H)   (F)   (H)   (F)   (H)"
```

Program 2.1—This program tabulates Chebyshev lowpass filter element values normalized for a ripple cutoff frequency of one rad/s and 1 Ω terminations. The four levels of maximum passband ripple amplitude selected for this program may be changed by listing the program and editing the data in the first line.

panded to account for the increased number of components. The design procedures using normalized element values are explained in Paragraph 2.3.3.

2.2.1.2 Table of Frequencies vs. Stopband Attenuation

To select an appropriate Chebyshev filter for a particular application, it is necessary to know what amount of attenuation is required at a particular stopband frequency, and then select a filter having that level of attenuation at that frequency. Table 2.2 gives normalized frequencies versus stopband attenuation levels of Chebyshev lowpass filters relative to a ripple cutoff frequency of one radian per second (rad/s). For example, if a lowpass filter with a 0.01 dB passband ripple is desired with a stopband attenuation of about 50 dB at twice the cutoff frequency, then a seven-element design is required. This is determined by scanning the 50 dB column and seeing that a seven-element filter with a 0.01 dB ripple will have a 50 dB stopband frequency of about twice the cutoff frequency. Of course, if a higher passband ripple amplitude is acceptable, the attenuation slope can be increased. For example, the

Table 2.2—Frequencies vs. Stopband Attenuation
Levels of Chebyshev Lowpass Filters
Normalized for a Ripple Cutoff Frequency of 1 rad/s

N	A_p (dB)	Attenuation Levels in dB							
		1.0	3.01	6.0	10	20	30	40	50
3	0.0100	1.564	1.877	2.199	2.600	3.795	5.526	8.076	11.830
3	0.0437	1.310	1.538	1.779	2.082	3.000	4.342	6.329	9.258
3	0.1000	1.202	1.389	1.590	1.847	2.634	3.794	5.517	8.062
3	0.1773	1.139	1.301	1.477	1.705	2.410	3.457	5.016	7.323
5	0.0100	1.192	1.291	1.388	1.504	1.819	2.222	2.742	3.409
5	0.0437	1.108	1.184	1.261	1.353	1.613	1.952	2.394	2.963
5	0.1000	1.071	1.135	1.201	1.282	1.513	1.819	2.220	2.740
5	0.1773	1.049	1.105	1.164	1.237	1.450	1.733	2.109	2.596
7	0.0100	1.097	1.145	1.192	1.247	1.394	1.574	1.797	2.068
7	0.0437	1.055	1.093	1.130	1.176	1.299	1.455	1.649	1.888
7	0.1000	1.036	1.068	1.101	1.141	1.252	1.394	1.573	1.796
7	0.1773	1.025	1.053	1.083	1.119	1.222	1.355	1.524	1.735

50 dB stopband attenuation of a seven-element filter with a 0.1773 dB passband ripple is reached at only 1.735 times the cutoff frequency.

Program 2.2 lists the BASIC program used to generate Table 2.2. By changing the data in line 10, any level of stopband attenuation may be specified, but the column headings (in dB) should also be changed. And by changing the data in line 20, any level of passband ripple attenuation may be specified. If N > 7 is desired, the FOR/TO loop in line 60 should be changed to the maximum odd degree of N desired. This program gives the user the capability of evaluating the attenuation response of any Chebyshev filter if the number of elements and the ripple amplitude are known.

If the percentage of reflection coefficient or VSWR is known, the maximum level of passband ripple amplitude (A_p) can be calculated. The following equations show the relationships between A_p, RC and VSWR:

$$A_p = -4.342945 \times l_n \, [1 - (RC/100)^2] \qquad (2.1)$$

```
10 DATA  1, 3.0103,  6,  10,  20,  30,  40,  50 : REM STOPBAND ATTENUATION LEVELS.
20 DATA .01, .04365, .1, .1773, 10    : REM MAX. PASSBAND RIPPLE AMPLITUDES (Ap).
30 PRINT "Table 2-2.  Frequencies vs. stopband attenuation levels of Chebyshev lowpass"
40 PRINT "            filters normalized for a ripple cutoff frequency of one rad/sec."
50 PRINT " N   Ap(dB)    1.0      3.01    6.0     10     20      30      40      50"
60 FOR N=3 TO 7 STEP 2 : REM LN 50 PRINTS COLUMN HEADINGS OF ATTENUATION LEVELS.
70 FOR J=1 TO 8 : READ A(J)     : NEXT J : REM READS ATTEN. LEVELS INTO ARRAY A.
80 READ AP : IF AP >5 THEN 150 : READS AP VALUES FROM DATA STATEMENT IN LN 20.
90 PRINT N; : PRINT USING " #.#### ";AP;    : REM PRINTS N AND Ap.
100 E = SQR(10^(.1*AP)-1)       : REM E = RIPPLE FACTOR.
110 FOR J = 1 TO 8              : REM LN 130 PRINTS NORMALIZED FREQUENCY, W.
120     V = 10^(A(J)/20) : T=(SQR(V^2-1))/E : M = 1/N*LOG(T+SQR(T^2-1))
130     W = .5*(EXP(M) + EXP(-M)) : PRINT USING "##.### "; W;
140 NEXT J : PRINT : GOTO 80 : REM READS NEXT Ap VALUE FOR ANOTHER RUN.
150 RESTORE : PRINT : NEXT N  : REM RESTORES ALL DATA AND STARTS WITH NEXT N.
160 END
```

Program 2.2—This program tabulates frequencies vs. stopband attenuation levels of Chebyshev lowpass filters normalized for a ripple cutoff frequency of one rad/s. Use the reciprocals of the frequencies for highpass filters. The stopband attenuation levels (1 to 50 dB) and maximum passband amplitudes (A_p) selected for this program may be changed by editing the data in the first two lines.

2.9

where,

RC = the reflection coefficient in percent
A_p = the maximum passband ripple amplitude in dB
l_n = natural log

$$\text{VSWR} = \frac{1 + (RC/100)}{1 - (RC/100)} \tag{2.2}$$

$$\text{RC (\%)} = 100 \times \frac{\text{VSWR} - 1}{\text{VSWR} + 1} \tag{2.3}$$

$$\text{RC (\%)} = 100 \times \sqrt{1 - (0.1^x)} \tag{2.4}$$

where,

$X = A_p/10$

For example, for a VSWR of 1.295, the corresponding RC and A_p are 12.854 percent and 0.0723559 dB, respectively.

To use the lowpass data of Table 2.2 in selecting highpass filters, first transform the desired normalized highpass attenuation frequency into a lowpass frequency by taking the reciprocal of the normalized highpass frequency. Then search the table for a design corresponding to the transformed normalized lowpass frequency. For example, assume a highpass filter with a 0.01 dB passband ripple is desired with a stopband attenuation of about 50 dB at half the cutoff frequency. Since the reciprocal of one-half is two, look for a lowpass design under the 50 dB column with a stopband frequency of about two. A suitable highpass design with a 0.01 dB passband ripple and having 50 dB of attenuation at half the cutoff frequency requires seven elements.

2.2.1.3 Table of Stopband Attenuation for a Given Stopband Frequency

It frequently is desired to know the amount of stopband attenuation available at a particular frequency, and for a given number of filter elements and a given passband ripple amplitude. Table 2.3 gives the stopband attenuation levels at 2.6 times the ripple cutoff frequency for lowpass filters of N = 3, 5 and 7 for three levels of passband attenuation. For example, for a lowpass filter having a passband ripple amplitude of 0.01 dB (the corresponding reflection coefficient is 4.796 percent), the stopband attenuation at 2.6 times the cutoff frequency is 10 dB. This agrees with the data in Table 2.2 where a lowpass filter of N = 3 has 10 dB attenuation at a normalized frequency of 2.60. As the A_p levels and the number of elements increase in Table 2.3, the stopband attenuation at 2.6 times the cutoff frequency also increases (from 10 to 75.5 dB). The data in this table clearly demonstrate the effectiveness of increasing the filter reflection coefficient and passband ripple amplitude to obtain a corresponding increase in the stopband attenuation.

This table is also applicable to highpass filters if the highpass requirements are transformed into equivalent lowpass requirements by taking the reciprocal of the highpass normalized frequency. For example, a highpass filter with N = 3 and A_p = 0.01 dB has 10 dB of attenuation at 1/2.6 = 0.3846 times the highpass cutoff frequency.

Program 2.3 lists the BASIC program used to generate Table 2.3. By changing the data in line 10, any value of reflection coefficient may be specified. The reflection coefficient was selected as the variable upon which the table was based so designs could be evaluated in which this parameter is specified. If the ripple amplitude, A_p, is desired to be the controlling variable, use Eq. (2.4) to change A_p into the corresponding percentage reflection

Table 2.3—Stopband Attenuation Levels of Chebyshev Lowpass Filters for a Given Stopband Frequency of $F_s = F_{co} \times 2.6$, and for N = 3, 5 and 7 and a Given Percent RC

N	RC (%)	A_p (dB)	VSWR	Ret. Loss (dB)	Atten. (dB) @$F_s = F_{co} \times 2.6$
3	4.796	0.0100	1.101	26.382	10.0
3	10.000	0.0436	1.222	20.000	16.1
3	15.087	0.1000	1.355	16.428	19.6
5	4.796	0.0100	1.101	26.382	37.5
5	10.000	0.0436	1.222	20.000	43.9
5	15.087	0.1000	1.355	16.428	47.5
7	4.796	0.0100	1.101	26.382	65.5
7	10.000	0.0436	1.222	20.000	71.9
7	15.087	0.1000	1.355	16.428	75.5

2.11

coefficient (RC). Then modify Program 2.3 to take A_p as data. For each A_p value, the corresponding RC must be calculated for use in line 140. A similar procedure may be used if VSWR is to be the input variable. In this case, Eq. (2.3) is used to transform VSWR into percent reflection coefficient.

The input statement in line 50 permits any normalized stopband frequency to be specified. In addition to the A_p and percentage reflection coefficient, the VSWR and Return Loss are also listed. Equations for N = 3, 5, 7 and 9 are available within the program for stopband attenuation calculation. If stopband data for a nine-element filter is desired, the FOR/TO loop in line 120 must be

```
10 DATA 4.796, 10, 15.087,  99 : CLS : REM %RC FOR Ap(dB) = .01, .04365, AND .1.
20 PRINT "To find the attenuation of a Chebyshev lowpass filter at a desired frequency,"
30 PRINT "specify the ratio between the stopband frequency, FS, and the ripple cutoff"
40 PRINT "frequency, Fco.  This ratio MUST BE GREATER THAN ONE.  Input 2.6 for Table 2-3."
50 INPUT W : IF W>1 THEN PRINT : GOTO 70
60 PRINT : PRINT "FREQ. RATIO MUST BE GREATER THAN ONE.  Try again." : PRINT : GOTO 30
70 PRINT "Table 2-3.  Stopband attenuation levels of Chebyshev"
80 PRINT "lowpass filters for a given stopband frequency of"
90 PRINT "FS=Fco*"W", and for N=3, 5 & 7 and given % R.C." : PRINT
100 PRINT " N     R.C.      Ap     VSWR RET. LOSS Atten. (dB)"
110 PRINT "        (%)      (dB)    ----     (dB)    @ FS=Fco*"W""
120 FOR N=3 TO 7 STEP 2 : REM  CALCULATES ONLY FILTERS WITH AN ODD NUMBER OF ELEMENTS.
130 READ RC : IF RC> 50 THEN 320    : REM READS RC VALUES <50 FOR ODD VALUE OF N.
140 P = RC/100 : E = P/(SQR(1- P^2)) : REM  CALCULATES E BASED ON R.C.%
150 AP = -4.34295*LOG(1-P^2)          : REM  AP= MAX. PASSBAND RIPPLE AMPL.(dB)
160 VS = (1+P)/(1-P) : RL = -8.68589*LOG(P) : REM CALCULATES VSWR AND RET. LOSS.
170 IF N=3 THEN 210
180 IF N=5 THEN 220  : REM *** TO CALCULATE DATA FOR N=9, CHANGE THE "7" TO "9"
190 IF N=7 THEN 230  : REM *** IN LINE 120 WHERE THE FOR/NEXT LOOP STARTS.
200 IF N=9 THEN 240  :
210 C = 4*W^3 - 3*W         : GOTO 250 : REM CHEBYSHEV POLYNOMIALS FOR SA WHERE THE HIGHEST
220 C = 16*W^5 - 20*W^3 + 5*W  : GOTO 250 : REM         POWER = NUMBER OF ELEMENTS.
230 C = 64*W^7 - 112*W^5 + 56*W^3 - 7*W  : GOTO 250
240 C = 256*W^9 - 576*W^7 + 432*W^5 - 120*W^3 + 9*W : GOTO 250
250 SA = 4.34295*LOG(1+ (E*C)^2) : REM CALCULATES STOPBAND ATTEN. AT FS.
260 PRINT N; : PRINT USING " ##.###";RC; : PRINT USING "  .####";AP;
270 PRINT USING "  #.###";VS; : PRINT USING " ##.###";RL; : REM  VSWR & RET. LOSS.
280 IF SA>9.99 THEN 300 : REM PRINTS TO ONE DECIMAL PLACE FOR SA>9.99
290 PRINT USING " ###.##"; SA : GOTO 310 : REM PRINTS STOPBAND ATTEN.(dB) AT FS.
300 PRINT USING " ###.#"; SA : REM PRINTS STOPBAND ATTEN.(dB) AT FS.
310 GOTO 130 : REM READS NEXT RC VALUE UNTIL RC IS GREATER THAN 50.
320 RESTORE  : PRINT : NEXT N : END
```

Program 2.3—This program tabulates the stopband attenuation of Chebyshev lowpass filters for a given normalized stopband frequency equal to the ratio of F_S and F_{CO} (F_S = stopband frequency and F_{CO} = ripple cutoff frequency).

changed to stop at nine instead of seven. Since a Chebyshev filter with more than nine elements is seldom used, equations for N greater than nine are not included in the program. If a more abrupt attenuation rolloff is desired, an elliptic design is preferable to a Chebyshev design having more than nine elements.

2.2.2 Elliptic Filters

Most filtering applications do not need the high attenuation (>70 dB) provided by the monotonic Chebyshev response at two or more octaves from the cutoff frequency. Instead, high attenuation within an octave of the cutoff frequency is frequently desired. This more selective response is provided by a filter type known as the **elliptic** because it is based on elliptic functions. This filter type is also known as the **Cauer** in honor of the German network

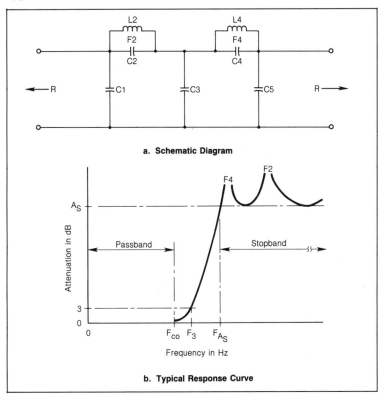

Figure 2.5—Fifth-Degree Elliptic Lowpass Filter, C-in/out

theorist, Prof. Wilhelm Cauer. The more selective response of the elliptic filter is achieved by using resonant sections tuned to frequencies in the stopband close to the filter cutoff frequency. By properly placing the resonant frequencies of these circuits, it is possible to maintain a specific level of minimum attenuation (for example, 45 dB) throughout the entire stopband. Like the Chebyshev, the elliptic also can be designed to have a particular level of equi-ripple passband attenuation.

Figures 2.5 and 2.6 show the most frequently used networks and responses of the fifth-degree elliptic lowpass and highpass filters, respectively. These networks are derived from the fifth-degree Chebyshev lowpass and highpass filters shown in Figs. 2.1a and 2.3a, respectively. The transmission zeroes (frequencies of maximum attenuation) responsible for the selectivity of the elliptic lowpass response are provided by parallel resonant circuits in the series arms of the networks as shown in Fig. 2.5a. In the highpass network, the transmission zeroes are provided by series resonant

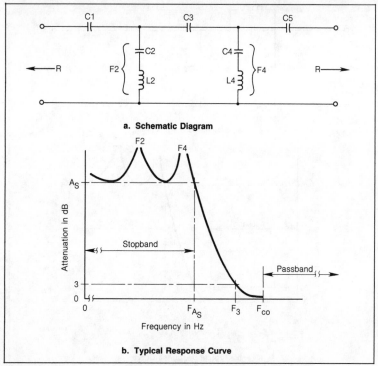

a. **Schematic Diagram**

b. **Typical Response Curve**

Figure 2.6—Fifth-Degree Elliptic Highpass Filter, C-in/out

circuits in the shunt arms as shown in Fig. 2.6a. The close relationship between the elliptic and Chebyshev networks becomes more obvious with the explanation that when the resonating capacitors, C2 and C4, of these elliptic networks approach zero capacity for the lowpass and infinite capacity for the highpass, the networks degenerate into the Chebyshev lowpass and highpass networks from which the elliptic networks were derived. Elliptic filters of higher degree are derived in a similar manner from correspondingly higher degree Chebyshev designs.

Unlike the Chebyshev designs, which have repeating element values, the elliptic designs have all dissimilar element values and are not as convenient to realize. In spite of this inconvenience, the elliptic response is often preferred because of its superior magnitude response and its design versatility (the ability to specify a maximum passband ripple amplitude and a minimum level of stopband attenuation).

2.2.2.1 Standard Odd-Degree Elliptic Designs

The odd-degree elliptic designs discussed in this chapter are the fifth (see Figs. 2.5 and 2.6) and the seventh (see Fig. 2.7). The fifth-degree elliptic lowpass and highpass computer-calculated 50 Ω designs are tabulated in Tables 2.7 and 2.10, respectively (see Sections 2.3.1.1 and 2.3.1.2). The fact that the odd-numbered (nonresonating) capacitors in these designs have standard values alleviates somewhat the inconvenience of realizing these special designs. Scaling procedures allow these tabulated standard-value capacitor designs to be used for any impedance level and for virtually any cutoff frequency. Also, Program 2.4 lists a BASIC program that designs odd-degree lowpass or highpass elliptic filters that are automatically scaled to any desired impedance level and cutoff frequency. Consequently, there is no need for normalized design tables for the elliptic filter. A special elliptic design of the seventh degree is discussed in the next paragraph.

2.2.2.2 Special Seventh-Degree Elliptic Filter Designs where L4 = L6

There is a special group of seventh-degree elliptic filter designs where the values of L4 and L6 are identical. In some cases, this unique characteristic may be useful. For example, in the audio frequency range, the most convenient impedance level is between 400 and 1,000 Ω, and it may be more convenient to use standard-value inductors instead of standard-value capacitors. If so, the fact that L4 = L6 may have advantages in realizing the filter if the other filter parameters, such as reflection coefficient, the $F - A_s/F_{co}$ ratio (an indication of the relative abruptness of the attenuation rise), and the minimum stopband attenuation level, A_s, are satisfactory.

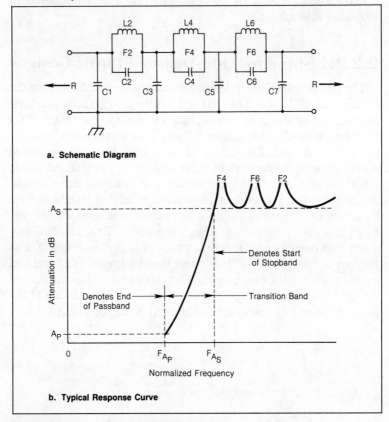

a. **Schematic Diagram**

b. **Typical Response Curve**

Figure 2.7—Seventh-Degree Elliptic Lowpass Filter

Figure 2.7a shows the schematic diagram of the seventh-degree elliptic filter, and Fig. 2.7b shows the typical filter response curve. All the design parameters of this unique family are listed in Table 2.4a, where seven different designs have reflection coefficients ranging from about 8 to 15 percent. The A_s levels vary from 45 to 64 dB, and this range is suitable for audio filter designs. Table 2.4b lists component values normalized to a ripple cutoff frequency of one rad/s and 1 Ω terminations. The reciprocals of the component values in Table 2.4b can be used for designing highpass filters. In this case, all the odd-value capacitors in Fig. 2.1a change from shunt to series elements, and the parallel-tuned series circuits (C2 and L2, etc.) become series-tuned shunt circuits. An example will demonstrate an application of this design data where L4 and L6 have the same values.

Assume five high-Q encapsulated 22 mH toroidal inductors are available, and it is desired to use them to construct a lowpass filter to limit the bandwidth of speech signals to a maximum of about

Table 2.4—Seventh-Degree Elliptic Filter Designs where L4 = L6

a. Design Parameters and Normalized Frequencies

Design No.	RC (%)	F-A_s	A_s (dB)	A_p (dB)	F_2	F_4	F_6	L2/L4 Ratio
1	15.361	1.37033	64.496	0.10370	2.73428	1.39413	1.64044	1.250
2	12.797	1.31661	59.159	0.07171	2.58181	1.33828	1.56426	1.300
3	11.559	1.28879	56.185	0.95842	2.50079	1.30931	1.52428	1.333
4	10.232	1.25728	52.609	0.04571	2.40690	1.27644	1.47847	1.380
5	9.769	1.24585	51.249	0.04164	2.37219	1.26450	1.46170	1.400
6	8.981	1.22575	48.768	0.03517	2.31017	1.24348	1.43195	1.440
7	8.058	1.20121	45.559	0.02829	2.23250	1.21777	1.39515	1.500

b. Component Values of Seventh-Degree Elliptic Filters where L4 = L6, Normalized to a Ripple Cuttoff Frequency of 1 rad/s and 1 Ω Terminations

Design No.	C1 (F)	C2 (F)	C3 (F)	C4 (F)	C5 (F)	C6 (F)	C7 (F)	L2 (H)	L4, L6 (H)	L2/L4 Ratio
1	1.106	0.1022	1.678	0.4913	1.532	0.3548	0.9035	1.3091	1.0473	1.250
2	1.012	0.1151	1.568	0.5569	1.414	0.4076	0.7878	1.3034	1.0026	1.300
3	0.9645	0.1234	1.509	0.6002	1.352	0.4428	0.7255	1.2959	0.97194	1.333
4	0.9099	0.1345	0.1441	0.6601	1.279	0.4920	0.6519	1.2832	0.92985	1.380
5	0.8899	0.1391	0.1415	0.6855	1.252	0.5130	0.6241	1.2773	0.91241	1.400
6	0.8545	0.1481	1.369	0.7361	1.204	0.5551	0.5734	1.2652	0.87861	1.440
7	0.8102	0.1609	1.310	0.8112	1.143	0.6180	0.5076	1.2469	0.83127	1.500

3 kHz. Because the inductors are encapsulated, turns cannot be removed, and the inductors must be used as they are.

Examining the L2/L4 ratios available in Table 2.4, the 1.500 ratio appears promising. For example, L4 and L6 could both be separate 22 mH inductors, and the 33 mH value of L2 could be made from a combination of a single 22 mH inductor connected in series with the remaining two 22 mH inductors in parallel. The L2/L4 ratio requirement of 1.500 is then fulfilled, and design no. 7 can be used. Of course, using three 22 mH inductors for L2 is justifiable only if it is necessary that the inductor requirements be immediately satisfied. This may be the case when it is desired that a prototype design be constructed as soon as possible to verify by operation that the filter performance will be adequate. A review of the parameters of design no. 7 indicates that the design will be satisfactory. That is, the 8.058 percent reflection coefficient, the 1.20 $F - A_s$ and the 45.56 dB A_s are all satisfactory for this audio filtering application.

The next step is to select a cutoff frequency and a suitable impedance level. Because frequencies above 3 kHz are not required for speech intelligibility, the lowpass filter can have a cutoff frequency somewhere between 2,800 and 3,200 Hz, and the exact cutoff frequency is selected to get the most convenient impedance level. Some trial calculations using common audio circuit impedance levels quickly allow a suitable compromise to be reached. As a start, assume an impedance level of 500 Ω and find the corresponding cutoff frequency. If the cutoff frequency is close enough to 3 kHz, it will be used as a basis for the lowpass design.

The basic inductance scaling equation is: $L' = L \times R/(2 \times \pi \times F)$, where L' is the scaled inductance in henries, L is the normalized inductance in henries, R is the impedance level in ohms, and F is the ripple cutoff frequency in hertz. From design no. 7, L4 = 0.83127. The desired scaled value of L'4 is to be 22 mH, and R is to be 500 Ω. The scaling equation is arranged to solve for the ripple cutoff frequency, F in hertz:

$$F(Hz) = L4 \times R/(2 \times \pi \times L'4)$$

$$= 0.83127 \times 500/(2 \times \pi \times 22 \times 10^{-3})$$

$$F(kHz) = 415.635/138.23 = 3.007 \text{ kHz}$$

Thus, the 500 Ω impedance level is satisfactory because it gives a cutoff frequency close to 3 kHz. Therefore, 500 Ω will be used to calculate a lowpass filter using the normalized data of design no. 7.

The inductance and capacitance scaling factors (L_s and C_s) are calculated based on a 500 Ω impedance level and a 3,007 Hz ripple-cutoff frequency:

$$L_s = R/(2 \times \pi \times F) = 500/(2 \times \pi \times 3,007)$$

$$= 26.464 \times 10^{-3}$$

$$C_s = 1/(R \times 2 \times \pi \times F) = 1/(500 \times 2 \times \pi \times 3,007)$$

$$= 0.10586 \times 10^{-6}$$

The scaled inductance values of L'2, L'4 and L'6 are calculated by multiplying the normalized inductance values of design no. 7 by L_s:

$$L'2 = 1.2469 \times 26.464 \times 10^{-3} = 33 \text{ mH}$$

$$L'4 \text{ and } L'6 = 0.83127 \times 26.464 \times 10^{-3} = 22 \text{ mH}$$

The scaled capacitance values are calculated by multiplying the normalized capacitance values of design no. 7 by C_s:

$$C'1 = 0.8102 \times 0.10586 \times 10^{-6} = 0.08577 \text{ } \mu F,$$

$$C'2 = 0.1609 \times 0.10586 \times 10^{-6} = 0.01703 \text{ } \mu F$$

$$C'3 = 1.310 \times 0.10586 \times 10^{-6} = 0.1387 \text{ } \mu F$$

The remaining C-values are calculated in the same manner.

The scaled frequencies of $F' - A_s$, F'_2, F'_4 and F'_6 are calculated by multiplying the normalized values of design no. 7 by the 3.007 kHz ripple cutoff frequency:

$$F'_{co} = 1.00000 \times 3.007 \text{ kHz} = 3.007 \text{ kHz}$$

$$F' - A_s = 1.20121 \times 3.007 \text{ kHz} = 3.612 \text{ kHz}$$

$$F'_2 = 2.23250 \times 3.007 \text{ kHz} = 6.713 \text{ kHz}$$

$$F'_4 = 1.21777 \times 3.007 \text{ kHz} = 3.662 \text{ kHz}$$

$$F'_6 = 1.39515 \times 3.007 \text{ kHz} = 4.1952 \text{ kHz}$$

The RC, A_s and A_p values of design no. 7 are copied directly from Table 2.4a. This concludes the calculations associated with the lowpass speech filter in which L4 and L6 have the same value.

2.3 Simplified Chebyshev and Elliptic Filter Design

In the recent past, all modern design procedures for lowpass, highpass, bandpass and bandstop filters required the scaling and transformation of normalized lowpass values into a design having the desired characteristics. Although the scaling and transformation procedures were relatively straightforward, one had to have available an appropriate reference and then perform the scaling and transformation calculations without error. Invariably, the calculated capacitor values would be nonstandard, thus unnecessarily complicating the filter construction. In this section, a new and simplified method of modern filter design will be explained in which tables of computer-calculated 50 Ω standard-value capacitor (SVC) filter designs are used to obtain a suitable filter for applications where the attenuation response is of primary interest. All lowpass and highpass designs are of the capacitor input/output configuration to minimize the number of inductors.

Because of the increased availability of the personal computer, it is now feasible for the average electronics engineer and technician to use this tool to further refine the SVC design procedure. Instead of being restricted to only the exact SVC values of a particular Chebyshev design, a BASIC computer program calculates a unique design based on the actual capacitor values on hand. Another BASIC computer program calculates odd-order elliptic filters scaled to the desired performance parameters. For the more unusual designs requiring special phase or impulse responses or the less common configurations, one or two of the references in Section 4 must be used. But for the majority of non-stringent filtering requirements, the filter design procedures discussed in this section will suffice.

2.3.1 Filter Design Using Standard-Value Capacitor Tables

The passive LC equally-terminated filter is optimum for non-stringent filtering applications, such as harmonic attenuation or wideband preamplifier preselection, where the amplitude response of sinusoidal signals is of primary concern. For most of these applications, it is not necessary that the actual cutoff frequency exactly match the desired cutoff frequency. Consequently, it is more convenient to use SVC design tables instead of the normalized design tables that require calculations and are restricted to specific published values of reflection coefficient or passband ripple.

The five- and seven-element Chebyshev and five-branch elliptic designs with the capacitor input/out configuration were selected for tabulation because they are easy to construct and will satisfy the majority of non-stringent filtering requirements where the amplitude response is of primary interest. All filter designs were calculated for an equally terminated impedance of 50 Ω because it is the most common impedance level. The 50 Ω designs are presented in six tables: three lowpass types and three highpass types, with cutoff frequencies covering the 1 to 10 MHz decade. In addition to the component values, attenuation versus frequency data and VSWR are also included in the tables.

The SVC filter tables were computer calculated for only the E12 capacitor preferred value series (10 percent tolerance values). Smaller increments of cutoff frequency increase are possible using the E24 series, and published tables using this series may be found in the references. All SVC designs use capacitor value combinations that produce maximum VSWR levels less than 1.7:1 to minimize excessive input impedance fluctuations and to make the designs less sensitive to variations in component values.

2.21

2.3.1.1 Lowpass Filters

Tables 2.5 through 2.7 are for the five- and seven-element Chebyshev and the five-branch elliptic configurations. Figures 2.1, 2.2 and 2.5 show the attenuation versus frequency response of these filters. The cutoff frequency (F_{co}) is that frequency where the passband attenuation first exceeds the maximum ripple amplitude. The passband attenuation ripples are not shown in the response curves because the low VSWR designs have ripple amplitudes that are so small they are swamped by the losses of the filter components. In both the Chebyshev designs, all the capacitor values are standard; however, in the elliptic, only the nonresonating (odd-numbered) capacitors have standard values.

Table 2.5—Five-Element 50 Ω
Chebyshev Lowpass SVC Filters, C-in/out

| No. | Frequency in MHz | | | | | Max. | C1, 5 | L2, 4 | C3 |
	F_{co}	3 dB	6 dB	20 dB	40 dB	VSWR	(pF)	(μH)	(pF)
1	1.04	1.37	1.48	1.94	2.94	1.085	2,200	9.82	4,700
2	1.32	1.50	1.59	2.01	2.96	1.332	2,700	8.29	4,700
3	1.23	1.65	1.78	2.34	3.55	1.076	1,800	8.19	3,900
4	1.55	1.79	1.90	2.41	3.55	1.295	2,200	7.05	3,900
5	1.43	1.94	2.10	2.77	4.21	1.068	1,500	6.96	3,300
6	1.76	2.07	2.20	2.81	4.17	1.238	1,800	6.21	3,300
7	1.70	2.36	2.56	3.40	5.17	1.057	1,200	5.73	2,700
8	2.20	2.56	2.72	3.46	5.11	1.268	1,500	4.98	2,700
9	2.14	2.91	3.14	4.16	6.31	1.068	1,000	4.64	2,200
10	2.64	3.11	3.31	4.22	6.25	1.238	1,200	4.14	2,200
11	2.63	3.56	3.84	5.08	7.71	1.069	820	3.79	1,800
12	3.30	3.84	4.08	5.19	7.67	1.268	1,000	3.32	1,800
13	3.14	4.26	4.61	6.10	9.26	1.067	680	3.17	1,500
14	3.88	4.56	4.85	6.20	9.17	1.241	820	2.82	1,500
15	4.06	5.36	5.78	7.61	11.5	1.083	560	2.51	1,200
16	5.07	5.84	6.19	7.84	11.5	1.304	680	2.16	1,200
17	4.91	6.45	6.95	9.13	13.8	1.087	470	2.09	1,000
18	6.00	6.95	7.37	9.37	13.8	1.282	560	1.83	1,000
19	4.86	7.69	8.39	11.4	17.5	1.023	330	1.76	820
20	6.07	7.89	8.49	11.1	16.8	1.095	390	1.70	820
21	5.73	9.27	10.1	13.7	21.2	1.020	270	1.46	680
22	7.48	9.56	10.3	13.4	20.2	1.110	330	1.40	680
23	9.02	11.6	12.5	16.3	24.6	1.105	270	1.16	560
24	11.5	12.9	13.6	17.1	25.1	1.391	330	0.949	560
25	10.4	13.7	14.8	19.4	29.4	1.085	220	0.982	470

Table 2.6—Seven-Element 50 Ω
Chebyshev Lowpass SVC Filters, C-in/out

No.	Frequency (MHz)					Max. VSWR	C1, 7 (pF)	L2, 6 (µH)	C3, 5 (pF)	L4 (µH)
	F_{co}	3 dB	6 dB	20 dB	40 dB					
1	1.04	1.16	1.21	1.40	1.79	1.142	2,700	10.9	5,600	12.6
2	1.03	1.30	1.36	1.63	2.15	1.030	1,800	9.52	4,700	11.9
3	1.21	1.37	1.42	1.66	2.13	1.119	2,200	9.27	4,700	10.8
4	1.25	1.57	1.65	1.97	2.59	1.031	1,500	7.90	3,900	9.85
5	1.44	1.64	1.71	1.99	2.56	1.109	1,800	7.73	3,900	9.04
6	1.40	1.83	1.93	2.33	3.08	1.019	1,200	6.64	3,300	8.47
7	1.68	1.93	2.01	2.35	3.03	1.099	1,500	6.58	3,300	7.72
8	1.75	2.25	2.37	2.84	3.75	1.023	1,000	5.45	2,700	6.89
9	2.02	2.34	2.44	2.86	3.70	1.086	1,200	5.41	2,700	6.40
10	2.16	2.76	2.91	3.49	4.60	1.024	820	4.44	2,200	5.61
11	2.52	2.89	3.01	3.52	4.54	1.099	1,000	4.38	2,200	5.15
12	2.67	3.38	3.56	4.26	5.61	1.027	680	3.64	1,800	4.57
13	3.09	3.54	3.69	4.31	5.55	1.100	820	3.59	1,800	4.21
14	3.17	4.05	4.26	5.12	6.75	1.024	560	3.03	1,500	3.82
15	3.69	4.24	4.42	5.17	6.66	1.097	680	2.99	1,500	3.52
16	4.13	5.11	5.36	6.39	8.38	1.035	470	2.43	1,200	3.01
17	4.72	5.35	5.57	6.49	8.34	1.116	560	2.37	1,200	2.76
18	4.93	6.12	6.43	7.67	10.1	1.034	390	2.03	1,000	2.51
19	5.69	6.44	6.70	7.80	10.0	1.122	470	1.97	1,000	2.29
20	6.17	7.52	7.88	9.36	12.2	1.043	330	1.66	820	2.04
21	7.01	7.89	8.20	9.53	12.2	1.131	390	1.61	820	1.86
22	7.36	9.04	9.48	11.3	14.8	1.039	270	1.38	680	1.70
23	8.58	9.59	9.96	11.6	14.8	1.148	330	1.32	680	1.52
24	8.86	11.0	11.5	13.7	18.0	1.036	220	1.14	560	1.40
25	10.4	11.6	12.1	14.0	17.9	1.142	270	1.09	560	1.26

2.3.1.2 Highpass Filters

Tables 2.8 through 2.10 are for the five- and seven-element Chebyshev and the five-branch elliptic configurations. Figures 2.3, 2.4 and 2.6 show the attenuation versus frequency response of these filters. The previous comments concerning the lowpass filters also apply to the highpass filters. Although the highpass elliptic schematic diagram shows inductors L2 and L4 grounded, it may be more convenient when assembling the filter to have one end of the capacitors grounded.

Table 2.7—Five-Branch 50 Ω Elliptic Lowpass SVC Filters, C-in/out (continued next page)

No.	F-co	F₃ dB	F-Aₛ	Aₛ	Max. VSWR	C1	C3	C5	C2	C4	L2	L4	F2	F4
	(MHz)	(MHz)		(dB)		(pF)					(µH)		(MHz)	
1	0.795	0.989	1.57	47.4	1.092	2,700	5,600	2,200	324	937	12.1	10.1	2.54	1.64
2	1.06	1.20	1.77	46.2	1.234	2,700	4,700	2,200	341	982	9.36	7.56	2.82	1.85
3	1.47	1.57	2.15	45.4	1.586	2,700	3,900	2,200	364	1,045	6.32	4.88	3.32	2.23
4	0.929	1.18	1.91	48.0	1.077	2,200	4,700	1,800	257	743	10.2	8.59	3.11	1.99
5	1.27	1.45	2.17	46.7	1.215	2,200	3,900	1,800	271	779	7.85	6.39	3.45	2.26
6	1.69	1.82	2.54	45.9	1.489	2,200	3,300	1,800	287	821	5.64	4.42	3.96	2.64
7	1.12	1.44	2.41	49.8	1.071	1,800	3,900	1,500	192	549	8.45	7.25	3.95	2.52
8	1.49	1.73	2.70	48.8	1.183	1,800	3,300	1,500	200	570	6.75	5.62	4.33	2.81
9	2.11	2.27	3.27	47.8	1.506	1,800	2,700	1,500	213	604	4.55	3.64	5.12	3.40
10	1.28	1.66	2.63	46.3	1.064	1,500	3,300	1,200	192	561	7.20	6.00	4.28	2.74
11	1.79	2.06	2.99	44.8	1.195	1,500	2,700	1,200	204	592	5.52	4.42	4.75	3.11
12	2.52	2.70	3.63	43.8	1.525	1,500	2,200	1,200	220	636	3.71	2.82	5.58	3.76
13	1.56	2.08	3.55	50.1	1.055	1,200	2,700	1,000	127	363	5.88	5.07	5.83	3.71
14	2.23	2.59	4.04	48.8	1.183	1,200	2,200	1,000	133	380	4.50	3.75	6.50	4.22
15	3.17	3.41	4.90	47.8	1.506	1,200	1,800	1,000	142	402	3.03	2.42	7.68	5.10
16	1.94	2.52	4.15	48.4	1.064	1,000	2,200	820	115	331	4.79	4.06	6.78	4.34
17	2.73	3.14	4.73	47.0	1.199	1,000	1,800	820	121	348	3.66	2.99	7.56	4.93
18	3.73	4.02	5.63	46.2	1.491	1,000	1,500	820	129	368	2.56	2.01	8.76	5.85

Table 2.7—Five-Branch 50 Ω Elliptic Lowpass SVC Filters, C-in/out (Continued)

No.	F_{co} (MHz)	$F_{3\,dB}$ (MHz)	$F\text{-}A_s$	A_s (dB)	Max. VSWR	C1 (pF)	C3	C5	C2	C4	L2 (µH)	L4	F2 (MHz)	F4
19	2.39	3.11	5.20	49.4	1.065	820	1,800	680	89.3	256	3.910	3.350	8.51	5.44
20	3.26	3.79	5.85	48.2	1.185	820	1,500	680	93.6	267	3.070	2.54	9.39	6.10
21	4.83	5.17	7.30	47.2	1.569	820	1,200	680	100	286	1.950	1.540	11.4	7.58
22	2.85	3.71	6.15	48.8	1.063	680	1,500	560	76.6	220	3.260	2.780	10.1	6.43
23	4.16	4.74	7.14	47.3	1.221	680	1,200	560	81.3	233	2.400	1.970	11.4	7.44
24	5.72	6.13	8.58	46.5	1.547	680	1,000	560	86.3	246	1.650	1.300	13.3	8.91
25	3.67	4.69	7.95	50.5	1.076	560	1,200	470	57.6	164	2.590	2.230	13.0	8.31
26	5.02	5.77	9.01	49.4	1.212	560	1,000	470	60.3	171	2.010	1.680	14.5	9.40
27	7.18	7.68	11.1	48.6	1.582	560	820	470	64.1	181	1.320	1.060	17.3	11.5
28	4.40	5.60	9.24	49.3	1.079	470	1,000	390	51.4	147	2.160	1.840	15.1	9.66
29	6.17	7.01	10.6	48.0	1.236	470	820	390	54.2	155	1.630	1.340	17.0	11.1
30	8.63	9.20	12.9	47.3	1.604	470	680	390	57.6	164	1.090	0.857	20.1	13.4
31	5.47	6.91	11.8	51.3	1.086	390	820	330	38.5	109	1.760	1.520	19.3	12.3
32	7.55	8.59	13.5	50.2	1.242	390	680	330	40.4	114	1.340	1.120	21.7	14.1
33	10.9	11.5	16.8	49.5	1.659	390	560	330	42.8	120	0.862	0.695	26.2	17.4
34	6.59	8.17	13.0	47.7	1.096	330	680	270	39.0	112	1.460	1.220	21.1	13.6
35	9.10	10.2	15.0	46.5	1.267	330	560	270	41.2	118	1.090	0.881	23.7	15.6
36	12.4	13.2	18.1	45.8	1.635	330	470	270	43.9	125	0.741	0.573	27.9	18.8

**Table 2.8—Five-Element 50 Ω Chebyshev
Highpass SVC Filters, C-in/out**

No.	Frequency (MHz)					Max. VSWR	C1, 5 (pF)	L2, 4 (μH)	C3 (pF)
	F_{co}	3 dB	6 dB	20 dB	40 dB				
1	1.14	0.978	0.920	0.723	0.490	1.268	2,700	5.09	1,500
2	1.43	1.06	0.977	0.738	0.486	1.068	3,300	4.44	1,500
3	1.45	1.24	1.16	0.909	0.614	1.238	2,200	3.99	1,200
4	1.84	1.32	1.22	0.921	0.605	1.057	2,700	3.54	1,200
5	1.71	1.47	1.38	1.08	0.734	1.268	1,800	3.39	1,000
6	2.15	1.58	1.47	1.11	0.730	1.068	2,200	2.96	1,000
7	2.12	1.81	1.70	1.33	0.898	1.241	1,500	2.73	820
8	2.61	1.93	1.79	1.35	0.890	1.069	1,800	2.43	820
9	2.45	2.13	2.01	1.58	1.08	1.304	1,200	2.36	680
10	3.17	2.33	2.16	1.63	1.07	1.067	1,500	2.01	680
11	3.02	2.60	2.45	1.93	1.31	1.282	1,000	1.92	560
12	3.72	2.81	2.61	1.98	1.31	1.083	1,200	1.67	560
13	3.49	3.05	2.88	2.28	1.55	1.327	820	1.66	470
14	4.39	3.34	3.10	2.36	1.56	1.087	1,000	1.41	470
15	4.20	3.68	3.47	2.75	1.87	1.328	680	1.38	390
16	5.22	4.02	3.73	2.84	1.88	1.095	820	1.17	390
17	6.03	4.72	4.39	3.36	2.23	1.110	680	1.00	330
18	7.70	4.87	4.46	3.30	2.14	1.023	820	0.962	330
19	7.43	5.78	5.38	4.11	2.73	1.105	560	0.817	270
20	9.63	5.96	5.45	4.02	2.60	1.020	680	0.788	270
21	7.61	6.60	6.22	4.90	3.33	1.295	390	0.760	220
22	9.43	7.15	6.63	5.04	3.33	1.085	470	0.658	220
23	9.69	8.24	7.74	6.06	4.09	1.238	330	0.597	180
24	11.7	8.77	8.13	6.16	4.06	1.076	390	0.536	180
25	11.4	9.78	9.20	7.23	4.90	1.268	270	0.509	150

2.3.1.3 Scaling the Tables to Other Frequency Decades and Impedance Levels

Although the SVC tables are for the 1 to 10 MHz decade and a 50 Ω impedance level, the designs are easily scaled to other frequency decades and other impedance levels.

Frequency Scaling

To scale the frequency and component values to the 10 to 100 or 100 to 1,000 MHz decades, multiply all tabulated frequencies by 10 or 100, respectively, and divide all C and L values by the same number. The attenuation and VSWR data remain unchanged.

Table 2.9—Seven-Element 50 Ω
Chebyshev Highpass SVC Filters, C-in/out

No.	Frequency (MHz)					Max. VSWR	C1, 7 (pF)	L2, 6 (µH)	C3, 5 (pF)	L4 (µH)
	F_{co}	3 dB	6 dB	20 dB	40 dB					
1	1.00	0.880	0.845	0.724	0.563	1.109	3,900	5.67	1,800	4.86
2	1.16	0.922	0.878	0.734	0.558	1.030	4,700	5.55	1,800	4.45
3	1.22	1.06	1.02	0.871	0.676	1.099	3,300	4.70	1,500	4.01
4	1.39	1.11	1.05	0.880	0.670	1.031	3,900	4.63	1,500	3.71
5	1.55	1.34	1.28	1.09	0.845	1.086	2,700	3.74	1,200	3.16
6	1.82	1.40	1.32	1.10	0.831	1.019	3,300	3.73	1,200	2.92
7	1.82	1.59	1.53	1.31	1.01	1.099	2,200	3.14	1,000	2.67
8	2.15	1.67	1.59	1.32	1.00	1.023	2,700	3.10	1,000	2.45
9	2.22	1.94	1.86	1.59	1.24	1.100	1,800	2.57	820	2.19
10	2.61	2.03	1.93	1.61	1.22	1.024	2,200	2.54	820	2.01
11	2.69	2.34	2.25	1.92	1.49	1.097	1,500	2.13	680	1.81
12	3.10	2.45	2.33	1.94	1.47	1.027	1,800	2.10	680	1.67
13	3.19	2.82	2.71	2.32	1.81	1.116	1,200	1.77	560	1.52
14	3.81	2.98	2.83	2.36	1.79	1.024	1,500	1.73	560	1.37
15	3.79	3.35	3.22	2.76	2.15	1.122	1,000	1.49	470	1.28
16	4.35	3.52	3.35	2.81	2.14	1.035	1,200	1.45	470	1.17
17	4.52	4.02	3.86	3.32	2.59	1.131	820	1.24	390	1.07
18	5.27	4.24	4.04	3.39	2.58	1.034	1,000	1.20	390	0.969
19	5.26	4.71	4.53	3.91	3.05	1.148	680	1.06	330	0.924
20	6.07	4.98	4.75	4.00	3.06	1.043	820	1.02	330	0.829
21	6.46	5.77	5.55	4.78	3.74	1.142	560	0.867	270	0.752
22	7.50	6.11	5.82	4.89	3.74	1.039	680	0.831	270	0.675
23	8.11	7.16	6.89	5.91	4.60	1.119	470	0.697	220	0.599
24	9.28	7.51	7.16	6.00	4.58	1.036	560	0.677	220	0.548
25	10.0	8.80	8.45	7.24	5.63	1.109	390	0.567	180	0.485

To scale the filter tables to the 1 to 10 kHz, 10 to 100 kHz or the 0.1 to 1 MHz decades, divide the frequencies by 1,000, 100 or 10, respectively, and multiply the component values by the same number. In all tables but 2.10, changing the column headings of MHz, pF and µH to kHz, nF and mH changes the tables from the 1 to 10 MHz decade to the 1 to 10 kHz decade, and the table values may be read directly. In the case of Table 2.10, the nF heading becomes µF.

Because the impedance level is still at 50 Ω, the component values may be awkward for the 1 to 10 kHz decade, but this can be corrected by increasing the impedance level by 10 times using the impedance scaling procedure explained next.

Impedance Scaling

All the SVC designs are easily scaled to impedance levels other

Table 2.10—Five-Branch 50 Ω Elliptic Highpass SVC Filters, C-in/out (continued next page)

No.	F_{co}	$F_{3\,dB}$ (MHz)	$F-A_s$	A_s (dB)	Max. VSWR	C1	C3	C5 (nF)	C2	C4	L2	L4 (µH)	F2	F4 (MHz)
1	1.01	0.936	0.670	45.9	1.489	2.7	1.8	3.3	20.7	7.24	6.58	8.40	0.431	0.646
2	1.14	0.976	0.608	50.4	1.186	3.3	1.8	3.9	32.3	11.4	5.53	6.54	0.377	0.582
3	1.30	1.01	0.604	49.4	1.071	3.9	1.8	4.7	35.8	12.5	5.19	6.07	0.369	0.578
4	1.19	1.11	0.810	45.4	1.543	2.2	1.5	2.7	16.4	5.71	5.65	7.28	0.523	0.780
5	1.38	1.20	0.797	46.8	1.199	2.7	1.5	3.3	22.0	7.66	4.61	5.65	0.499	0.765
6	1.56	1.19	0.685	51.6	1.064	3.3	1.5	3.9	33.7	11.9	4.32	4.97	0.417	0.655
7	1.51	1.40	1.01	45.9	1.489	1.8	1.2	2.2	13.8	4.82	4.39	5.60	0.646	0.968
8	1.75	1.51	1.00	46.6	1.180	2.2	1.2	2.7	17.7	6.14	3.65	4.47	0.627	0.961
9	2.02	1.52	0.92	48.3	1.055	2.7	1.2	3.3	23.4	8.09	3.44	4.04	0.562	0.880
10	1.78	1.65	1.15	47.8	1.506	1.5	1.0	1.8	12.7	4.47	3.71	4.64	0.733	1.10
11	2.07	1.80	1.20	46.8	1.199	1.8	1.0	2.2	14.7	5.11	3.07	3.77	0.749	1.15
12	2.38	1.83	1.13	47.8	1.064	2.2	1.0	2.7	18.6	6.43	2.87	3.40	0.689	1.08
13	2.22	2.08	1.55	43.7	1.531	1.2	0.82	1.5	8.2	2.83	3.05	4.02	1.01	1.49
14	2.52	2.17	1.39	48.7	1.186	1.5	0.82	1.8	13.5	4.73	2.51	3.01	0.865	1.33
15	2.89	2.23	1.36	48.2	1.065	1.8	0.82	2.2	15.5	5.37	2.36	2.78	0.833	1.30
16	2.57	2.40	1.68	47.8	1.560	1.0	0.68	1.2	8.40	2.96	2.60	3.27	1.08	1.62
17	3.05	2.68	1.85	44.7	1.215	1.2	0.68	1.5	8.77	3.02	2.10	2.64	1.17	1.78
18	3.48	2.66	1.57	49.9	1.063	1.5	0.68	1.8	14.1	4.94	1.96	2.28	0.957	1.50

Table 2.10—Five-Branch 50 Ω Elliptic Highpass SVC Filters, C-in/out (Continued)

No.	Fco (MHz)	F3 dB (MHz)	F-As	As	Max. VSWR	C1	C3	C5 (nF)	C2	C4	L2	L4 (µH)	F2 (MHz)	F4 (MHz)
19	3.17	2.96	2.13	46.1	1.554	0.82	0.56	1.0	6.31	2.21	2.13	2.72	1.37	2.05
20	3.62	3.16	2.05	48.6	1.210	1.0	0.56	1.2	8.93	3.14	1.74	2.10	1.28	1.96
21	4.19	3.30	2.11	46.1	1.076	1.2	0.56	1.5	9.30	3.19	1.61	1.94	1.30	2.02
22	4.30	3.79	2.55	46.9	1.233	0.82	0.47	1.0	6.69	2.33	1.48	1.82	1.60	2.45
23	4.89	3.84	2.31	49.7	1.079	1.0	0.47	1.2	9.34	3.27	1.36	1.59	1.41	2.21
24	5.87	3.89	2.31	47.4	1.021	1.2	0.47	1.5	9.71	3.32	1.35	1.58	1.39	2.20
25	4.44	4.17	3.01	46.5	1.618	0.56	0.39	0.68	4.37	1.53	1.54	1.97	1.94	2.90
26	5.14	4.52	2.99	48.0	1.236	0.68	0.39	0.82	5.88	2.06	1.23	1.50	1.87	2.87
27	5.88	4.67	2.90	48.0	1.085	0.82	0.39	1.0	7.05	2.45	1.13	1.34	1.78	2.78
28	5.99	5.34	3.60	47.1	1.269	0.56	0.33	0.68	4.63	1.62	1.06	1.31	2.27	3.46
29	6.81	5.48	3.37	49.0	1.096	0.68	0.33	0.82	6.15	2.15	0.961	1.13	2.07	3.22
30	8.07	5.50	3.17	49.3	1.026	0.82	0.33	1.0	7.33	2.54	0.945	1.09	1.91	3.02
31	6.38	5.99	4.26	47.3	1.609	0.39	0.27	0.47	3.18	1.12	1.06	1.34	2.74	4.10
32	7.34	6.47	4.18	49.2	1.241	0.47	0.27	0.56	4.33	1.53	0.856	1.03	2.61	4.01
33	8.39	6.73	4.17	48.4	1.092	0.56	0.27	0.68	4.90	1.71	0.784	0.930	2.57	4.00
34	7.92	7.36	4.98	49.6	1.522	0.33	0.22	0.39	3.05	1.08	0.828	1.02	3.17	4.79
35	9.21	8.05	5.27	48.1	1.217	0.39	0.22	0.47	3.40	1.19	0.686	0.832	3.30	5.06
36	10.40	8.18	4.84	50.5	1.077	0.47	0.22	0.56	4.56	1.60	0.636	0.740	2.95	4.62

than 50 Ω while keeping the convenience of standard-value capacitors and the "scan mode" of design selection. If the desired new impedance level differs from 50 Ω by a factor of 0.1, 10 or 100, the 50 Ω designs are scaled by inspection by shifting the decimal points of the component values. The other data remain unchanged. For example, if the impedance level is increased by 10 times (to 500 Ω), the decimal points of the capacitor and inductor values are shifted one place to the left and right, respectively. That is, with increasing impedance, the capacitor values become smaller and the inductor values become larger. The opposite is true if the impedance decreases.

When the desired impedance level differs from the standard 50 Ω level by a factor such as 1.5 or 1.86 (75 or 93 Ω), the following scaling procedure is used:

1. Calculate the impedance scaling ratio: $R = Z_x/50$, where Z_x is the desired new impedance level in Ω.
2. Calculate the cutoff frequency (F_{50co}) of a trial 50 Ω filter, where $F_{50co} = R \times F_{xco}$. R is the impedance scaling ratio and F_{xco} is the desired cutoff frequency of the desired filter at the new impedance level.
3. From the appropriate SVC table select a design having its cutoff frequency closest to the calculated F_{50co} value. The tabulated capacitor values of this design are taken directly, but the frequency and inductor values must be scaled to the new impedance level.
4. Calculate the exact F_{xco} values, where $F_{xco} = F'_{50co}/R$ and F'_{50co} is the tabulated cutoff frequency of the selected design. Calculate the other frequencies of the new design in the same way.
5. Calculate the inductor values for the new design by multiplying the tabulated inductor values of the selected design by the square of the scaling ratio, R.

For example, assume a 600 Ω elliptic lowpass filter is desired with a cutoff frequency of 1 kHz. The elliptic lowpass table is frequency scaled by inspection to the 1 to 10 kHz decade by changing the table headings to kHz, nF and mH. A suitable design is then selected for scaling to 60 Ω. The 60 Ω design is next scaled to 600 Ω by shifting decimal points of the component values to complete the scaling procedure.

The calculations for this example follow with the same paragraph numbers previously used:

1. $R = Z_x/50 = 60/50 = 1.2$
2. $F_{50co} = 1.2 \times 1$ kHz $= 1.2$ kHz
3. From the elliptic lowpass table, design nos. 5 and 10 have cutoff frequencies closest to the F_{50co} of 1.2 kHz, and either design is suitable. Design no. 5 is selected because of its better selectivity. The tabulated capacitor values of 2,200, 3,900, 1,800, 271 and 779 nF are copied directly.
4. All frequencies of the final design are calculated by dividing the tabulated frequencies (in kilohertz) by the impedance scaling ratio of 1.2. Thus, the new F_{co}, $F-3$ dB, $F-A_s$, F_2 and F4 frequencies are 1.06, 1.21 and 1.81, 2.88 and 1.88 kHz. Note that a cutoff frequency of 1 kHz was desired, but a 1.06 kHz cutoff frequency will be accepted in exchange for the convenience of using an SVC design.
5. The L2 and L4 values of design no. 5 are scaled to 60 Ω by multiplying them by the square of the impedance ratio where $R^2 = 1.44$, L2 $= 1.44 \times 7.85$ mH $= 11.3$ mH, and L4 $= 1.44 \times 6.39$ mH $= 9.20$ mH.

The 60 Ω design is now impedance scaled to 600 Ω by shifting the decimal points of the capacitor and inductor values to the left and right, respectively. The final scaled component values for the 600 Ω filter are: C1 $= 0.22$ μF, C3 $= 0.39$ μF, C5 $= 0.18$ μF, C2 $= 27.1$ nF, C4 $= 77.9$ nF, L2 $= 113$ mH and L4 $= 92.0$ mH.

This completes the demonstration showing how the SVC tables may be used to calculate Chebyshev and elliptic designs for any impedance level and virtually any cutoff frequency. The use of the SVC tables will next be demonstrated in designing bandpass and bandstop filters.

2.3.1.4 Bandpass Filters

Bandpass filter (BPF) design is based on transforming a prototype lowpass filter (LPF) into a BPF, in which the LPF prototype has the same bandwidth as the desired bandwidth of the BPF. The LPF components are then resonated to the desired center frequency of the BPF. Only those BPFs having a geometric-mean symmetry about a center frequency are considered. The easiest way to explain this procedure is with a simple example.

Assume a 50 Ω equally terminated BPF is desired having a 3 dB bandwidth of 1.3 MHz and a geometric-mean center frequency of 1.7 MHz. For the purpose of demonstration, the skirt selectivity is not important at this time, and a five-element Chebyshev lowpass will be used as the prototype.

1. The percentage bandwidth of the filter is calculated to get an indication of the relative difficulty in realizing the filter:

$$BW\% = 100 \times (F_b/F_c) = 100 \times (1.3/1.7) = 76.5\%$$

where,

F_b = 3 dB bandwidth
F_c = center frequency

This is a convenient percentage bandwidth, and the component values should be easily realized. As the percentage bandwidth decreases, the spread of component values becomes greater until the design becomes impractical. For example, for percentage bandwidths less than 10 percent the spread of the component values becomes so great that the standard filter configuration must be modified to reduce the spread so the design becomes more feasible. Geffe discusses this problem in his book, *Simplified Modern Filter Design* (see Chapter 4, "Refinements in Bandpass Design"). The steps in the lowpass-to-bandpass transformation follow:

2. Refer to Table 2.5 (Five-Element 50 Ω Chebyshev Lowpass SVC Filters) and select a filter having a 3 dB bandwidth closest to the desired bandwidth of 1.3 MHz. (Note: The designs in Tables 2.5 to 2.10 are referenced in the text using the last digit of the table number followed by a dash and the number of the individual design. For example, design no. 25 of Table 2.5 is referenced as design no. 5-25.) Design 5-1 has a 3 dB bandwidth of 1.37 MHz, and this design will be used as the LPF prototype.

3. Draw the schematic diagram of a capacitive input/output (C-in/out) five-element lowpass filter and label all components. These components are responsible for setting the filter bandwidth (see Fig. 2.8a).

4. Resonate all the capacitors and inductors to the desired center frequency where F_c = 1.7 MHz. Of course, the series inductors, L2 and L4, must be series resonated to pass the center frequency signal through the filter, whereas the shunt capacitors, C1, C3 and C5, must be parallel resonated so the signal will not be attenuated. The equations for calculating the resonating inductors, L1,5 and L3 are:

$$L1,5(\mu H) = 25,330/(F_c^2 \times C1)$$

$$= 25,330/(1.7^2 \times 2,200)$$

$$= 25,330/6,358$$

$$= 3.984 \ \mu H$$

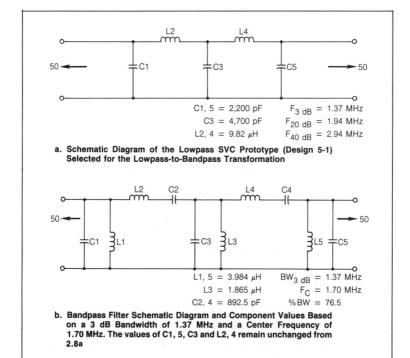

C1, 5 = 2,200 pF $F_{3 \ dB}$ = 1.37 MHz
C3 = 4,700 pF $F_{20 \ dB}$ = 1.94 MHz
L2, 4 = 9.82 μH $F_{40 \ dB}$ = 2.94 MHz

a. **Schematic Diagram of the Lowpass SVC Prototype (Design 5-1) Selected for the Lowpass-to-Bandpass Transformation**

L1, 5 = 3.984 μH $BW_{3 \ dB}$ = 1.37 MHz
L3 = 1.865 μH F_C = 1.70 MHz
C2, 4 = 892.5 pF   %BW = 76.5

b. **Bandpass Filter Schematic Diagram and Component Values Based on a 3 dB Bandwidth of 1.37 MHz and a Center Frequency of 1.70 MHz. The values of C1, 5, C3 and L2, 4 remain unchanged from 2.8a**

Figure 2.8—Schematic Diagram Showing Lowpass-to-Bandpass Transformation

where,

$$F_c = \text{center frequency in MHz}$$

$$C = \text{capacitance in pF}$$

$$L3 = 25{,}330/(1.7^2 \times 4{,}700)$$

$$= 1.865 \ \mu H$$

In a similar manner, the resonating capacitors C2 and C4 are calculated:

$$C2{,}4(\text{pF}) = 25{,}330/(F_c^2 \times L2)$$

$$= 25{,}330/(1.7^2 \times 9.82)$$

$$= 25{,}330/(28.38)$$

$$= 892.5 \ \text{pF}$$

where,

$$F_c = \text{center frequency in MHz}$$

$$L = \text{inductance in } \mu H$$

This completes the bandpass design. See Fig. 2.8b for the bandpass filter schematic diagram and the component values.

5. Review the design, and note especially that the maximum spread of the component values is about five. This is a reasonable ratio, and indicates that all the values can be conveniently realized. This confirms the expectation that a bandpass filter with a percentage bandwidth of about 76 percent would be practical.

Note that the nonstandard value of 892.5 pF for C2,4 complicates the realization of the filter. If the center frequency could be shifted upward, C2,4 could be made to become a standard value of 820 pF. The factor for raising the center frequency to make C2,4 820 pF is calculated:

$$\text{Factor} = \sqrt{892.5/820} = \sqrt{1.0884146} = 1.04327$$

The new center frequency is equal to 1.7 MHz × 1.04327 = 1.77356 MHz, or about four percent higher than the old center frequency. This new center frequency is assumed to be acceptable, and it will be used to allow all capacitors to have standard values. The new values of the resonating capacitors and inductors are:

$$C2, 4 = 25{,}330/(1.77356^2 \times 9.82)$$
$$= 820 \text{ pF (standard value as desired)}$$

$$L1{,}5 = 25{,}330/(1.77356^2 \times 2{,}200) = 3.660 \ \mu H$$

$$L3 = 25{,}330/(1.77356^2 \times 4{,}700) = 1.713 \ \mu H$$

The original values of C1, C5, C3 and L2 and L4 remain unchanged.

The fact that the inductors do not have standard values is not important as they can be hand wound using iron-powder toroidal cores to give the exact value required by the design. However, when in the audio frequency range, it may be preferable to use standard inductor values while paralleling capacitors to get odd capacitor values. In this case, a similar shifting of the center frequency can be performed to get a particular standard inductor value.

The expected response of the bandpass filter is calculated using the following equations. The response curve is shown in Fig. 2.9.

1. $BW_{(3 \text{ dB})} = F_{3Up} - F_{3Lo}$

   where,
   $BW_{(3 \text{ dB})}$ is the 3 dB bandwidth
   F_{3Up} and F_{3LO} are the upper and lower 3 dB frequencies

2. $F_{3Lo} = -X + \sqrt{F_c^2 + X^2}$

   where,

   $X = 0.5 \times BW_{(3 \text{ dB})}$
   $F_c = $ the center frequency

3. $F_c = \sqrt{F_{3Up} \times F_{3Lo}}$

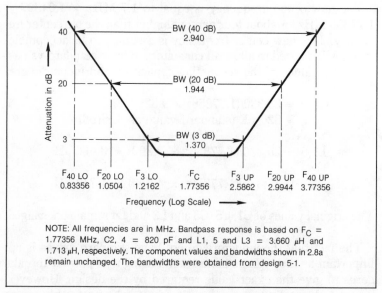

NOTE: All frequencies are in MHz. Bandpass response is based on F_C = 1.77356 MHz, C2, 4 = 820 pF and L1, 5 and L3 = 3.660 μH and 1.713 μH, respectively. The component values and bandwidths shown in 2.8a remain unchanged. The bandwidths were obtained from design 5-1.

Figure 2.9—Response Curve of Bandpass Filter after Transformation and Adjustment of F-Center to Give All Standard-Value Capacitors

The frequencies of the BPF at the 20 dB and 40 dB attenuation levels are calculated in a similar manner using the bandwidths at the 20 dB and 40 dB levels (taken from design no. 5-1). The bandpass response curve may then be sketched as shown in Fig. 2.9 using the new center frequency of 1.77356 MHz. Of course, these calculations may be performed before calculating the component values, and if the five-element prototype gives a response having inadequate skirt selectivity, then a seven-element SVC prototype may be tried. The upper and lower frequencies associated with the ripple cutoff bandwidth and the 6 dB bandwidth are not shown but are calculated in the same manner as the other frequencies.

An interesting aspect of the bandpass filter response is that at the same attenuation level, the lower frequency is the reciprocal of the upper frequency when both are normalized to the center frequency. For example, for the 40 dB frequencies in Fig. 2.9, the lower and upper normalized frequencies are 0.8336/1.77356 = 0.4700, and 3.774/1.77356 = 2.128. The reciprocal of 2.128 is 0.4700. Thus, the upper skirt is a mirror image of the lower skirt when the bandpass response is plotted on a logarithmic horizontal scale.

2.3.1.5 Bandstop Filters

A bandstop filter (BSF) is calculated in the same way as the BPF, except a highpass filter having a 3 dB bandstop equal to the desired bandstop of the BSF is chosen as the HPF prototype. For example, assume a 50 Ω BSF is desired having a 3 dB bandstop of 1.5 MHz and a center frequency of 2 MHz. As in the BPF design example, a five-element SVC Chebyshev prototype will be used, except for the BSF design a suitable highpass filter from Table 2.8 will be selected.

1. The percentage bandwidth, %BW, is first calculated:
   %BW = 100 × F_b/F_c = 100 × 1.5/2 = 75%
2. Refer to Table 2.8 (Five-Element Chebyshev Highpass SVC Filters) and select a filter having a 3 dB bandstop closest to the desired stopband of 1.5 MHz. Design 8-5 has 3 dB bandstop of 1.47 MHz, and this design will be used as the HPF prototype.

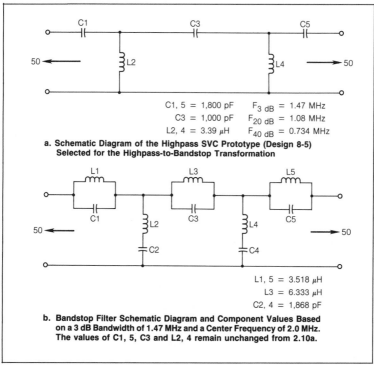

C1, 5 = 1,800 pF $F_{3\ dB}$ = 1.47 MHz
C3 = 1,000 pF $F_{20\ dB}$ = 1.08 MHz
L2, 4 = 3.39 μH $F_{40\ dB}$ = 0.734 MHz

a. Schematic Diagram of the Highpass SVC Prototype (Design 8-5) Selected for the Highpass-to-Bandstop Transformation

L1, 5 = 3.518 μH
L3 = 6.333 μH
C2, 4 = 1,868 pF

b. Bandstop Filter Schematic Diagram and Component Values Based on a 3 dB Bandwidth of 1.47 MHz and a Center Frequency of 2.0 MHz. The values of C1, 5, C3 and L2, 4 remain unchanged from 2.10a.

Figure 2.10—Schematic Diagrams Showing Highpass-to-Bandstop Transformation

2.37

3. Draw the schematic diagram of a C-in/out five-element highpass filter and label all components using the values of design 8-5. These are the components that set the width of the filter stopband (see Fig. 2.10a).

4. Resonate all the capacitors and inductors to the center frequency of 2 MHz. The series capacitors must be parallel resonated, and the shunt inductors must be series resonated so all the tuned circuits offer maximum attenuation at 2 MHz. The equations to find the resonating capacitors and inductors are the same as for the bandpass filter. The calculated values of L1,5, L3 and C2,4 are 3.518 μH, 6.333 μH and 1,868 pF, respectively. If desired, the nonstandard value of C2,4 can be made standard by shifting the center frequency using the same procedure previously described in the bandpass filter calculations. Figures 2.10 and 2.11 show the schematic diagrams and response curve associated with the bandstop filter.

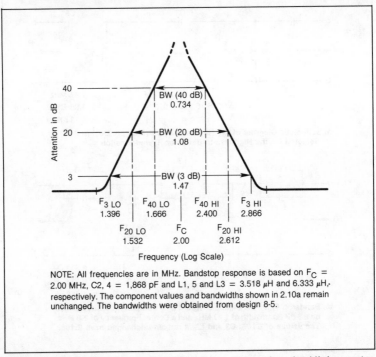

Figure 2.11—Response Curve of Bandstop Filter after the Highpass-to-Bandstop Transformation

2.3.2 Filter Design Using BASIC Computer Programs

Most previously published filter books use tables of normalized filter designs based on specific values of reflection coefficient for the design of filters. However, in this section, the personal computer (PC) will be used to design filters instead of normalized tables.

The increased availability and lower cost of the PC now makes it feasible to use this powerful tool in the design of simple passive LC filters. Included in this section are two BASIC programs that are short enough to be copied into your computer for designing Chebyshev and elliptic passive LC filters. Although the programs are restricted to odd-order filters having equal terminations, there is no restriction on the filter reflection coefficient. The fact that the programs design only odd-order filters is of little concern as the majority of filtering requirements can be satisfied with this type of filter. These noncompiled BASIC programs are easily modified to obtain other output formats or additional data.

2.3.2.1 Chebyshev Filters

The design of the Chebyshev passive LC filter has been greatly simplified by the SVC filter tables; however, the expected filter performance is assured only if close-tolerance capacitors are used. Such capacitors are not always conveniently available. A more satisfactory procedure is to use the SVC filter tables in combination with a simple BASIC computer program. After finding what standard value capacitors are required, about 10 of the proper value capacitors are obtained and measured. A 96-line program is then used to calculate a unique Chebyshev design based on the exact capacitor values on hand. In this way, the need for close-tolerance capacitors is eliminated.

Program 2.4 is a listing of a 96-line BASIC program that calculates equally terminated 50 Ω Chebyshev filters for 5, 7 or 9 elements. All designs are based on two capacitor values that are entered in response to the program prompt statements. In addition to the component values, the computer also calculates the ripple cutoff frequency, the frequencies at the 3, 6, 20 and 40 dB attenuation levels, and the maximum VSWR. Although the program is written for an impedance level of 50 Ω, this can be changed by listing the program and changing the "Z" parameter to the desired impedance level. The program is written in a form of BASIC that should be acceptable to any IBM-compatible computer.

All the PRINT USING statements are directed to the CRT monitor, so if a printer output is desired, the proper coding must be added to the program. The output format gives frequencies in MHz and component values in pF and μH. However, audio frequency filters may be calculated by changing the screen prompts and tables headings from "MHz, pF and μH" to "kHz, nF and mH."

Figure 2.12 shows an example of the output from the program where the capacitor values of lowpass design no. 1 of Table 2.5 are both increased by five percent. Because both capacitor values are increased by the same percentage, the C3/C1 ratio remains unchanged, and therefore the VSWR is the same as before. However, as expected, the frequencies and inductor values are different.

	5-Element 50-Ohm Low-Pass Filter Design							
	—Frequency (MHz)—				Max.	C1, 5	L2, 4	C3
F_{co}	3 dB	6 dB	20 dB	40 dB	VSWR	(pF)	(μH)	(pF)
0.990	1.31	1.41	1.85	2.80	1.085	2,310	10.3	4,935

Figure 2.12—Example of Calculation Output Produced by Program 2.4

2.3.2.2 Elliptic Filters

Elliptic lowpass and highpass filters of odd degree and having equal terminations may be designed using a BASIC program in which the design parameters are the ripple cutoff and stopband frequencies, the number of attenuation peaks and the minimum stopband attenuation level. Program 2.5 gives the 48-line listing of the elliptic design program. The design parameters are entered into the program via a DATA statement (line 10) and a READ statement (line 40) where the variables FP, FS, M and S1 are assigned to represent the ripple cutoff frequency, the frequency at the start of the stopband, the number of attenuation peaks and the minimum stopband attenuation level. After the program has been copied and all syntax and copying errors have been eliminated, the user may use INPUT statements for those variables that require frequent changes during the development of a design.

```
10 REM  PROGRAM CALCULATES 50-OHM CHEBYSHEV FILTER DESIGNS
20 REM  BASED ON C-VALUE INPUTS FOR MAX. VSWR <1.6.
30 Z= 50  : CLS : PI=3.1415927# : X9 =1 : REM X9= COUNTER.
40 PRINT "CHEBYSHEV FILTER DESIGNS: C-IN/OUT FORM"
50 PRINT "WITH MAXIMUM VSWR LIMIT LESS THAN 1.6."
60 PRINT "ALL DESIGNS ARE CALCULATED USING THE"
70 PRINT "C1 AND C3 CAPACITOR VALUES ENTERED." : PRINT
80 INPUT "ENTER FILTER TYPE: 1=LOW, 2=HIGH, 3=EXIT"; XP
90 IF XP = 3 THEN 960
100 IF XP = 1 THEN 120
110 T$= "HIGH" : GOTO 130
120 T$= "LOW"
130 INPUT "ENTER NUMBER OF ELEMENTS: 5, 7 or 9    "; N
140 PRINT "Enter C1 in pF (must be < 10001 pF). ";
150 PRINT "Enter 0 to start over. "; : INPUT C1
160 PRINT : IF C1=0 THEN 30
170 IF C1 <10001 THEN 190
180 PRINT "C1 must be < 10001 pF." : PRINT : GOTO 140
190 IF XP =2 THEN 220
200 X1=C1*1.63 : X2=C1*2.74 : REM  VSWR range for LPF.
210 GOTO 230
220 X1=C1/2.74 : X2=C1/1.63 : REM  VSWR range for HPF.
230 PRINT "For "N"-element,"Z"-ohm "T$"-pass Filter, ";
240 PRINT "C1 = "C1"pF."
250 PRINT "C3 must be greater than" INT(X1);
260 PRINT "and less than "INT(X2)"pF." : PRINT
270 INPUT "Enter C3 capacity in picofarads"; C3 : PRINT
280 IF C3 <X1 THEN 250 : REM Out-of-range traps for C3.
290 IF C3 >X2 THEN 250
300 IF XP=1 THEN C=C3/C1 ELSE C=C1/C3
310 IF X9>1 THEN 360 : REM TABLE HEADING FOR ALL FILTERS.
320 PRINT
330 PRINT "Table of"N"-element "Z"-ohm "T$"-pass Designs"
340 PRINT " for VSWR <1.60 and Selected Capacitor Values"
350 PRINT
360 PRINT " No. ----- Frequency (MHz) ----- Max.";
370 H$ = " -- F-co 3-dB 6-dB 20dB 40dB VSWR"
380 H1$ = "   (pF)  (uH)  (pF)"
390 IF N=5 THEN 900 : REM For printing Table Headings.
400 IF N=7 THEN 920 ELSE 940
410 U =C*(SIN(PI/(2*N))/SIN(5*PI/(2*N)))
420 W1=((SIN(PI/N))^2)-U*((SIN(2*PI/N))^2)
430 W = SQR(W1/(U-1)) : X =(W+SQR(W^2+1))^(2*N)
440 R =8.68589*LOG((X+1)/(X-1)) : R1=R/17.3718
450 RC=100*SQR(1-.1^(.1*R))    : REM  RC = R.C.(%).
460 VS=(1+RC/100)/(1-RC/100)   : REM  VS = VSWR.
470 B =LOG((EXP(R1)+EXP(-R1))/(EXP(R1)-EXP(-R1)))
480 D =(EXP(B/(2*N))-EXP(-B/(2*N)))/2
```

Program 2.4—BASIC Program for Calculating 50 Ω Chebyshev Filters Based on Selected C1 and C3 Capacitor Values (continued next page)

2.41

```
490 FOR K=1 TO N  :  A(K) = SIN((((2*K)-1)*PI)/(2*N))
500 B(K) =((D)^2)+(1-COS((2*K*PI)/N))/2 : NEXT K
510 G(1) =2*A(1)/D
520 FOR K=2 TO N:G(K)=4*A(K-1)*A(K)/(B(K-1)*G(K-1)):NEXT K
530 IF XP=2 THEN 560 : REM Branch to calculate F-co (MHz).
540 F0=1E+06*G(1)/(C1*Z*2*PI)
550 GOTO 580 : REM  For Lowpass G Values.
560 F0=1E+06/(G(1)*C1*Z*2*PI) : FOR K=1 TO N
570 G(K)=1/G(K) : NEXT K : REM For Highpass G Values.
580 FOR K=1 TO N STEP 2  : T(K) =(G(K)/(Z*2*PI*F0*1E+06))
590 IF K+1>N THEN 610    : REM Calculates odd G Values.
600 T(K+1)=G(K+1)*Z/(2*PI*F0*1E+06) : REM Even G values.
610 NEXT K
620 PRINT USING "### ";X9; : S = F0 : GOSUB 790
630  E =SQR((.01*RC)^2/(1-(.01*RC)^2))
640 V(1) =10^(3/20) : V(2)=10^(6/20)
650 V(3) =10^(20/20) : V(4)=10^(40/20)
660 FOR J=1 TO 4    : T=(SQR(V(J)^2-1))/E
670  M =1/N*LOG(T+SQR(T^2-1)) : W1=.5*(EXP(M)+EXP(-M))
680 IF XP=2 THEN 700
690 F(J) =F0*W1 : S=F(J) : GOTO 720
700 F(J) =F0/W1 : S=F(J)
710 REM F(1-4) are 3, 6, 20 and 40-dB frequencies.
720 GOSUB 790  : NEXT J
730 PRINT USING "##.### ";VS; : REM  Prints VSWR.
740 FOR K=1 TO N STEP 2       : IF K>(N/2+1) THEN 780
750 S=T(K)*1E+12 : GOSUB 790  : IF K>N/2 THEN 780
760 S=T(K+1)*1E+06 : GOSUB 790
770 REM C and L values based on K and (K+1)
780 NEXT K : PRINT : X9=X9+1 : PRINT : GOTO 140
790 REM   OUTPUT FORMAT SUBROUTINE
800 IF S<999.9 THEN 820
810 PRINT USING "##### ";S; : RETURN
820 IF S<99.9 THEN 840
830 PRINT USING "  ### ";S; : RETURN
840 IF S<9.99 THEN 860
850 PRINT USING " ##.# ";S; : RETURN
860 IF S<.999 THEN 880
870 PRINT USING " #.## ";S; : RETURN
880 PRINT USING " .### ";S; : RETURN
890 REM HEADINGS FOR N= 5, 7 or 9 LP & HP FILTER DESIGNS.
900 PRINT "  C1,5 L2,4  C3"            : PRINT H$;
910 PRINT H1$                          : GOTO 410
920 PRINT "  C1,7 L2,6 C3,5  L4"       : PRINT H$;
930 PRINT H1$; : PRINT " (uH)"         : GOTO 410
940 PRINT "  C1,9 L2,8 C3,7 L4,6  C5" : PRINT H$;
950 PRINT H1$; : PRINT " (uH) (pF)"   : GOTO 410
960 PRINT : PRINT "  *** PROGRAM EXIT ***" : END
```

Program 2.4—(continued)

2.42

```
10 DATA 1.06291, 1.77419, 2, 46.2450,    1.74746, 1.00158, 2, 46.5529, 0,0,0,0
20 REM DATA: Fco(MHz), STOPBAND FREQ.(MHz),  NO. PEAKS, STOPBAND ATTEN, As(dB).
30 CLS  : DN=LOG(10)/10 : PI=3.1415926# : RR = 50 : REM IMPEDANCE LEVEL =50 ohms.
40 CN=1 : READ FP, FS, M, S1 : IF FP=0 THEN 480 : REM  Fco, FAs, No. of Peaks & As.
50 N=2*M+1 : FC=SQR(FS*FP) : R = FC+FC  : FOR K=1 TO 2 : S=FS+FP
60 FOR J = 1 TO 6 : PX= SQR(S*R) : S = (S+R)/2  : IF 1E+08*(S-PX)<S GOTO 80
70 R=PX    : NEXT J           : REM  N = DEGREE (MUST BE ODD).
80 IF K>=2 GOTO 100           : REM  FOR AUDIO FILTER DESIGNS,
90 Q=N/S   : R=ABS(FS-FP) : NEXT K : REM  CHANGE ALL MHz TO kHz AND
100 Q = Q*S                   : REM  ALL pF AND uH TO nF AND mH.
110 S=EXP(-PI/Q)   : Y=S  : CQ=Q/(4*(1-S)*S^M) : S=EXP(S1*DN/2) : R=EXP(PI*Q)
120 AP=(LOG(1+(S*S-1)/(R/4+1/R)^2))/DN  : RC=100*SQR(1-(.1^(AP/10)))
130 R=R/(2*(S+SQR(S*S-1)))   : R=LOG(R+SQR(R*R+1))/(2*Q) : R=SIN(R)/COS(R) : W=R
140 F3 = FP+(FS-FP)/(1+FC/(FP*R*R))     : REM  F3 = approx. 3-dB Frequency.
150 Z=Y    : E(M)=W : W=W*W  : FOR J= 1 TO N-1 : F(J)= 1 : NEXT J
160 K=1    : FOR J=1 TO 1024  : F(K)=F(K)*(1-Z)/(1+Z)   : IF K<N-1 GOTO 180
170 Z=Z*Y  : X=((1-Z)/(1+Z))^2 : E(M)=E(M)*(W+X)/(1+W*X)  : K=0
180 Z=Z*Y  : IF Z< 1E-12 GOTO 200
190 K=K+1  : NEXT J
200 FOR J=1 TO M   : F(J)=F(J)*F(N-J) : F(N-J)=F(J) : NEXT J
210 FOR J=1 TO M   : D(J)=F(2*J)*(1-F(J)^4)/F(J)  : B(J)=E(M)*F(J) : NEXT J
220 C(1)=1/B(M)    : FOR J= 1 TO M-1 : C(J+1)=(C(J)-B(M-J))/(1+C(J)*B(M-J))
230 E(M-J)=E(M+1-J)+E(M)*D(J)/(1+B(J)*B(J))     : NEXT J
240 FOR J=1 TO M   : B(J)=((1+C(J)*C(J))*E(J)/D(J)-C(J)/F(J))/2
250 C(J)=C(J)*F(J)  : D(J)=F(J)*F(J)           : NEXT J
260 B(M+1)=B(M)    : C(M+1)=C(M):D(M+1)=D(M)    : IF M=1 GOTO 300
270 FOR L = 1 TO 2 : FOR K=L+2 TO M+1 STEP 2
280 FOR J=L TO K-2 STEP 2 : Y=C(J)-C(K) : Z=1/(Y/(B(J)*(D(K)-D(J)))-1)
290 B(K)=(B(K)-B(J))*Z*Z-B(J)*(1+Z+Z)  : C(K)=Y*Z  : NEXT J : NEXT K : NEXT L
300 Q=1/(2*PI*FC)  : P=Q*RR : Q=Q/RR : IF FS<FP GOTO 340 : REM PICKS LP or HP FLTR.
310 PRINT"   ** EQUALLY-TERMINATED "RR"-ohm  LOWPASS FILTER DESIGN **" : GOSUB 440
320 FOR J=1 TO M   : C(J)=Q*1E+06*C(J) : D(J)=Q*1E+06*B(J)*D(J)   : B(J)=P/B(J)
330 F(J)=FC/F(J)   : NEXT J : C(M+1)=Q*1E+06*C(M+1) : GOTO 370
340 PRINT"   ** EQUALLY-TERMINATED "RR"-ohm  HIGHPASS FILTER DESIGN **" : GOSUB 440
350 FOR J=1 TO M   : C(J)=Q*1E+06/C(J) : D(J)=Q*1E+06/(B(J)*D(J)) : B(J)=P*B(J)
360 F(J)=FC*F(J)   : NEXT J  : C(M+1)=Q*1E+06/C(M+1)
370 PRINT "No.  C(pF)   L(uH)  F(MHz)" : FOR J=1 TO M STEP 2
380 GOSUB 470 : PRINT USING " #####";C(J)
390 GOSUB 470 : PRINT USING " #####";D(J);  : PRINT USING " ####.### ";  B(J);
400 PRINT F(J) : NEXT J : GOSUB 470 : PRINT USING " ####";C(M+1) : IF M=1 GOTO 40
410 L=(INT((M+1)/2))*2  : K=N-1-L : FOR J= L+2 TO N-1 STEP 2 : GOSUB 470
420 PRINT USING " #####";D(K);  : PRINT USING " ####.### ";B(K);  : PRINT F(K)
430 GOSUB 470 : PRINT USING " #####";C(K) : K=K-2 : NEXT J : PRINT : GOTO 40
440 PRINT "Ripple F-co = "FP"MHz,   A-s = "S1"dB,    No. of peaks = "M"
450 PRINT "       F3-dB = "F3"MHz,   A-p = "AP"dB,
460 PRINT "       F-As = "FS"MHz,  R.C.= "RC" %,    Critical Q  = "CQ : RETURN
470 PRINT CN;  : CN = CN+1 : RETURN : REM   CN = COMPONENT AND FREQUENCY NUMBER.
480 END
```

Program 2.5—BASIC Program for Calculating 50 Ω Odd-Degree Elliptic
Filters. For this listing, the units are MHz, pF and μH, but they may be
changed by inspection to kHz, nF and mH. The DATA gives examples
of SVC 50 Ω lowpass and highpass fifth order elliptic filters.

The design variables listed in line 10 produce fifth-degree lowpass and highpass SVC designs, and the two output examples are shown in Fig. 2.13. Most of the output data is self-explanatory; however, the **critical Q** factor requires some explanation. This parameter provides an indication of stopband degradation due to component dissipation which is usually primarily associated with the inductors. When the inductor Q equals the critical Q, the attenuation peak nearest the passband is just erased. Consequently, to maintain the first attenuation peak, the inductor Q should be many times greater than the critical Q.

Although the program is written for an impedance level of 50 Ω, other impedance levels may be specified by editing line 30 and changing "RR = 50" to the desired impedance level. Other possible variations are mentioned in the program remark statements and in the program caption. To obtain other designs, line 10 must be listed and the original data replaced with data provided by the user. The concluding four zeroes indicate the end of data.

—EQUALLY-TERMINATED 50 Ω ELLIPTIC LOWPASS FILTER DESIGN—

Ripple F-co = 1.06291 MHz,   A-s = 46.245 dB,   No. of peaks = 2
F3-dB = 1.20497 MHz,   A-p = 4.79715E-02 dB,
F-As = 1.77419 MHz,   R.C. = 10.481 %,   Critical Q = 9.6674

No.	C(pF)	L(μH)	F(MHz)
1	2700		
2	341	9.359	2.81628
3	4700		
4	982	7.559	1.8473
5	2200		

—EQUALLY-TERMINATED 50 Ω ELLIPTIC HIGHPASS FILTER DESIGN—

Ripple F-co = 1.74746 MHz,   A-s = 46.5529 dB,   No. of peaks = 2
F3-dB = 1.50623 MHz,   A-p = 2.97964E-02 dB,
F-As = 1.00158 MHz,   R.C. = 8.26884 %,   Critical Q = 9.48923

No.	C(pF)	L(μH)	F(MHz)
1	2200		
2	17684	3.648	0.62663
3	1200		
4	6139	4.468	0.961031
5	2700		

Figure 2.13—Examples of Calculation Output Produced by Program 2.5

2.3.3 Design Procedures Using Normalized Element Values

Sometimes a special filter configuration or response is desired that is not available from the SVC filter design tables or from any of the computer programs presented in this chapter. In this case, the appropriate normalized design tables in filter references, such as Zverev's *Handbook of Filter Synthesis*, must be used. The following paragraphs explain the design procedures using filter tables normalized to a ripple cutoff frequency of 1 rad/s and 1 Ω terminations. The tables are based on a ripple cutoff frequency of 1 rad/s so that the reciprocals of the lowpass values may be used to calculate the highpass values. This would not be possible if the tables were normalized to a cutoff frequency of 1 Hz.

2.3.3.1 Normalized Lowpass

A five-element 50 Ω Chebyshev lowpass filter with capacitive input-output is desired having a maximum passband ripple amplitude of 0.1 dB and a ripple cutoff frequency of 1 MHz. The normalized component values for this design may be obtained from Chapter 3, Table 2.1 of this book or from Table 4.4 of White's *Handbook on Electrical Filters*. The normalized component values are: C1 and C5 = 1.147, L2 and L4 = 1.371 and C3 = 1.975. The following steps demonstrate the scaling procedure:

1. Calculate the capacitor scaling factor, C_s:

$$C_s = 1/(R \times 2\pi \times F_c)$$
$$= 0.003183 \times 10^{-6}$$

or,

$$C_s = 3,183 \times 10^{-12}$$

where,

$$R = 50$$
$$2\pi = 6.2832$$
$$F_c = 1 \times 10^6$$

2. Calculate the inductor scaling factor, L_s:
$$L_s = R/(2\pi \times F_c)$$
$$= 50/(6.2832 \times 1 \times 10^6)$$
$$= 7.958 \times 10^{-6}$$

3. Use the C and L scaling factors to scale the normalized component values to an impedance level of 50 Ω and a cutoff frequency of 1 MHz:

   a. $C1,5 = 1.147 \times 3,138 \times 10^{-12} = 3,651$ pF
   b. $C3 = 1.975 \times 3,183 \times 10^{-12} = 6,286$ pF
   c. $L2,4 = 1.371 \times 7.958 \times 10^{-6} = 10.9$ μH

This completes the scaling procedure using normalized component values. The correctness of the calculations can be confirmed by using Program 2.4.

2.3.3.2 Normalized Highpass

A highpass filter is designed in the same manner as the lowpass filter, except the reciprocals of the normalized lowpass values are used as the highpass normalized values. If a highpass filter is desired having the same characteristics as the lowpass filter, the normalized highpass component values are first calculated: C1 and C5 = $1/1.147 = 0.8718$, L2 and L4 = $1/1.371 = 0.7294$, and C3 = $1/1.975$ = 0.5063.

1. Calculate the capacitor scaling factor (same as in Paragraph 2.3.3.1):

   $$C_s = 3,183 \times 10^{-12}$$

2. Calculate the inductor scaling factor (same as in Paragraph 2.3.3.1):

   $$L_s = 7.958 \times 10^{-6}$$

3. Use the C and L scaling factors to scale the normalized highpass component values to an impedance level of 50 Ω and a cutoff frequency of 1 MHz.

   a. $C1,5 = 0.8718 \times 3,183 \times 10^{-12} = 2,775$ pF

   b. $C3 = 0.5063 \times 3,183 \times 10^{-12} = 1,612$ pF

   c. $L2,4 = 0.7294 \times 7.958 \times 10^{-6} = 5.80$ μH

This completes the highpass filter scaling procedure using normalized component values. The correctness of the calculations can be confirmed by using Program 2.4.

2.3.3.3 Normalized Bandpass and Bandstop

The Chebyshev normalized data in Table 2.1 and the frequencies versus stopband attenuation levels in Table 2.2 are used to design bandpass and bandstop filters when an appropriate SVC lowpass prototype design is not available. However, the BASIC programs used to generate these tables may require minor changes in the variables to provide new tables that will calculate data having smaller increments to allow the selection of a design having the desired skirt selectivity.

An example demonstrates the use of normalized lowpass data to design a bandpass filter:

Assume a 50 Ω Chebyshev BPF is desired having lower and upper ripple cutoff frequencies of 1 and 4 MHz, a ripple bandwidth of 3 MHz and a center frequency of 2 MHz. The desired bandwidth at the 50 dB attenuation level is 6.2 MHz. The maximum passband ripple amplitude desired is 0.01 dB (corresponding to a maximum reflection coefficient of 4.8 percent). What is an optimum design for this application?

The ratio of the 50 dB BW relative to the ripple BW is 6.2/3 = 2.067. The lowpass prototype upon which the BPF will be based will have the same ratio of bandwidths. Referring to Table 2.2, the frequencies in the 50 dB column are examined to find a design having a bandwidth ratio closest to 2.067. It is obvious that there are no suitable designs for N = 3 or N = 5 over the A_p range of 0.01 to 0.1773 dB. However, a design of N = 7 and A_p = 0.01 dB has a 50 dB bandwidth of 2.068 which is suitable for this application. Although N = 7 designs with higher passband attenuation amplitudes are available with better skirt selectivities, the 0.01 dB design is preferred to minimize VSWR. If appropriate designs are not available in Table 2.1, the A_p data used to generate this table (see Program 2.1, line 10) is modified to include additional A_p values that will give other designs that will be more likely to be suitable.

Referring to Table 2.1 for N = 7 and A_p (dB) = 0.01, the listed normalized lowpass prototype values are: C1,7 = 0.7969, L2,6 = 1.392, C3,5 = 1.748 and L4 = 1.633. The bandpass filter is calculated using the same procedure previously described in Paragraph 2.3.1.3. For the LP-to-BP transformation, the ripple bandwidth is 3 MHz and the center frequency is 2 MHz. The corresponding inductor and capacitor scaling factors are 2.65258×10^{-6} and $1,061.03 \times 10^{-12}$, respectively. Figure 2.14 shows the schematic diagrams and component values associated with the LP-to-BP transformation. Figure 2.15 shows the response curve of the bandpass filter.

A similar procedure is used in the design of bandstop filters, ex-

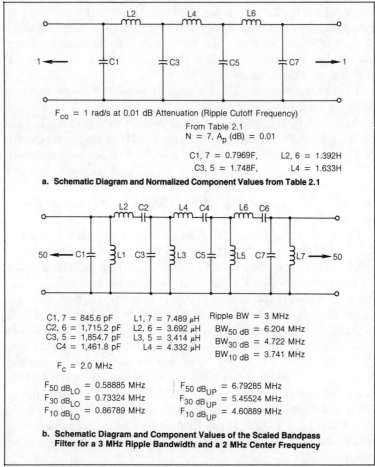

$F_{co} = 1$ rad/s at 0.01 dB Attenuation (Ripple Cutoff Frequency)

From Table 2.1
N = 7, A_p (dB) = 0.01

C1, 7 = 0.7969F,   L2, 6 = 1.392H
C3, 5 = 1.748F,   L4 = 1.633H

a. Schematic Diagram and Normalized Component Values from Table 2.1

C1, 7 = 845.6 pF   L1, 7 = 7.489 μH   Ripple BW = 3 MHz
C2, 6 = 1,715.2 pF   L2, 6 = 3.692 μH $BW_{50\ dB}$ = 6.204 MHz
C3, 5 = 1,854.7 pF   L3, 5 = 3.414 μH $BW_{30\ dB}$ = 4.722 MHz
C4 = 1,461.8 pF   L4 = 4.332 μH $BW_{10\ dB}$ = 3.741 MHz

F_c = 2.0 MHz

$F_{50\ dB_{LO}}$ = 0.58885 MHz $F_{50\ dB_{UP}}$ = 6.79285 MHz
$F_{30\ dB_{LO}}$ = 0.73324 MHz $F_{30\ dB_{UP}}$ = 5.45524 MHz
$F_{10\ dB_{LO}}$ = 0.86789 MHz $F_{10\ dB_{UP}}$ = 4.60889 MHz

b. Schematic Diagram and Component Values of the Scaled Bandpass Filter for a 3 MHz Ripple Bandwidth and a 2 MHz Center Frequency

Figure 2.14—Schematic Diagrams Showing Lowpass-to-Bandpass Transformation of Normalized Chebyshev Design for N = 7 and A_p = 0.01 dB

cept the normalized lowpass values are first transformed into highpass values by calculating the reciprocals of the lowpass values. The highpass filter is then transformed into a bandstop filter using the procedure previously explained in Paragraph 2.3.1.4.

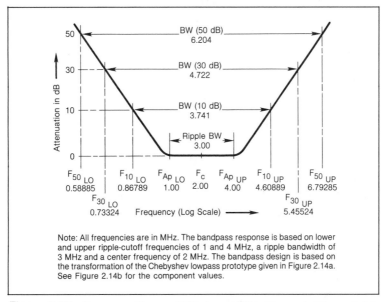

Note: All frequencies are in MHz. The bandpass response is based on lower and upper ripple-cutoff frequencies of 1 and 4 MHz, a ripple bandwidth of 3 MHz and a center frequency of 2 MHz. The bandpass design is based on the transformation of the Chebyshev lowpass prototype given in Figure 2.14a. See Figure 2.14b for the component values.

Figure 2.15—Response Curve of Bandpass Filter Shown in Figure 2.14b

2.4 References and Bibliography

2.4.1 Image Parameter Filter Design

Although Zobel's image parameter filter design procedures have been largely replaced by modern design procedures using network synthesis, there are occasions when an authoritative reference is needed, either to design a Zobel filter or to check the correctness of a published design. The eight references listed below on image parameter design are by widely recognized authors, and these references are recommended as reliable sources of design information.

Grammer, G., "Eliminating TVI with Lowpass Filters," Parts 1, 2 and 3, QST, February, March and April 1950, published by The American Radio Relay League, Inc., Newington, CT.

2.49

Kerchner, R.M. and Corcoran, G.F., *Alternating-Current Circuits,* (New York, Wiley, 3rd edition, 1953), Chapter 13, "Electric Wave (Image Parameter) Filters," pp. 436-487.

Laurent, T., *Frequency Filter Methods,* (New York: Wiley, 1964).

Orchard, H.J., commentary on the use of partisan image-parameter design examples in the book, *Frequency Filter Methods,* IEEE Transactions on Circuit Theory, p. 276, June 1965.

Reference Data for Radio Engineers, (Indianapolis: Howard W. Sams, sixth edition, 1975), Chapter 7, "Filters—Image Parameter Design."

Skilling, H.H., Electric Transmission Lines, (New York: McGraw-Hill, 1951), Chapter 10, "Introduction to (Image Parameter) Filters," pp. 224-257.

Terman, F.E., *Radio Engineers' Handbook,* (New York: McGraw-Hill, 1943), Section 28: "M-derived (Ladder) Filters," pp. 226-238.

Van Valkenburg, M.E., *Network Analysis,* (Englewood Cliffs, NJ: Prentice-Hall, 1955), "Image Parameter Theory," pp. 344-353.

2.4.2 Modern Filter Design

2.4.2.1 References

The 23 listed books span a quarter-century period of modern filter development, and some of the earlier publications may no longer be in print. For those wishing to assemble a library on modern filter design, the following books and authors are recommended:

Geffe provides an easy to understand introduction to modern filter design with many useful suggestions on filter design, construction and testing.

Zverev's book is one of the most authoritative and widely quoted filter synthesis references. It contains many normalized design tables for both magnitude and linear phase responses.

Co-authors Blinchikoff and Zverev provide a 494-page book suitable for the nonspecialist graduate engineer. The topics covered include insertion loss, group delay, delay equalization and the various tradeoffs involved in obtaining specified responses in both time and frequency domains. The book is intended to complement Zverev's handbook.

Lindquist provides an extensive theoretical background on filtering, discussing both passive and active types. Chapters on oscillators and component selection are also included in this authoritative 749-page reference. The treatment is more suited to the graduate student rather than to one designing filters on an infrequent basis.

Williams' book includes many of Zverev's tables and has many simplified and easy to follow explanations and procedures with worked out design examples. This kind of treatment is suited to engineers and technicians not trained in filter synthesis procedures but nevertheless responsible for designing and building filters.

Christian's book treats the design, testing and manufacturing of filters on a commercial basis. The design and application of pot-core inductors is emphasized.

Those interested in using computers to design filters will want the Cuthbert book.

Blinchikoff, H.J. and Zverev, A.I., *Filtering in the Time and Frequency Domains*, (New York: Wiley, 1976).

Bonebreak, R.L., *Practical Techniques of Electronic Circuit Design*, (New York: Wiley, second edition, 1987), Chapter 7, "Filters."

Bowick, C., *RF Circuit Design*, (Indianapolis: Howard Sams, 1982), Chapter 3, "Filter Design."

Christian, E., *LC-Filters: Design, Testing and Manufacturing*, (New York: Wiley, 1983).

Cuthbert, T.R., Jr., *Circuit Design Using Personal Computers*, (New York: Wiley, 1983), Chapter 9, "Other Direct Filter Design Methods."

Daniels, R.W., *Approximation Methods for Electronic Filter Design*, (New York: McGraw-Hill, 1974).

Geffe, P., *Simplified Modern Filter Design*, (New York: John F. Rider, 1964).

Graf, R.F., editor, *Electronic Databook*, (Blue Ridge Summit, PA: TAB Books Inc., third edition, 1983), "Passive LC Filter Design," pp. 117-143.

Hansell, G.E., *Filter Design and Evaluation*, (New York: Van Nostrand Reinhold, 1969).

Hardy, J., *High Frequency Circuit Design*, (Reston, VA: Reston Publishing Co., 1979), Chapter 4, "Filters."

Hayward, W.H., *Introduction to Radio Frequency Design*, (Englewood Cliffs, NJ: Prentice-Hall, 1982), Chapter 2, "Filter Basics."

Jordan, E.C., editor-in-chief, *Reference Data for Engineers: Radio, Electronics, Computer, and Communications*, (Indianapolis: Howard W. Sams, seventh edition, 1985), Chapter 9, "Filters, Modern-Network-Theory Design," pp. 9-1 to 9-26).

Lindquist, C.S., *Active Network Design with Signal Filtering Applications*, (Long Beach, CA: Steward & Sons, 1977), Chapter 4, "Classical Filter Response."

Mattaei, G.L., Young, L. and Jones, E.M.T., *Microwave Filters, Impedance-Matching Networks and Coupling Structures*, (New York: McGraw-Hill, 1964).

Orr, W.I., editor, *Radio Handbook*, (Indianapolis: Howard W. Sams, twenty-third edition, 1987), "Passive LC Filters," pages 3-17 to 3-29.

Pasahow, E., *Electronics Ready Reference Manual*, (New York: McGraw-Hill, 1985), pp. 109-124, Section 5-3, "Chebyshev (50 Ω SVC) Filters."

Saal, R., *The Design of Filters using the Catalog of Normalized Lowpass Filters*, (Backnang, West Germany: Telefunken AG, 1966).

Temes, G.C. and Mita, S.K., *Modern Filter Theory and Design*, (New York: Wiley, 1973).

Weinberg, L., *Network Analysis and Synthesis*, (New York: McGraw-Hill, 1962).

White, Donald R.J., *Electrical Filters—Synthesis, Design and Applications* (Gainesville, VA: Interference Control Technologies, Inc., 1980), formerly published as *A Handbook on Electrical Filters—Theory and Practice*, (Rockville, MD: White Electromagnetics, 1963).

Williams, A.B., *Electronic Filter Design Handbook*, (New York: McGraw-Hill, 1981).

Wilson, M., editor, *The 1988 ARRL Handbook for the Radio Amateur*, (Newington, CT: American Radio Relay League, Inc., sixty-fifth edition, 1987), "Passive LC Filter Design," pages 2-41 to 2-50.

Zverev, A.I., *Handbook of Filter Synthesis*, (New York: Wiley, 1967).

2.4.2.2 Bibliography

The 91 listed magazine articles give a good background on the development of modern filter design. Any of the articles by Geffe and Zverev are recommended in assembling a library of useful reference material. The content of most articles may be inferred from their titles.

"Application of Filters to Analog and Digital Signal Processing, The" Rockland Systems Corp., West Nyack, NY, Copyright 1976.

"Capacitors—A Comprehensive EDN Report," reprinted from *EDN*, May 1966.

"Fixed Capacitors Now and in '69," reprinted from *EDN*, 11 Nov. 1968.

"Modern Crystal Filters, An Engineering Manual for Circuit Engineers," Bulletin 5001, Bulova Frequency Control Products, Electronics Division of Bulova Watch Co., Inc. Woodside, NY, Copyright 1970.

"RF Capacitor Handbook, The" American Technical Ceramics, 1 Norden Lane, Huntingdon Station, NY.

"Tchebycheff or Chebyshev?" Correspondence: p. 105, *IRE Transactions*, 1955.

Allen, W.H., "Modern Filter Design for the Radio Amateur," *Radio Communication* (Journal of the Radio Society of Great Britain), August 1971.

Amstutz, P., "Elliptic Approximation and Elliptic Filter Design on Small Computers," pp. 1001—1011, *IEEE Transactions on Circuits and Systems*, Vol. CAS-25, No. 12, December 1978.

Bain, R., "Filter Response Program (BASIC Program Calculates the Response of Butterworth or Chebyshev Filters)," *RF Design*, January 1985.

Blinchikoff, H. "Toroidal Inductor Design," *Electro-Technology*, November 1964.

Bostick, G., Kinnetz G.F. and Parker, T.W., "Designing High-Power Series Inductors and Shunt Capacitors," *Microwaves & RF*, October 1987.

Burwasser A.J. and Bossaler, E.F., Jr., "Simple Bandpass Filters," *RF Design*, March 1986, and RF Letters, Corrections, by K. Pullen, Jr., p. 13, May 1986.

Cohn, S.B., "Direct-Coupled-Resonator Filters," *Proceedings of the IRE*, Vol. 45, No. 2, pp. 187-196, February 1957.

Dabrowski, G., "9 Test Hints for Coils and Capacitors," Reprint No. 68/1 of articles from "News from Rohde & Schwarz," Nos. 14, 15, 16, 17, 18, 23, 24, 27 and 28 of 1965 to 1967.

DeMaw, M.F., "Magnetic Cores in RF Circuits," *RF Design*, April 1980.

DePalma, H., "Pico-Chip Passive RF Components: Inductors—Capacitors—Resistors," *RF Design*, June 1980.

Drentea C. and Watkins, L.R., "Automatically Switched Half-Octave Filters," Parts 1 and 2, *Ham Radio* magazine, February and March 1988.

Eggen, C.P. and McAllister, A.S., "Modern Lowpass Filter Characteristics," *Electro-Technology*, August 1966.

Feeney R. and Hertling, D., "Microstrip and Lumped Element Ladder Network Analysis Program," *RF Design*, July 1987.

Frymoyer, E., Johnson, R. and Schindelbeck, F., "Passive Filters: Today's Offerings and Tomorrow's Promises," *EDN*, October 5, 1973.

Fuchs, M.L., "Shrink Passive Filter Size with Lower Q Inductors," *EDN*, 5 May 1979.

Geffe, P., "Bandpass Filter Shapes up from a Lowpass Network," *Electronics*, 6 July 1970.

Geffe, P., "Comprehensive Tables for Resistive Attenuator Design," *EEE* magazine, pp. 61-65, November 1964.

Geffe, P., "EDN Designers' Guide to Active Bandpass Filters," Parts 1 to 6, *EDN* February 5, 1974 to June 5, 1974.

Hayward, W., "General Purpose Ladder Analysis with the Hand-Held Calculator," *RF Design*, September/October 1983.

Hayward, W., "The Peaked Lowpass: A Look at the Ultraspherical Filter," *Ham Radio*, June 1984.

Home Study Course 69/51, "Passive LC Filter Design," and Home Study Course 71/53, "Component Selection and Test Procedures for LC Filters, Measurements & Data Corp., 2994 West Liberty Ave., Pittsburgh, PA, 1978.

Kefer, M., "A Programmable Calculator Method for Chebyshev Filter Selection," *RF Design*, March/April 1982.

Kefer, M., "An Easy Method for Measuring Unloaded Q (Qu) for an Inductor or Filter Tank." *RF Design*, March/April 1983.

Kochen, D., "Practical VHF and UHF Coil-Winding Data," *Ham Radio* magazine, April 1971.

Kost, R.E., "Equal-Ripple LC Filter Synthesis (Computer Program Synthesizes Arbitrary Stopband Characteristics)," *RF Design*, February 1988.

Levy, R., "Design Considerations for Lumped-Element Microwave Filters," *Microwave Journal*, February 1988.

Medley, M.W., Jr., "Calculate Dispersive Microstrip Line Width in Minutes!" *Microwaves*, July 1978.

Milligan, T., "Nomographs Aid the Filter Designer," *Microwaves & RF*, October 1985.

Niemeyer, E., "Network-Analysis Program Runs on Small Computer System," *EDN*, 4 February 1981.

Niewiadomski, S., "Elliptic Lowpass Audio Filter Design Using Miniature Preferred Value Components," *Radio Communication*, October 1984.

Niewiadomski, S., "Passive Audio Filter Design," Parts 1-3, *Ham Radio*, September and October 1985 and January 1986.

Noble, F., "Take a Fresh Look at Filters," *Electronic Design*, 4 January 1967.

Olson, H., "How to Use Ferrite and Powdered-Iron for Inductors," *Ham Radio* magazine, April 1971.

Olson, W., "Chip Capacitors," QEX, p. 14, September 1986. Published monthly by The American Radio Relay League, Inc., (ARRL), Newington, CT.

Olson, W., "Solid-State Construction Practices (Microstrip Notes)," *QEX*, p. 13, April 1987.

Orchard, H.J., "Filter Design by Iterated Analysis," pp. 1089—1096, *IEEE Transactions on Circuits and Systems*, Vol. CAS-32, No. 11, November 1985.

Perna, V.F., Jr. and Klein, S.J., "To You It's a Capacitor—But What Does the Circuit See?" *EDN*, 5 November 1973.

Porter, J., "Noise bandwidth of Chebyshev filters," *RF Design*, Summer 1980.

Pro, S., "Toroid Design Analysis," *Electro-Technology*, August 1966.

Przedpelski, A., "Special Lowpass Filters," *RF Design*, Sept./Oct. 1982.

Rubinstein, I. and Sleven, R.L., "Need a Really Low-Loss Filter? Elliptic Function to the Rescue!" *Microwaves*, December 1966.

Saal R. and Ulrich E., "On the Design of Filters by Synthesis," *IRE Transactions on Circuit Theory*, December 1958.

Sabin, W.E., "Designing Narrow Band-Pass Filters with a BASIC Program," *QST*, May 1983.

Sanders, K., "Insertion Loss Testing of Common-Core Filters," *RF Design*, July/August 1982.

Silver, S.C., "Special Report on Filters," *Electronic Products*, pp. 18-42, September 1968.

Stolarczyk L.G. and Jackson, J.R., "Electrical Wave Filters," A.R.F. Products, Inc., Raton, NM, Copyright 1968.

Tam, A., "Microstrip Lowpass Filter Design," *RF Design*, June 1987.

Ticknor, S., "Magnetic Core Calculations—A BASIC Program," *RF Design*, August 1986.

Vizmuller, P., "Elliptic Filter Wins a Comparison Test," *RF Design*, pp. 45-50, October 1985.

Wainwright, D., "Specifying High-Power Filters," *RF Design*, August 1987.

Watkins, L., "Narrowband Butterworth or Chebyshev Filter Design Using the TI-59 Calculator," *RF Design*, November/December 1980.

Watkins, L., "Need a Helical Filter?" *RF Design*, May/June 1981.

Webb, J.K., "Highpass Filters for Receiving Applications," *QST*, October 1983.

Wetherhold, E., "Inductance and Q of Modified Surplus Toroidal Inductors," *QST*, September 1968.

Wetherhold E., and Lee, H.A., Jr., "Pick a Filter from This Chart," *Electronic Design* 24, 23 November 1972.

Wetherhold, E., "Lowpass Filters for Amateur Radio Transmitters," *QST*, December 1979.

Wetherhold, E., "Chebyshev Filters Using Standard-Value Capacitors," *RF Design*, February 1980, and "Correction," p. 19, RF Design, June 1980.

Wetherhold, E. "Lowpass Chebyshev Filters Use Standard-Value Capacitors," Engineer's Notebook, *Electronics*, 19 June 1980.

Wetherhold, E., "Modern Design of a CW Filter Using 88- and 44-mH Surplus Inductors," *QST*, December 1980.

Wetherhold, E., "Elliptic Lowpass Filters for Transistor Amplifiers," *Ham Radio* January 1981.

Wetherhold, E., "Design 7-Element Lowpass Filters Using Standard-Value Capacitors," *EDN*, 7 January 1981.

Wetherhold, E., "Highpass Chebyshev Filters Use Standard-Value Capacitors," Engineer's Notebook, *Electronics*, 27 January 1981.

Wetherhold, E., "Tables of Precalculated Chebyshev Lowpass Filters with Inductive Input and Output," *RF Design*, July/August and Sept./Oct. 1981.

Wetherhold, E., "Practical 75- and 300-Ohm Highpass Filters," *QST*, February 1982.

Wetherhold, E., "Table Picks Standard Capacitors for Lowpass Elliptic Filters," Designer's Casebook, *Electronics*, 30 November 1982.

Wetherhold, E., "Passive Elliptic Filters Using Standard-Value (E24) Capacitors," *Interference Technology Engineers' Master (ITEM),* 1983.

Wetherhold, E., "Table Picks Standard Capacitors for Highpass Elliptic Filters," Designer's Casebook, *Electronics*, 24 February 1983.

Wetherhold, E., "Simplified Elliptic Lowpass Filter Construction Using Surplus 88-mH Inductors," *Radio Communication*, April 1983.

Wetherhold, E., "Lowpass Filters for Attenuating RF Amplifier Harmonics," Parts 1 & 2, *Short Wave* magazine, December 1983 and January 1984.

Wetherhold, E., "Simplified Design of LC Bandpass Filters," *ITEM* 1984.

Wetherhold, E., "Elliptic Lowpass Audio Filter Design," *Ham Radio*, February 1984.

Wetherhold E., "Practical LC Filter Design," Parts 1-6, *Practical Wireless* magazine, July 1984–January 1985.

Wetherhold, E., "Simplified Passive LC Filter Design for the EMC Engineer," from the record of the 1985 IEEE International Symposium on Electromagnetic Compatibility, pp. 575-584, August 1985, IEEE Catalog No. 85CH2116-2.

Wetherhold, E., "Simplified Passive LC Filter Design for the EMC Engineer," *ITEM* 1986.

Wetherhold, E., "Calculate 5- and 7-Element Chebyshev Filter Components," *QEX*, May 1987.

Wetherhold, E., "BASIC Program Designs Equally Terminated Chebyshev Filters," *EMC Technology*, July-August 1987.

Wetherhold, E., "BASIC Program Analyzes Simple Ladder Networks," *Ham Radio*, August 1987.

Wetherhold, E., "Simplified Design and Evaluation of Chebyshev Passive LC Filters," *ITEM* 1988.

Wetherhold, E., "How to Design Standard-Value L-C Filters Using the SVC Filter Tables," *QEX*, June 1988.

Wetherhold, E., "BASIC Program Designs Equally Terminated Elliptic Filters," *EMC Technology*, July-August 1988.

Wilkinson, J., "An Introduction to Elliptic Filters for the Radio Amateur," *Radio Communication*, February 1983.

Wyatt, K., "A Ladder Network Analysis Program," *RF Design*, November 1986.

Zverev, A.I., "Introduction to Filters," *Electro-Technology*, June 1964.

Zverev, A.I., "Lowpass Filter Design," *Electro-Technology*, March 1966.

Zverev, A.I., "The Golden Anniversary of Electric Wave Filters," *IEEE Spectrum*, pp. 129-131, March 1966.

Chapter 3

Signal Line EMI Suppression

by Steven F. Srebranig and Leonard F. Crane
Coilcraft, Inc., Cary, IL 60013

3.1 Signal Line Noise

There are two types of electromagnetic interference (EMI); these are radiated emissions (RE) and conducted emissions (CE). Radiated emissions are free-space currents and potentials which depend upon the time rate of changes of the electric field intensity and magnetic flux density. Conducted emissions are noise currents which are transmitted and occur within conductors and travel the usual current paths of a device. Conducted emissions can become radiated under appropriate circumstances, and this is almost always the source of RFI. EMI may be separated into two distinct kinds of noise potentials: differential-mode (DM, also known as normal-mode) and common-mode (see Fig. 3.1).

Differential or normal-mode noise is a noise potential occurring between current paths. A differential noise potential is not necessarily identified with reference to earth ground.

Common-mode noise is a noise potential occurring simultaneously on all current paths with respect to some unique reference. The reference may be chassis ground or, where the chassis ground detects the same noise potential as the regular current paths, earth ground. Two types of common-mode noise then may be observed

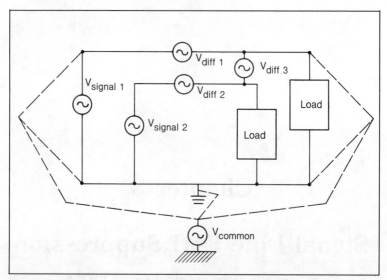

Figure 3.1—Differential-Mode and Common-Mode Noise

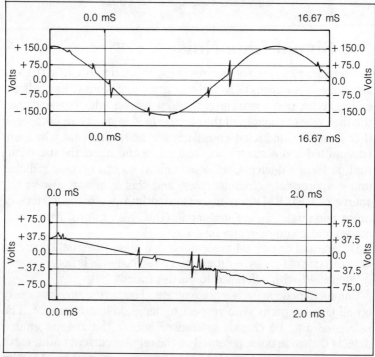

Figure 3.2—Example of Noise on Unfiltered Power Mains

from the reference chosen to measure the noise potential: a common noise potential existing between all current paths and chassis (safety) ground; or a common noise potential existing between all current paths, chassis (safety) ground and earth ground.

As shown in Fig. 3.2, the power mains can be a prime distribution system of conducted EMI, particularly in a manufacturing environment. A device connected to the power mains may be a likely source of noise if its power conversion section is not adequately filtered. The noise from the device may easily enter the line, modulating the low frequency power waveform or creating high frequency transients which can enter other equipment connected to the same power line. The noise transients can attain tens to hundreds of volts for microsecond durations and can be transmitted as both conducted DM and CM noise as well as radiated CM noise. Radiated CM noise can be especially destructive to data line transmissions; such signals are inherently low level with predefined transition thresholds which can be severely obfuscated by power line aberrations (see Fig. 3.3).

Power converters are inherently noisy. The radiated emissions of power converters are either mostly due to the creation of an electric field or a magnetic field. The field created by the power converter becomes electromagnetic only at a great distance from the converter.

Conducted emissions from power converters are attributable to the inherent character of converter operation itself (rectification of the line frequency, emissions of switching waveforms). Other conducted EMI sources are the transformer and other circuit magnetics, capacitive effects of components and structures and semiconductor components of the converter circuit. Both DM and CM noise are exhibited by converters. Common-mode emissions are primarily composed of harmonics of the switching frequency, while DM noise will contain wideband as well as harmonics of the switching frequency.

When a converter is powered up, the relatively large filter capacitance of the converter input circuitry draws a substantial current transient; this current will quickly saturate the core of an input filter inductor and render it useless in the suppression of the high harmonic content of the surge current. Electromagnetic interference is reflected back to the source of the current, the power mains. Usually, a shunting or commutating scheme is used to bypass the converter circuitry until the input capacitors have been charged;

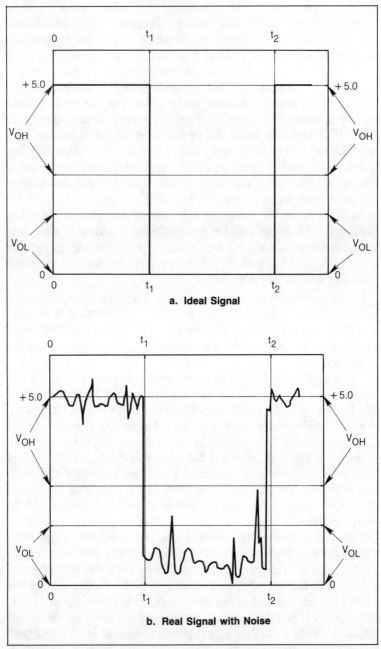

a. Ideal Signal

b. Real Signal with Noise

Figure 3.3—TTL Signals

this saves the converter from the lower frequencies of the transient, but the power line still produces the current surge unabatedly with the full effect of EMI. Rectifying or commutating diodes may be prime EMI sources, and contact bounce is a source of EMI. There are semiconductor noise sources associated with temperature (thermal noise), with the junction of differing materials (contact noise) and electron-hole movement in junction devices (shot noise). There exists low-frequency noise attributed to dc current-carrying electronic devices (modulation, flicker or 1/f noise*), due to the non-ohmic behavior of semiconductors at high fields (hot carrier noise), the generation and recombination of charge carriers (generation-recombination noise) and induced noise at the gate of a field-effect transistor (FET) due to the alteration of the source to drain currents by the induced charge at the gate.

The switching of digital current inherent in logic ICs and microprocessors of the TTL, CMOS, MOS, ECL and other technologies creates a form of severe EMI via their clock signals. Digital clocks are generally designed for short rise times, high-frequency state changes, precise periodicity and simultaneous support of a high number and digital ICs. The sought-after attributes of digital clocks are also good characteristics for the generation of problematic EMI. The noise generated from digital components are at the harmonics of the clock frequencies and extend through hundreds of megahertz. Also of consequence are the high-rate clock generators of video displays operating in the tens of megahertz. The RFI thus created can easily migrate to input-output (I/O) lines and any other cabling which uses the same ground (signal) reference or signal paths of the associated printed circuit boards. The cabling then acts as an "antenna farm" and therefore constitutes the primary emission source for computer devices such as modems and personal computers.

---

*i.e., noise whose intensity varies inversely with frequency, f.

3.5

3.2 Signal Line Specifications and Standards

3.2.1 Radiated Emissions Specifications: VDE/FCC

FCC regulations on EMI (CFR 47, Part 0-19) cover all equipment which uses digital techniques and has clock rates or generate similar timing signals or pulses of greater than 10 kHz.

CFR 47, Part 15, Subpart J (MP-4 measurement procedure) of the FCC regulations specifies two categories of equipment: Class A, intended for use within industrial and commercial environments; and Class B, intended for a residential environment. The distinction between FCC Class A and Class B equipment is made depending upon the targeted environment to which a piece of equipment is marketed. Class A devices, marketed for commercial and industrial environments, are placed under looser federal scrutiny than Class B. Examples of Class A equipment are measurement apparatus and mainframe computers. Examples of Class B equipment are personal computers, digital watches and video games (see Fig. 3.4).

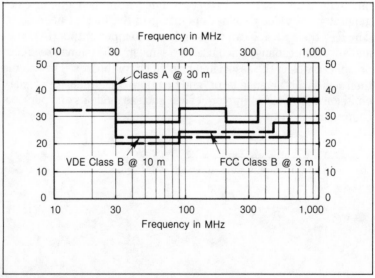

Figure 3.4—Typical Noise Specification Limits

Subpart H of the FCC Part 15 rules deal with Class I television devices (devices which connect to a television). Subpart H specifies more tests than Subpart J, but similar standards for EMI.

Other equipment which uses or somehow generates RF potentials is already covered by various FCC regulations.

The FCC rules regulate both radiated emissions limits and conducted EMI. Conducted EMI is the object of concern below 30 MHz, where interference affects lower frequency transmissions such as short wave and AM signals via the power mains. EMI radiating directly off suspect equipment into the air primarily occurs in significant quantity above 30 MHz, affecting FM, television and other VHF signals. The radiated limits appertain to equipment and peripherals (associated cabling and equipment) of the targeted devices measured at a specified distance from the machine under test. The conducted limits are referenced from the allowable voltage feedback into the power mains from the machine under test.

Until standards are available, some special equipment types are exempt from the FCC limits. These include signal generators and oscilloscopes used for electrical testing, systems for industrial control, electronic devices which are limited to an automotive environment and most medical equipments which are not intended for residential use. For more information on United States commercial and industrial EMC standards, see Volume 9 of this handbook series.

The German Postal Service (Deutsche Bundespost) is the agency which, via the FTZ (Telecommunications Central Office) regulates RFI limits in Germany, using the VDE limits as guidelines and the VDE as the verification agency. Though largely holding an advisory position, when indicated in German law, the VDE specifications are legally viable regulations.

The German postal authorities have divided equipment types and noise limits in a similar fashion to that of the FCC (see Fig. 3.4) and these limits are generally accepted throughout Europe. The distinction of equipment type for the FCC depends upon how the equipment is marketed. The VDE relegates the classification of equipment to the manufacturer. If a manufacturer chooses to meet and classify equipment per the relatively more liberal Class A limits, the end-use customer informs VDE of the equipment and intended application. By meeting the stricter Class B requirements and classifying the equipment as such, the end user need not notify the VDE.

Because the frequencies of normal broadcasting are not the same for both the U.S.A. and West Germany, the VDE regulations cover lower frequencies than the FCC limits for both radiated and conducted EMI.

The VDE Class A limits fall between 0.15 and 1,000 MHz, while VDE Class B limits fall between 0.01 and 1,000 MHz. The B limits below 0.15 MHz are recommendations of the VDE, but the FTZ (Fernmelde Technisches Zentralamt) Vfg. 1046/1984 invokes the entire frequency range.

The VDE Class B limits apply to portable equipment as well as the VDE Class A equipment. Included in the VDE Class B limits are printers, typewriters, small home computers and general equipment which are completely portable and operate under microprocessor control.

The VDE Class B limits allow manufacturers to seek out independent laboratories for verification (so-called "self-certification"). The Class B limits involve power line RFI conducted emissions and radiated RFI. For equipment 1 m or less in overall length (i.e., the major dimension, including cabling completely extended), conducted RFI power may be measured instead of radiated RFI. The RFI power for the Class B limits must be within 30 dBpW and 43 dBpW at 30 MHz and 300 MHz respectively. Below 30 MHz, equipment may be measured for RFI at a distance of 3 m rather than the 0871 requirement of 30 m. Certain frequencies which apply to certain computer peripheral devices (CRTs and switched-mode power supplies, for example, and including television scan frequencies through the ninth harmonic) will have the less stringent limits of 114 dBμV/m at 3 m (or 65 μV/m at 30 m). The indicated frequencies are (in MHz): 0.015 through 0.019; 0.030 through 0.038; 0.045 through 0.047; 0.077525 through 0.078725; 0.09305 through 0.094450; 0.108575 through 0.110175; 0.1241 through 0.1259 and 0.139625 through 0.141625.

VDE noise limits in Germany and most other countries are essentially similar to those of the FCC, and they are all collectively based upon the CISPR (International Special Committee for Radio Interference) procedures and limits. CISPR specifications can be used as a general guide for noise limits throughout the world. For a more detailed discussion of international EMC standards, refer to Volume 10 in this handbook series.

The relevant EMI test procedures in Germany (similar to those throughout the world for equipment using digital techniques) are covered in the following: VDE 0871/6.78, VDE 0872/7.72, VDE

0871 Limit A, VDE 0871 Limit C, VDE 0871 Limit B, VDE 0872 and VDE 0871.

For Class A equipment, conducted limits specified by the CISPR Publication 22 are 66 dBμV from 0.15 MHz through 0.50 MHz and 60 dBμV between 0.50 MHz and 30.0 MHz. Radiated limits are specified as 50 dBμV/m at 3 m from 30.0 MHz to 230.0 MHz and 57 dBμV/m at 3 m from 230.0 MHz through 1,000.0 MHz.

Class B conducted limits are specified by the CISPR Publication 22 as 56 dBμV to 46 dBμV from 0.15 MHz through 0.50 MHz, 46 dBμV between 0.5 MHz to 5.0 MHz and 50 dBμV between 5.0 MHz and 30.0 MHz. Mean radiated limits are specified as 40 dBμV/m at 3 m from 30.0 MHz to 230.0 MHz and 47 dBμV/m at 3 m from 230.0 MHz through 1,000.0 MHz.

Electromagnetic interference standards via the Japanese VCCI organization are based on the CISPR recommendations and will use CISPR Publication 22 limits by the year 1990. The VCCI standards are voluntary at present, but they are observed throughout the Japanese electronics industry.

Similar to the VDE and FCC EMI specifications, the VCCI divides equipment types into two **information technology equipment** (ITE) categories: Class 1 and Class 2. Class 1 limits correspond to Class A (FCC/VDE) equipment; that is, equipment intended for commercial or industrial environments. Class 2 limits apply to equipment used in residential districts and environments.

Filter components, including capacitors and inductors (chokes) must meet VDE 0565, Parts 1 through 3 for parameters such as insulation resistance. Underwriters Laboratories (UL) in the United States and the Canadian Standards Association (CSA) in Canada also have similar requirements for passive filter components.

Power lines may vary in output impedance by as much as 40 dB from location to location, making the repeatability of line-based evaluations very unreliable between differing locations. A **line impedance stabilization network** (LISN) as shown in Fig. 3.5 allows uniform line based testing regardless of locality. This device is also called an **artificial mains network** (AMN), primarily in Europe.

A line impedance standard has been devised and is specified by several licensing and independent standards agencies (e.g., the FCC and VDE). The LISN is used as the terminating impedance for conducted emissions testing.

For noise evaluations of OEM devices, the LISN allows the nor-

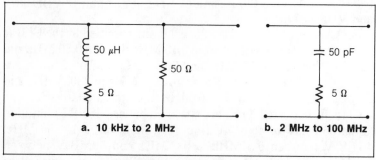

Figure 3.5—LISN Test Termination Circuits

mal power flow required of the device while yielding a stable impedance to conducted emissions. The LISN provides a low impedance at the line frequency, increasing impedance through the noise frequencies (5.4 Ω at 0.010 MHz with 50 Ω above about 0.400 MHz).

3.2.2 IEEE 802 Network Performance Standard

The proliferation of the **local area network** (LAN) to link personal computers and peripherals has created a vast new area of concern for data line filtering. LANs have all the filtering needs of computing devices plus the demands of the associated cabling. As computing devices intended primarily for office use, the equipment that constitutes a LAN must meet the requirements for Class B devices.

IEEE 802.3, 802.4 and 802.5 define the physical layer for LANs using **carrier sense multiple access with collision detection** (CSMA/CD), **token-passing bus,** and **token ring** media access methods, respectively. Each of these standards defines acceptable EMI emissions as well as the level of EMI susceptibility to be maintained.

IEEE 802.3, which defines LANs including those similar to the popular Ethernet® and Starlan® types, specifically states (Paragraph 8.7.2.2) that conformance to FCC 20780-1980 is required. IEEE 802.4 includes the same requirement in various sections, and IEEE 802.5 Paragraph 7.5.1 specifically lists the required attenuation of higher harmonics of the fundamental data rate.

The data rate specified by IEEE 802.3 is 10 megabits per second (Mb/s), although the standard was intended to cover possible data rates from 1 to 20 Mb/s. IEEE 802.4 includes data rates of

1, 5 and 10 Mb/s, and IEEE 802.5 specifies the rate to be either 1 or 4 Mb/s.

All specified data rates are well within the area of concern for line conducted limits. Higher harmonics can easily cause radiated emissions. Most LANs use as the transmission medium a shielded cable; either coaxial or twisted pair wire.

In addition to shielded cable, LANs also employ inductive (often common-mode) or capacitive filters or combinations of the two on both the transmit and receive lines at the DTE-cable interface. These filters may be in the form of board-mounted components or filtered connectors.

The receive filter may also function to shape the wave of signal pulses. IEEE 802.5 Paragraph 7.5.1, for example, delineates allowable signal pulse distortion of the received signal.

The IEEE LAN standards include specifications for EMI susceptibility that may also require filtering. IEEE 802.3, IEEE 802.4 and IEEE 802.5 each specify that the LAN hardware must meet specifications when operating in a plane wave field of 2 V/m from 10 KHz to 30 MHz and 5 V/m from 30 MHz to 1 GHz. IEEE 802.3 further specifies operation with an interference voltage of 1 V/ns peak slope applied between the coaxial cable shield and the **data terminal equipment** (DTE) earth ground connection.

Supplements a, b, c, and e to IEEE 802.3 introduce slightly changed requirements for attachment units of several different network types.

IEEE 802.3 Supplement e specifically defines type **1Base5** (1 MHz baseband with maximum segment length of 500 m). Networks utilizing this scheme are, for the most part, expected to utilize existing building wiring in the form of unshielded twisted pair (telephone) wire. Using twisted pair wiring increases the need for filtering for a network to be compatible with the appropriate emission and susceptibility specifications.

IEEE 802.3 Supplement e specifically defines limits for common-mode voltage that may be transmitted, and it requires receivers to meet a minimum level of common-mode rejection. To achieve acceptable levels of common-mode voltage transmitted to the twisted pairs, common-mode inductors are found to be particularly effective. Allowable levels of impulse noise and crosstalk are specified, as is the standard filter alignment for testing the received noise (two-pole Butterworth lowpass with a defined 3 dB cutoff frequency).

Noise immunity for receivers is defined such that a 560 mV squelch level and a 2 to 4 MHz, two-pole, lowpass Butterworth alignment will meet the requirement.

3.2.3 IEEE 488, EIA RS 232 and Similar Communication Standards

The EMI associated with I/O, whether it be defined by EIA serial interface standards RS-232-D (RS-422-A, RS-423-A, RS-449) or IEEE 488 or Centronics parallel or similar communications standards, is not necessarily due to the transmission of the data signals themselves.

EIA RS-232-D, for example, defines an interface standard for data rates not to exceed 20 kb/s. At a serial rate of 9,600 baud, an EIA-232-A signal consists of an 0.0048 MHz 18 V peak-to-peak square wave. Radiated emissions become evident above 30 MHz, and therefore only the higher harmonics of the square wave are an EMI concern. At 30 MHz the 7,000th harmonic of the signal waveform is approached, yielding an RF noise potential of approximately 250 μV (18 V/7,000). Even a very efficient unshielded cable antenna, using the noise generated by the 9,600 baud signal as a source, would transmit only about 25 μV/m (at 3 m) or 1/3 the EMI of the Class B limit.

EIA RS-422-A, RS-423-A and RS-449 are intended to gradually replace the interface as defined by RS-232 and have increased data rates to levels that can be more critical for controlling EMI emissions.

EIA standard RS-449, intended for use with RS-422 and RS-423, defines a serial interface at data rates up to 2 Mb/s. In this standard interface, connector pin 1 is reserved for a shield connection which may be required by the relatively higher data rate allowed by the standard. More specific shielding requirements are beyond the scope of this standard.

EIA-422-A defines the interface for balanced voltage expected to operate at 10 Mb/s or less. EIA-422-A recommends the use of a balanced circuit in preference to the unbalanced type defined by EIA-423-A when an interconnecting cable will be subjected to ± 1 V of extraneous noise between the signal conductor and circuit common. A balanced circuit is also indicated in any circumstance where interference with other signals is to be minimized.

EIA-423-A is intended for unbalanced voltage circuit interfaces expected to operate at 100 kb/s or less. It is noted in Paragraph 7.2 of both EIA-422-A and EIA-423-A that shielded cable may be necessary in some applications for EMI reduction and that the shield may be terminated to frame ground at either or both ends.

Further definition of shield and/or connector termination for EMI purposes is not included in the EIA specifications.

IEEE 488 interfaces are intended to be used for interconnection over short distances, so the EMI problems are less severe than, for example, LANs. IEEE 488 does not specifically deal with EMI regulations, so the equipment used is simply considered to be subject to regulatory requirements such as FCC at the appropriate frequencies. IEEE 488 Paragraph 5.2 gives recommended guidelines for data rates of 250, 500 and 1,000 kB/s.

3.3 Signal Line Filtering

Radiated EMI is more amorphous a problem than conducted EMI. Conducted EMI can often be ameliorated by using standard pi filters, and conducted noise sources are generally specific and identifiable. Radiated EMI occurs at higher frequencies than conducted EMI and occurs from numerous sources. Input-output and line cables are significant sources of radiated noise (approx. 30 to 200 MHz) which act as antennas and are subject to the same attributes as antennas (i.e., orientation and length).

Noise can radiate onto PC boards through an equipment enclosure via I/O cabling and board traces which act as antennas. The radiated EMI then becomes conducted. Slots and seams in enclosures can act as portals to radiated noise ("**slot antennas**"). Keyboards and video display apparatus contribute their own high-frequency EMI.

The I/O drivers of a communication system (generally a single printed circuit board) share a common reference, and if this reference "ground" is noisy, all lines of the drivers and the attached cabling will be subjected to the same noise. Most EMI due to I/O and emanating from computing equipment is the effect of common-mode noise which can reach levels of hundreds of microvolts.

The data transmitted via I/O lines can generally be ignored as sources of EMI themselves unless the data transmissions are approaching frequencies in the megahertz range.

Solutions to radiated EMI of I/O lines fall into three standard categories:

1. Filtering (standard pi, nth order or reactive/dissipative)
2. Shielding (enclosures, coaxial cabling)
3. Bypassing (largely the domain of bypass capacitors)

3.13

All of the solutions to radiated EMI have one main common feature: an effective "earth" ground. Creating a ground which is essentially perfect, that is, capable of accepting all incident (noise) currents with a negligible change in potential, is paramount to successfully bypassing, filtering or enclosing radiated and conducted fields of noise energy.

It is vitally important to prevent high-frequency currents of 30 MHz through 1,000 MHz from attaining the use of signal line "antennas." However, an upper limit of 300 MHz is usually sufficient for most applications. Employing reasonable Faraday shielding can yield a piece of equipment which will pass the regulatory limits.

Input-output lines are particularly antenna-like: they have individual resonances and nulls with their resonances dependent upon length and orientation. Held vertically, the I/O lines act as quarter-wave antennas, similar in operation to citizen's band (CB) radio antennas. Physically changing the I/O lines by modifying their length or by looping and bending, the resonant peaks of the cables can be modified. The **"I/O line" antennas** radiate common-mode noise most successfully at their particular resonant frequencies. Because common-mode EMI is broadband, composed of a large number of harmonics between 30 MHz and several hundreds of megahertz, I/O line antennas can generally find EMI to radiate at their particular resonances.

3.3.1 Coaxial Cable

At resonant frequencies, the characteristic model of an I/O line antenna is a simple resistance representing radiated potentials; that is, energy dissipated into the air as EMI. The resistance is the characteristic impedance of the line. As for a quarter-wave antenna, which the I/O line simulates, the characteristic impedance is very nearly 50 Ω. At frequencies away from resonance, the I/O line antenna model becomes increasingly dominated by a series combination of capacitance and inductance in series with the characteristic resistance (the capacitance and inductance still exist at resonance where their cumulative reactance becomes zero). Essentially, from an EMI viewpoint, computers and similar devices are broadband noise sources terminated with a 50 Ω load.

Coaxial or twisted pair cables are generally employed as the interconnection medium of computer systems, particularly LANs.

Coaxial-type cabling uses a center conductor for signal transmission and a 360° shielding conductor as a return path. Coaxial cabling can support signal transmissions of several hundreds of megahertz.

Because the outer conductor of a shielded cable is essentially an antenna, it must be grounded directly to the equipment chassis to minimize a potential occurring on the shield; this should be done via the shortest, most complete connection possible (generally a 360° connection using a metal shell attached directly and securely to the enclosure). If the adjoining of the shield to the chassis is made such that the connection (e.g., a length of wire) can present a significant impedance at an RF frequency, then an RF potential will be created on the shield at that frequency, and the potential will be radiated by the antenna-like structure of the shield (less or more so depending upon the cable's resonant frequencies and the actual broadband character of the noise).

Terminating the shield to the chassis at both ends changes the resonances of the shield, creating a half-wave antenna from a quarter-wave antenna (one end tied to ground); this is the only significant difference between terminating one or both ends as far as radiated EMI is concerned. Tying both shield ends to ground may, however, cause current loops for conducted EMI.

The characteristic impedance of a shielded cable is largely dependent upon the ratio of the center conductor diameter to the diameter of the outer conducting shield. Characteristic impedances of shielded cables generally fall between 50 and 300 Ω for an infinitely long cable or a cable terminated with its characteristic impedance. A cable which is mismatched with a load (the load is not equivalent to the cable's characteristic impedance or the finite length of cable is unterminated or capacitive: an RF short), could have standing waves of some fraction of the RF potential riding the center conductor. Fortunately, I/O cabling is very lossy at RF frequencies, and the transmission of the RF energy is mostly lost in heat instead of being reflected. Essentially, to an RF potential, I/O cabling appears terminated in its characteristic impedance regardless of its actual (signal frequency) termination.

The signal transmission capability of coaxial cable can be hundreds of megabits per second (several hundred megahertz in bandwidth).

3.3.2 Twisted-Pair Wiring

Twisted-pair cabling uses insulated conductors, one signal and one return, twisted together (see Fig. 3.6). Increasing the turns per inch of twist increases the reduction of spurious high-frequency common-mode noise. Twisted-pair cabling may be shielded for further EMI/RFI rejection (particularly if the shield reference is balanced with the associated circuit). The cost of unshielded twisted-pair cabling can be one-third that of the equivalent coaxial cabling, but a shielded twisted pair is comparable in cost to coaxial cabling. Twisted-pair cabling is generally capable of supporting signal transmissions up to approximately 10 MHz.

In large, local electromagnetic fields, coaxial cabling and shielded twisted-pair cabling can maintain a higher level of transmitted signal fidelity than an unshielded twisted pair.

Most LANs have a specified bit error rate (BER) equivalent to that of the Ethernet system (1 bit error in one billion bits transmitted). Very high local potentials (especially RFI) which occur primarily within an industrial environment mandate the use of special conductive rigid conduit shielding.

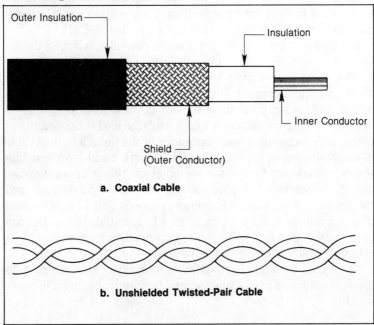

Figure 3.6—Coaxial and Twisted Pair Cabling

3.3.3 Capacitive Connectors and Planar Arrays

Another method of filtering employs modified connectors for specific standard types of cabling (e.g., DB-25 for RS-232 connections). Connector filters may involve feed-though capacitors, and sometimes ferrite beads or toroids, for each I/O line. The ferrite beads are generally insufficient for affecting EMI much below 100 MHz. Toroids function efficiently to reduce EMI in the critical range of 30 to 300 MHz. Prices for filter connectors are relatively high and are generally used only in specific situations where their use becomes imperative or unique (i.e., low production quantities).

Connectors which are specifically capacitive shunt high-frequency current directly to the chassis. It is imperative that the chassis or enclosure be as nearly "earth" ground as possible (very high normal potential between it and any where on the circuit board). The connectors generally employ a monolithic discoidal structure to minimize parasitic series inductances and resistances, and each line (connector pin) is provided a shunt capacitance of 100 to 1,000 pF. The capacitance acts with the effective impedance of the digital circuit board to create a lowpass filter to high-frequency noise in the range of 30 MHz to several hundred megahertz. The 3 dB point of the RFI filter thus created is high enough to let currents at signal line frequencies (such as RS-232 at 19.2 kilobaud and 500 kilobaud computer storage devices) unabated access. Another advantage of capacitive connectors is that individual I/O wires have greater isolation from one another.

Other types of capacitive connectors come in the form adapters which may be used between a cable and a noisy computer device. Similar capacitive planar arrays are also available for certain circuit board mounts and ICs which yield equivalent noise attenuation to the cable connectors (10 to 30 dB from 30 to 300 MHz).

Electrostatic discharge (ESD) is also reduced by the use of capacitive connectors and arrays because each I/O line or IC pin is capacitively coupled to ground. Capacitive connectors are relatively expensive (per-pin pricing of $.50 to $1.00); they are less expensive than discrete pi-type filters employed on each signal or I/O line and more expensive than magnetic filtering alone (using a single common-mode lossy ferrite structure for all I/O lines).

Ferrite beads or balance-to-unbalance transformers (baluns) may be used to augment the achievable attenuation of capacitive connectors, thus raising the effective circuit board impedance at noise frequencies (see Fig. 3.7). Applying beads to the circuit board source inputs and signal ground ("isolation beads"), which are main sources of noise, will keep much of the RF noise from the board circuitry and, thereby, the I/O lines and cabling.

Capacitive connectors and unshielded cables together are more effective in the reduction of EMI than shielded cabling alone. A shielded cable, while rejecting radiated potentials, will maintain high-frequency noise currents on the center conductor, (e.g., from a printed circuit board connection) and transmit the noise to another device which may itself radiate them. A filter connector attenuates the noise currents before they reach the cable.

Shielded cable shields are laced and fitted into a 360° conductive shell which itself can be securely attached to the device enclosure. Heavy braided shields are generally the most successful because of their durability (differences in shielding effectiveness are minor for high-frequency potentials) but are more expensive than simpler braids or foil. A capacitive connector must be securely fastened to the device enclosure, just as the shielded cable must be, and most connectors are specifically designed for such attachment.

The capacitive connector can allow the use of conventional flexible cabling; however, the use of ineffectual cabling (with regard to rejecting RFI) indicates the use of capacitive connectors at both ends of the cable.

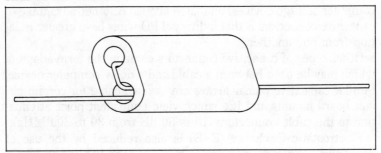

Figure 3.7—Ferrite Balun

3.3.4 Magnetic Filters

Since I/O lines are generally terminated in low-impedance (capacitive) loads, a series inductor makes an ideal impedance

3.18

because it provides a substantial impedance at EMI frequencies and negligible impedance at signal (low) frequencies.

Inductors using high turn count and high permeability cores can have inductances in the millihenry range. At low frequencies, these relatively high inductances can be used to deal with conducted EMI in the kilohertz range but may add ringing to the transmitted signal. As alluded to above, inductors having low inductances (tens of nanohenries to microhenry ranges), are suitable for dealing with radiated EMI in the high megahertz frequencies and without creating ringing of the transmitted signal.

Another method of filtering takes into account the common-mode nature of most EMI. Because the common-mode noise is the same on all I/O lines which relate to a common signal reference, common-mode attenuation is readily achieved by applying a single, common magnetic structure for all related I/O lines. The magnetic structure may be a sleeve surrounding all I/O lines, a large magnetic toroid on which the I/O lines are wound together, essentially composing a few turns of a common-mode inductor (see Figs. 3.8 through 3.10). It may be a common-mode, multi-line magnetic structure (a "data line" filter) which is interposed strategically between lengths of the I/O cabling (at the receive driver end, transmitting driver end or even in between, along the length of the cable).

The success of "common-mode" filtering of I/O lines lies in the fact that the signals transmitted via the lines are differential in nature and proceed through the magnetic structures without attenuation. Common-mode magnetic filter connectors and circuit board mountable arrays are available.

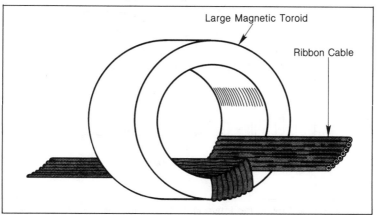

Figure 3.8—Multi-Line Common-Mode Inductor

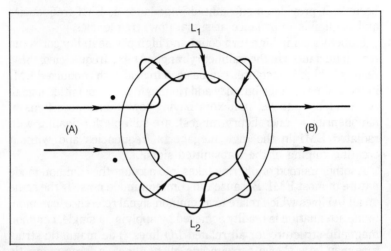

Figure 3.9—Two-Line Common-Mode Inductor

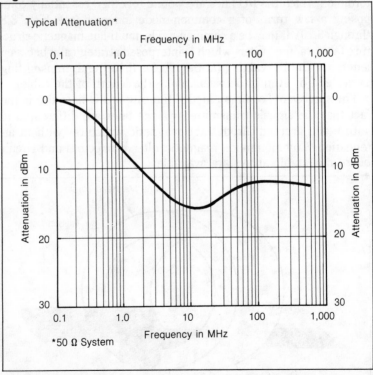

Figure 3.10—Typical Inductive Data Line Filter Response (courtesy of Coilcraft, Inc.)

3.3.5 Standard Reactive Filter Alignments

The filtering solution to EMI basically involves employing series impedances to absorb unwanted conducted energy and/or shunt impedances to deliver the unwanted energy to an equivalent "earth" ground. The ubiquitous pi filter is a good example of such a filter. The shunt impedances are capacitive in nature (almost exclusively RF capable capacitors). The series impedances are predominately inductive at conducted emission frequencies (below 30 MHz), less inductive, becoming dissipative at the low RF noise frequencies (between 30 and 100 MHz), and largely dissipative at the high EMI frequencies (100 to about 300 MHz). At the upper EMI frequencies (over 300 MHz), the series impedances become capacitive, beginning to transfer rather than curtail noise energy. For the majority of applications, particularly computer equipment, EMI is primarily limited to 300 MHz or less so that RF magnetics (inductors, baluns, ferrite beads) very successfully limit such EMI. At signal frequencies, filter inductors transfer energy unabatedly, essentially becoming a simple series short.

EMI line filters must be mounted to a conductive surface (the chassis), never to the circuit board. Filter leads should be as short and connected as directly as possible to minimize high-frequency common-mode noise. Open wire leads that are intended to use skin effect attenuation for filtering are not recommended because capacitive coupling between the wires creates high-frequency shorting of the filter, and lengths of wire can easily become antennas. Filter input and output wires should never be bundled together, thus avoiding coupling high-frequency noise around the filter.

An input LC smoothing filter is generally required in offline switching regulators, but these inductors and capacitors may themselves be sources of EMI. If the inductor is constructed with a relatively high-Q material, it will display substantial ringing and produce noise. Also, switching noise of the converter may be coupled through the distributed capacitance of the inductor and back into the line. The modulator transformer may ring and couple in ways similar to the filter inductor and produce its own EMI.

Passive filters serve as a very good means of eliminating the majority of conducted noise into a device (or out of a device and back into the line) when a relatively high current will be encountered (largely excluding the use of active filters). Many filter configurations exist, and each has its own advantages. Commonly considered filter alignments are the Bessel, Chebyshev and the Butterworth.

Ideally, Bessel filters maintain a very stable, linear phase response but at the expense of frequency response; the time response of Bessel filters is well behaved without substantial overshoot or ringing.

The ideal Chebyshev lowpass filter alignments allow a compromise between the amount of ripple in the passband (and damping) and the slope of attenuation at the crossover frequency. The stable behavior of the time response of Chebyshev filters is related to the damping factor, the allowed ripple and the slope of attenuation at the crossover frequency; as the slope of the attenuation at the crossover is increased, the transient response becomes less stable and prone to ringing, and the phase response becomes much less linear.

Butterworth lowpass filter alignments are Chebyshev filters designed for minimum ripple. They provide a flat response, no attenuation prior to the crossover frequency and a damping factor of approximately 0.7. After the crossover frequency, the attenuation continues at 20 times the order in decibels per decade. The time response for the Butterworth filter exhibits some ringing, and the phase response less than ideal but predictable. The overall response of Butterworth filters is well suited to quick and easy methods of approximation. Figure 3.11 illustrates the first three orders of lowpass filters and their Butterworth alignments.

In their use as noise suppressors, filters must be able to eliminate as much noise as possible beyond a predetermined frequency; the time response is not really important, especially in regard to common-mode noise. In a common-mode filter, the differential signal does not encounter the filter, thus any problems associated with phase or time response affect only the common-mode noise. When the filter is used to keep noise from entering the power mains from the device, phase and time responses become trivial to even the differential voltage. Ideally, then, Butterworth alignments for the design of EMI filters, because they are readily and easily modeled and approximated and provide good frequency response, seem the appropriate starting point for filter design.

Real passive filters, designed with idealized parameters, are not ideal themselves. Real filters, composed of real reactive elements, capacitors and inductors, are victims of anomalies which become more and more apparent as frequency increases. The reactive components become resistive at high frequencies; inductors become

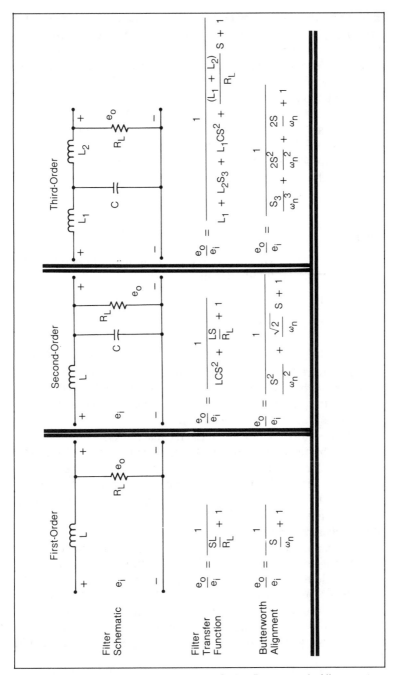

Figure 3.11—First, Second and Third Order Butterworth Alignments

capacitive, while the opposite is true of capacitors. There are several differing types of the standard reactive components (capacitors, inductors, transformers), and each has its own advantages and disadvantages. Also, reactive components, particularly inductors, may display high-frequency anomalous characteristics which can aid noise reduction.

Capacitance is ideally the amount of charge squared per unit energy (charge per volt) due to two equal area conductive plates which are isolated from one another by a dielectric material; this relationship between the plates and the dielectric is described in farads by the relation:

$$C = e \times A/D$$

where,

e = dielectric constant of the isolating material between the plates in farads per unit length

A = the area of each plate

D = the distance between the plates

The ideal capacitor provides an impedance which is inversely proportional to frequency and is stable for all frequencies. Because of the inverse proportionality, the capacity maintained by a capacitor at higher frequency needs to be lower to maintain equivalent impedance as that at lower frequency.

Real capacitors are not ideal. Each capacitor type and construction has a particular bandwidth of optimal application. Electrolytic capacitors, for example, are generally used at or near line frequencies and provide substantial capacitances (typically on the order of hundreds to thousands of microfarads), while ceramic chip capacitors are useful at high MHz frequencies and have capacities in the picofarad range.

All capacitors suffer to some degree from series resistance, series inductance and parallel resistance. The parallel resistance of a capacitor determines the self-resonance of the component [given by $1/(R \times C)$], the radian frequency above which the capacitor behaves as though it has switched circuit configuration. Above the resonant frequency, the parasitic series inductance and resistance become the effective parameters of the component as modeled in Fig. 3.12.

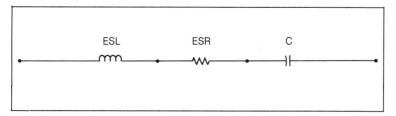

Figure 3.12—Typical Capacitor Model

There are various dielectrics used in the fabrication of capacitors, and there are a number of fabrication types. Usually, since the capacity of a structure is directly proportional to the area of its conductive plates, capacitors are made from very long, relatively narrow plates which are either interleaved, stacked or densely rolled to make a small package.

Electrolytic capacitors, made of tantalum or aluminum, achieve the highest capacitance of any normally available capacitors and are usually polarized. Electrolytics are generally used for extremely low-frequency energy storage and provide virtually none of the high-frequency capacitance required in most filtering applications (particularly for radio frequencies).

For filter applications, mylar, mica and ceramic capacitors are the most useful. Mylar capacitors are small, relatively inexpensive and can provide useful capacity though a few hundredths of a megahertz. Mica capacitors are more expensive than mylar, but they have very good electrical qualities and retain their original electrical parameters after temperature cycling. Ceramic capacitors have very small parasitic inductances, and they are useful for extended frequency bands (through the gigahertz range).

Ideally, inductors provide an impedance which is exactly proportional to frequency. Generally speaking, an air-core choke has an inductance which is largely frequency independent but very small; so small, its usefulness as a filter element (of the type with which we are concerned) is almost nil. Air has the permeability of free space, thus yielding low inductance in a coil. Much larger permeabilities are required for effective levels of inductance (thousands of times greater than air). Ferrites are generally used to provide the required permeability for filter chokes, yielding substantial inductance, but inductance which becomes frequency and current dependent rather quickly. Cores composed of high-permeability iron powder yield less inductance than the equivalent volume of ferrite but maintain their inductances through higher frequencies and larger currents. The winding of an inductor itself causes anomalies due to the decreasing skin depth as frequencies become high, contributing to higher resistive losses ($I^2 \times R$), and distributed capacity between the turns of an inductor winding lowers component self-resonant frequency.

The most usual types of core configuration for common-mode chokes are the "EE" and the toroid. The EE type of core is composed of two usually identical cores which are shaped like capital "Es" and which mate face-to-face to form a center path as well as a path about the perimeter of the core for magnetic flux to circulate. The toroid type of core is donut shaped and forces the magnetic flux to flow in a simple, circular unimpeded path.

The simplicity of the circular path makes the toroid a more efficient configuration than the EE; the EE essentially has eight 90° turns in the flux path, which somewhat diminishes the effective magnetic flux achievable by the core. However, the EE configuration has two major advantages over the toroid:

1. The windings of the choke can be made separate from the core, on a bobbin, and later slipped on the center leg prior to the gluing of the cores. (The windings of a toroid choke must be made on the core itself.)
2. EE chokes are easily gapped, yielding a second degree of freedom in adjusting inductance. (Changing the inductance of a toroid choke involves increasing or decreasing the number of wire turns alone.) Gapping an EE inductor also stabilizes the expected ideal characteristics of the component in respect to frequency and higher current capacity.

Figure 3.13 illustrates a typical inductor, and Fig. 3.14 shows "EE" and toroid core inductors.

Because the inductance of a toroidal coil cannot be adjusted by fractional turn count, the inductance is dependent on the core permeability tolerance (typically 15 to 25 percent). E cores are available with the same permeability tolerance; however, the inductance tolerance also depends on the precision with which the cores are assembled to each other. Therefore, using an ungapped E core

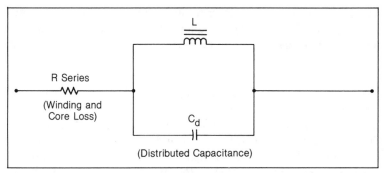

Figure 3.13—Typical Inductor Model

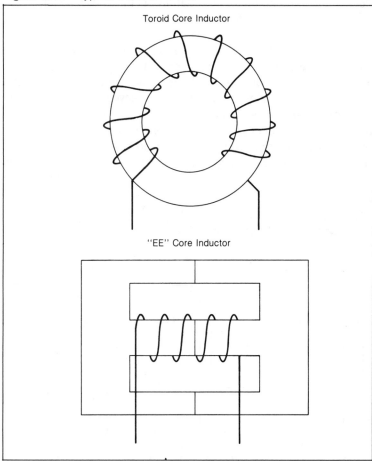

Figure 3.14—Typical "EE" and Toroid Inductor Shapes

typically yields a wider tolerance than a toroid. Gapping of E cores is a method of decreasing the tolerance of inductance because, as gap size increases, the inductance becomes proportional to the gap length instead of the permeability.

Above the self-resonant frequency, an inductor begins to display the full effects of its parasitic components. At high frequencies (a decade or so above the self-resonant frequency) the attenuation provided by an inductive lowpass filter can be expected to vary depending on the winding configuration and its associated distributed capacitance. The distributed capacitance allows a finite amount of high-frequency spectral energy to effectively short across the inductor and thus diminish attenuation at higher frequencies.

There are three standard winding configurations for an inductor (see Fig. 3.15). Simplest and least prone to distributed capacitance of all the standard configurations is the single-layer winding. The starts and finishes of a single layer winding are as far from one another as possible and thus inhibit capacitive coupling. A multi-layer wind (essentially, two or more interleaved single layers) provides capacitance between layers and from the start lead to the finish lead (which are generally as close to one another as possible with the finish lead ending where the start lead began). The multi-layer configuration displays the greatest capacitance of the winding con-

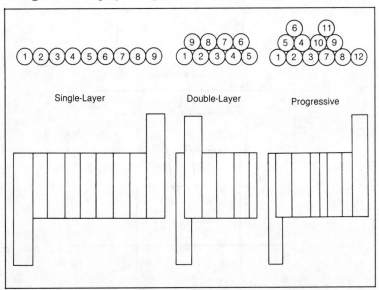

Figure 3.15—Single, Double and Progressive Layer Windings

figurations (thus the lowest attenuation at higher frequencies for an inductive lowpass filter).

A compromise between the single and multi-layer winding configurations is the progressive (banked) wind. A progressive winding is accomplished by winding a few turns, then backing up a couple of turns and repeating the process (three steps forward and two steps back). The starts and finish leads are thus as far apart as possible, with the same number of turns as a multi-layer wind, but without the interleaving. The progressive winding configuration yields a high frequency capacitance equivalent to the single-layer wind (and virtually the same high-frequency attenuating capability).

All multi-winding inductors exhibit leakage inductance. The leakage inductance of a winding is the amount of inductance which is not coupled to any other winds through the core. Leakage inductance is due to the winding itself. Leakage is undesirable in transformers in general because it stores energy without transforming it to other coils in the structure. However, in a lowpass filter, leakage inductance adds to the attenuation of the filter (also in line frequency common-mode chokes, where the differential signal passes unattenuated due to coupling of the windings, the uncoupled leakage inductance, much lower than the rated inductance of the choke, will help attenuate the undesirable higher frequency EMI).

The diameter of wire used in a choke is determined by the amount of current which it will be required to handle at the operating frequency of the associated circuit. The larger the current, the larger the wire. For example, at a line frequency current of 1 A, 26 AWG wire is required to provide 250 circular mils to support the current. As frequency increases, the amount of cross sectional area (for a single strand of wire) used by the current decreases (skin effect). For frequencies above about 100 kHz, multi-stranded wire (litz wire, with each strand insulated) should be used if the high-frequency current is to be supported. For a lowpass inductive filter which needs to pass only the line frequencies, further attenuation due to skin effect may be desirable.

The susceptibility of a material in powder form is one-third that of the homogeneous crystal form (the relative permeability is approximately one-third). The randomness of the magnetic domains of powder and the non-compactness of powder (relative to the high density of ferrite) provide minute gaps between domains which are able to store small energies; collectively, these small gaps provide a large effective gap. Because of the randomness and micro-gapping of powder, though the initial permeability begins much lower than that of high-density ferrite, the initial permeability (thus initial inductance) is well maintained through higher frequencies and for larger currents than the high-density materials.

At frequencies higher than the self-resonance of a filter inductor, the filter inductor characteristics become largely a function of shunt capacitance (distributed capacity). Likewise, the self-resonant character of a filter capacitor becomes largely a function of its series inductance and resistance. The design of a standard second-order filter should be made both via the Laplace transfer function of a circuit of ideal components and by way of determining the minimum value required for controlling the high-frequency peculiarities of the filter inductor(s) and the capacitor(s).

Below the self-resonant frequency, the measured response follows the ideal response (within a few decibels) of a standard filter alignment, with the measured response gaining attenuation by virtue of substantially increasing effective resistance near self-resonance.

Substantial resonant response peaks predicted from ideal component filter circuits are largely flattened in the real measurements. There exists a far greater damping factor in a real filter circuit than expected by ideal components; the Q of the real circuit is much less than predicted (attributable to a number of factors, including core loss, coupling of the choke winding to core, the much less than ideal coupling of components to one another).

The use of a smaller inductor in conjunction with a larger choke will provide a steeper slope of attenuation for a wider frequency range than either a single choke or two large value series inductors.

What is desired from a line filter is the removal of the harmonic content of the differential line input (usually signals above 60 Hz) so that ac line conducted noise is kept out of a load. At the same

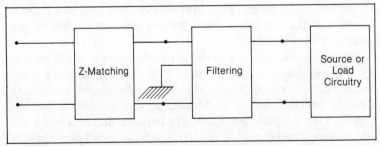

Figure 3.16—Conceptualized Filter Arrangement

time, the filter is removing the common-mode conducted noise of the load before entering the ac line.

Figure 3.16 shows the use of a common-mode filter for the ac line (via impedance matching circuitry) of a (noisy) power converter. The direction of common-mode noise (noise on both lines occurring simultaneously referred to earth ground) is from the converter and into the filter, where the noise common to both lines becomes attenuated.

The design of a common-mode filter is essentially the design of two identical differential filters, one for each of the two polarity lines with the inductors of each side coupled by a single core as shown in Fig. 3.9.

For a differential input [(A) to (B) through L1 and (B) to (A) through L2] the net magnetic flux which is coupled between the two inductors is nullified. Any inductance caused by the differential signal is then an effect of the decoupling of the two chokes; they perform as independent components with their leakage inductances responding to the differential signal.

When the inductors, L1 and L2, encounter an identical signal of the same polarity (referred to ground; common-mode signal), they each contribute a net non-zero flux in the shared core; the inductors thus perform as independent components with their mutual inductances responding to the common signal.

The simplest and least expensive filter to design is a first-order filter, using a single reactive component to store certain frequency bands of EMI energy without passing this energy to the load. In the case of a lowpass common-mode filter, a common-mode choke is the reactive element employed.

The value of inductance required of the choke is simply the load in ohms divided by the radian frequency at and above which the signal is to be attenuated. For example, attenuation at and above 1,000 Hz into a 50 Ω load would require $50/(1,000 \times 2 \times \pi)$ = 7.96 mH. The resulting filter configuration would have a 3 dB point at 1,000 Hz and a 6 dB per octave rolloff.

A 20 percent decrease in inductance would shift the crossover point upward to 1,250 Hz; a 40 percent decrease would shift the crossover point to 1,667 Hz. A 20 percent increase in inductance would shift the crossover point down to 833 Hz; an increase of 40 percent would yield a crossover point of 714 Hz.

Common-mode chokes are designed with a minimum inductance (usually at 15.75 kHz), therefore a first-order filter may be designed with a minimum inductance in mind. However, care should be observed in choosing a choke for a first-order lowpass filter because common-mode chokes are largely constructed to exceed a minimum value of inductance. A much higher than typical or minimum value of inductance may limit the choke's useful band of attenuation. Typically, the higher the inductance of a choke, the lower the self-resonant frequency. After the self-resonant frequency, the attenuation due to the single inductive filter rapidly decreases and may allow more noise at higher frequencies than should be allowed.

3.4 Other Signal Line Interference Control Techniques

3.4.1 Circuit Layout

The initial phase of solving an anticipated noise problem in a circuit is by defining the proper layout of the circuit. Integrated circuits are the primary sources of current transients. Other sources may be local magnetics and highly excited passive components. Nonlinear ICs, though, work in conjunction with and at the high frequencies of clock signals. Therefore, the design of the circuit board is of great EMI concern.

Component parts which are adjacent in the schematic of a device should be as close to one another as possible in the physical design. Leads or traces interconnecting component parts should be as short as possible and have as much surface area as practical. The return path (ground plane) should also have a very large surface area. All shield leads (only one end of each shield should be grounded to prevent undesirable current loops) should be as short as possible and make good electrical contact with the chassis ground. The chassis of the device should be of high conductivity and encapsulate the entire device as much as possible. Filters which form a physically integral part of the device should have respective inputs maintained directly opposite outputs (avoiding the cross coupling of these inputs and outputs). Filter mounts should be near the power input to the device as well.

It is important that nonisolated traces of the PC board not cross isolated sections or signal ground. It is also important that high-level signal wires be bundled separately from any and all wires supporting low level signals. Filter wires should never be bundled with any signal wire.

3.4.2 Grounding Techniques

Ground paths which are derived through circuit board traces are themselves inherently inductive (this becomes obvious at RF frequencies). In combination with high-frequency clock signals, they create current transients and, thereby, noise potentials at RF frequencies. Circuit boards generally share a common ground reference via common power supply connections, and wires connected to these boards radiate the created RF noise.

Breaking up a circuit board return or ground trace into a matrix of smaller traces will lower the effective impedance of the path at RF frequencies. Lowering the trace impedance will allow RF potentials to sink more successfully to ground.

Signal grounds are common points of signal reference which generally contain thin, inherently inductive paths and have a usually small overall cross-sectional area. Successful "earth" grounds have large seamless cross-sectional areas.

Bypass capacitors should shunt the I/O lines to chassis (not signal) ground at the I/O driver output (or input). The capacitor leads should be as short as possible to minimize parasitic inductances. Also shields should never be directly connected to the signal ground, primarily because this is generally the source of common-mode EMI.

3.4.3 Enclosures

The optimal chassis ground (enclosure) has a large, unipotential surface (negligible potential gradients over the entire surface). An enclosure is generally the largest conductive area of a piece of electronic equipment and serves as an "earth" ground as well as a Faraday shield.

Metalized enclosures can provide a piece of equipment with Faraday shielding; they also may provide "earth" grounding, if the enclosure provides suitable surface area to retain all return potentials attached to it. Metal impregnation of plastics and other nonconductive, electromagnetically transparent materials can serve as Faraday shields, limiting equipment radiated RF potentials to the field within the enclosure molded from these materials, but these materials cannot serve as "earth" grounds. An enclosure made of aluminum, steel or any similarly highly conductive material may serve as Faraday shielding and an equivalent "earth" grounding.

The perfect enclosure would be an entire metal structure of six seamless sides which contains no openings; such an enclosure lets an insignificant amount of radiated EMI to pass into or out of the enclosure. But seams, cracks and apertures are unavoidable aspects of equipment enclosures if the equipment will have any connection to the outside world (via the power line, I/O cabling, heat dissipation).

Seams of a metal enclosure perform in a similar fashion to antennas of the same shape and size, allowing RF radiation into space. Enclosure apertures are "slot antennas" which radiate any incident RF potentials. Like antennas, the longer the seams or apertures of an enclosure are, the lower the frequency of radiated potentials. Smaller apertures and seams created from larger ones increase the frequencies of radiation, effectively creating a highpass filter to very high-frequency RF potentials, limiting the more problematic lower-frequency EMI access.

The wavelength of a potential at 300 MHz is about 1 m (3 ft), increasing in length as frequency decreases. Seams and apertures of 51 mm (2 in) or less will be too small to radiate problem EMI in most cases. Metal screens can be used to cover large apertures (cooling vents, for example) and metal gaskets can be used around seams; both increase the radiating frequency of the antenna like structures (creating higher-frequency highpass filters to radiated potentials). Instead of gaskets, the seam (of an access door, for example) may be split up into several smaller seams by affixing conductive contact points around the seam at equal intervals.

Screens and gaskets must be securely fastened to an enclosure, and the connection must maintain the best possible conductivity without gaps (the screen or gasket mount must be free of nonconductive paint and films). Conductive protrusions coming through an enclosure should be bonded or otherwise maintain strong electrical contact with the enclosure to prevent radiating RFI from the enclosed circuitry.

3.5 Bibliography

ANSI/EIA-232-D-1986, "Interface between Data Terminal Equipment and Data Circuit-Terminating Equipment Employing Serial Binary Data Interchange" (New York: American National Standards Institute).

ANSI/IEEE Std 488-1978, "IEEE Standard Digital Interface for Programmable Instrumentation" (New York: Institute of Electrical and Electronics Engineers).

ANSI/IEEE Std 802.3-1985 (ISO/DIS 8802/3), "Carrier Sense Multiple Access with Collision Detection Access Method and Physical Layer Specifications" (New York: Institute of Electrical and Electronics Engineers).

ANSI/IEEE Std 802.3a, b, c and e-1988, "Supplements to Carrier Sense Multiple Access with Collision Detection Access Method and Physical Layer Specifications" (New York: Institute of Electrical and Electronics Engineers).

ANSI/IEEE Std 802.4-1985 (ISO/DIS 8802/4), "Token-Passing Bus Access Method and Physical Layer Specifications" (New York: Institute of Electrical and Electronics Engineers).

ANSI/IEEE Std 802.5-1985 (ISO/DIS 8802/5), "Token Ring Access Method and Physical Layer Specifications" (New York: Institute of Electrical and Electronics Engineers).

Bartee, Thomas, ed., *Data Communications, Networks and Systems* (Indianapolis: Howard W. Sams & Co., 1985).

Carsten, B.W., "Design Techniques for the Inherent Reduction of Power Converter EMI," Proceedings of Powercon 11, March 1984, P. D-2.

Corcom, "Noise Source Equivalent Circuit Model for Off-Line Converters and Its Use in Input Filter Design," Proceedings of Powercon 10, October 1985.

Crane, L.F. and Srebranig, S.F., "Common Mode Filter Inductor Analysis," Proceedings of the Power Electronics Design Conference, October 1985.

Dash, G., ed., "Design of the PC Board," *1985-86 Compliance Engineering*, 1985, pp. 87-110.

Dash, G., ed., "Shielding the Case," *1985-86 Compliance Engineering*, 1985, pp. 150-153.

Dash, G., ed., "Shielding, Filtering, and Bypassing of the I/O Cables," *1985-86 Compliance Engineering*, 1985, pp. 111-149.

EIA-422-A, "Electrical Characteristics of Balanced Voltage Digital Interface Circuits" (Washington, DC: Electronic Industries Association).

EIA-423-A, "Electrical Characteristics of Unbalanced Voltage Digital Interface Circuits" (Washington, DC: Electronic Industries Association).

EIA-449, "General Purpose 37-Position and 9-Position Interface for Data Terminal Equipment and Data Circuit-Terminating Equipment Employing Serial-Binary Data Interchange" (Washington, DC: Electronic Industries Association).

FCC Docket 20780-1980 [Part 15], "Technical Standards for Computing Equipment," Reconsidered First Report and Order, April 1980.

Hazzard, H. and Kiefer, R., "EMI Reduction Using Capacitive Filter Connectors." *ITEM 1986*, pp. 240-250.

Hoolihan, D. and Johnson, J., "Compliance with Japanese VCCI Standards," *Compliance Engineering 1988*, pp. 136-141.

Mertel, H., "VDE/FTZ Interference Regulations-West Germany," *ITEM 1986*, pp. 72-80.

Nave, M., "Line Impedance Stabilizing Networks: Theory and Use," *RF Design*, April 1985, p. 54.

Nye, F.J., *Physical Properties of Crystals* (London: Oxford University Press, Ely House, 1972).

Scidmore, A.K., "Noise in Amplifiers," Lecture Notes for ECE-341—Linear Active Circuits, University of Wisconsin, 1982.

Spencer, Peter, "Pitfalls of Filter Applications," *ITEM 1986*, p. 252.

Srebranig, S.F., "Data Line Filtering," *ITEM 1988*, pp. 130-138.

Srebranig, S.F. and Crane, L.F., Guide for Common-Mode Filter Design (Cary, IL: Coilcraft, Inc., 1985).

Williams, A.B., *Electronic Filter Design Handbook* (New York: McGraw-Hill, 1981).

Chapter 4

Power Line
Electromagnetic Interference

by Daryl Gerke, P.E.
Kimmel Gerke Associates, Ltd.
St. Paul, MN 55108

The proliferation of sophisticated electronic equipment in today's society has spawned numerous **electromagnetic interference (EMI)** and **electromagnetic compatibility (EMC)** problems. Many of these problems are associated with the commercial electrical power distribution system. Since most electronic equipments are connected to commercial power systems, the concern for both **power quality** and **power susceptibility** has increased dramatically in recent years by both the providers and users of electric power.

The problem has been aggravated as modern electronic systems incorporated embedded computers, microprocessors and other complex solid state components. By their nature, these devices operate at low energy levels and high speeds, making them particularly fragile and susceptible to power electrical noise. At the same time, these same devices often contribute to the power line noise levels in a system as well.

The objective of this chapter is to provide information and insights on electrical power disturbances and their effects upon modern electronic equipment. These disturbances include voltage fluctuations, electrical outages, spikes and transients, electrical **noise** and harmonic distortions of the voltage and current waveforms. The effects include undesired computing and data processing errors, analog instrumentation errors and even nuisances such as **hum** in a stereo system.

This chapter has four sections. The first three follow the EMI model of "source-path-victim." Section 4.1 discusses power line disturbances; Section 4.2 discusses the effects of these disturbances upon electronic equipment; and Section 4.3 discusses several power line coupling paths. The final section, 4.4, contains a list of references articles, standards and books.

Finally, this chapter is written from an EMC engineer's perspective, as a "user" of power rather than a "provider." From this vantage point, it would be easy to blame the electric utilities as the providers and demand that they provide "clean power." In most cases, however, the power utility is neither the cause of the power line EMI problem, nor does it typically have much control over the solutions. What is needed is more awareness and help from EMI engineers and design engineers to prevent and solve these problems. If this chapter helps only to increase that awareness, it has been a success.

4.1 Power Line Disturbances

This section describes typical power line disturbances, the "source" of power related EMI problems.

4.1.1 Some General Concepts

Before discussing the characteristics and sources of power line disturbances, it may be helpful to first review some general concepts and definitions.

Time Domain vs. Frequency Domain

An important parameter of disturbances is their frequency spectral content. These spectral characteristics dictate the frequency attenuation needed by protective devices. It is generally well understood that any variation from a pure sine wave results in harmonics of the fundamental repetition frequency. But single events such as transients have a "frequency content," too.

Working in the frequency domain rather than the time domain is important because the specifications and manufacturers literature for devices like filters use frequency-based, rather than time-based, units. In addition, important insights can be gained by examining both periodic and transient phenomena in the frequency domain.

Fourier analysis is the tool for moving between the time and frequency domains. In the purest sense, one uses the Fourier series for repetitive waveforms, and the Fourier transform for single events such as transients. In our case, however, we are simply interested in the "worst case" emission envelopes, which greatly simplifies the analysis.

Figures 4.1 and 4.2 show the time and frequency relationships for several representative waveforms. Note that for both the trapezoidal waveform and the unidirectional transient, the rate of decrease in spectral energy increases from 20 dB to 40 dB per decade at a frequency of $1/\pi \times$ rise time. This frequency is often

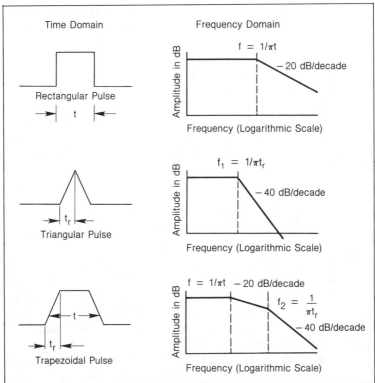

Figure 4.1—Frequency Spectrum for Digital Waveforms

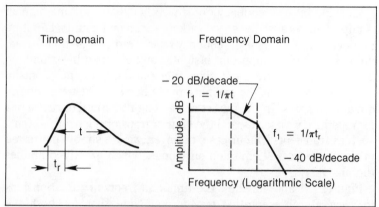

Figure 4.2—Frequency Spectrum for Transient Waveform

referred to as the critical frequency, or the bandwidth, since the majority of the energy is below this frequency. This frequency is often used as a design frequency for assessing filter performance, crosstalk and other frequency-dependent effects.

For example, a digital signal with a rise time of 5 ns has a critical frequency of about 60 MHz. A transient with a 2 ns rise time has a critical frequency of over 150 MHz.

This analysis also illustrates that limiting rise times (for both repetitive signals and transients) is a very effective method of controlling high-frequency noise components. For example, changing the rise time from 3 ns to 30 ns decreases the critical frequency from 100 MHz to 10 MHz.

Power Quality

The term **power quality** is commonly used within power utilities in regard to power-related EMI problems. High "quality" indicates a lack of power line disturbances.

The proliferation of electronic equipment has caused serious problems and concerns for the electric utilities. Customers are concerned about the "quality" of the power they receive, and the utilities are concerned about the pollution and/or waveform distortions caused by customers. The power quality problem has become so acute that many utilities are now providing both engineering services and power conditioning equipment to help resolve power EMI problems. Some utilities are even offering optional "clean" power feeders for users of sensitive equipment.

Inside vs. Outside the Meter

The power utilities use the **meter** as an arbitrary dividing line between the customer and the utility. In many cases, the root cause of the problem is "inside the meter." Most power line disturbances that can cause damage or upset are not caused by the utilities but, rather, by the consumer himself or other consumers on the same distribution line. One recent study by a manufacturer of power line monitors revealed that 85 to 95 percent of power disturbances in the United States originate at the customer site.

Since the utility has very little control of facilities "inside the meter," the EMI and design communities need a heightened awareness of the problems and a willingness to prevent and solve those problems at the equipment and system interconnect level.

EMI, EMC and RFI

Since these three terms are widely used (and abused), it may be beneficial to define these terms as they will be used here. Electromagnetic interference (EMI) refers to the impairment of desired operation by an electromagnetic disturbance. This disturbance can be coupled by direct conduction (such as through the power lines) or by electromagnetic radiation (such as to or from the power lines). Electromagnetic compatibility (EMC) is the desired state of functioning in an electromagnetic environment without either adversely affecting other equipment, or without being adversely affected by, the environment. Finally, radio frequency interference (RFI) is acknowledged as an "older" term for EMI, coined when most EMI problems were radio frequency related.

4.1.2 Types of Disturbances

At present, the terminology for power line disturbances has not been standardized. Some attempts have been made to separate disturbances on the basis of durations and levels. This section divides those disturbances into five areas: voltage variations (sags, surges, outages), waveform distortion (voltage and current), frequency variations, "continuous electrical noise" and transients. Table 4.1 gives an overview of these different disturbances.

Power Disturbances

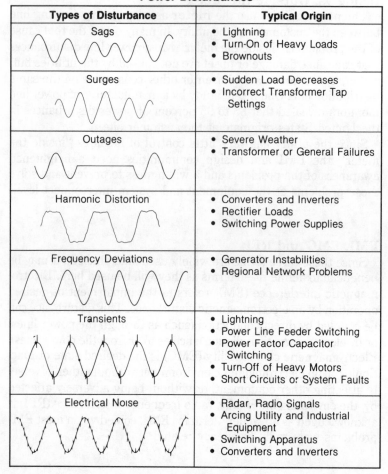

Types of Disturbance	Typical Origin
Sags	• Lightning • Turn-On of Heavy Loads • Brownouts
Surges	• Sudden Load Decreases • Incorrect Transformer Tap Settings
Outages	• Severe Weather • Transformer or General Failures
Harmonic Distortion	• Converters and Inverters • Rectifier Loads • Switching Power Supplies
Frequency Deviations	• Generator Instabilities • Regional Network Problems
Transients	• Lightning • Power Line Feeder Switching • Power Factor Capacitor Switching • Turn-Off of Heavy Motors • Short Circuits or System Faults
Electrical Noise	• Radar, Radio Signals • Arcing Utility and Industrial Equipment • Switching Apparatus • Converters and Inverters

4.1.2.1 Voltage Variations

In this case, the supplied voltage deviates from the specified operating range. Input below the range is a "sag," and input above the range is a "surge." Typically, sags and surges last more than one cycle (16.6 ms at 60 Hz); shorter duration deviations are generally considered transients. A total loss of voltage for one or more cycles is often referred to as an "outage." These are shown graphically in Fig. 4.3.

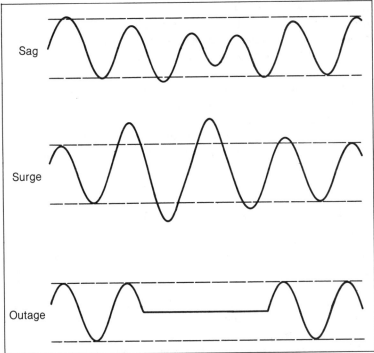

Figure 4.3—Voltage Sags, Surges and Outages

Sags can be caused by the utility or by the user. A prime example of a utility-caused sag is the "brownout," a deliberate cutback in voltage (typically 3 to 8 percent) during periods of peak demand. Utility sags also occur as a result of clearing faults due to lightning currents. Customer-induced sags are due to turn-on of heavy loads or by excessive inrush currents on equipment power-up. Long-term sags, greater than 30 cycles, are often referred to as **undervoltages**.

Surges are almost exclusively utility caused, resulting from sudden load decreases which can not be compensated or corrected instantly. Long-term surges, greater than 30 cycles, are often referred to as **overvoltages**. A common cause of overvoltages is a leading power factor, caused by either a capacitive load or too much capacitive correction to an inductive load.

Outages are total power failures lasting from about 0.5 s to several hours or more. Outages are usually utility caused, resulting from transformer or generator failures, severe weather or accidents involving power lines. Customer-induced outages occur whenever overcurrent devices, such as fuses or circuit breakers, are activated. Power outages are often further classified by duration as momentary, (0.5 to 2 s), temporary (2 s to 2 min), or permanent (longer than 2 min).

Sags and outages are much bigger problems than surges for electronic equipment operation. Both the magnitude and the duration of surges and outages are important parameters. For electronic equipment, the issue is energy storage. Can the equipment operate through the disturbance? Typical levels and limits will be discussed in a subsequent section.

4.1.2.2 Frequency Variations

These are changes in the sine wave frequency, caused by poor speed regulation of the generating equipment. This disturbance is almost nonexistent on commercial power in North America, where the frequency is typically held to within 0.5 Hz of the 60 Hz specification. In addition, any deviation is averaged out over a 24 hour period, because clocks and other time-based devices depend on a constant frequency for accuracy.

Although this is not typically a concern on commercial power, it can be a concern on independent ac power systems. Changing loads can cause frequency variations in small systems, particularly where the load changes constitute an appreciable fraction of the total load.

The effects upon users are varied. Most solid state electronic equipment is relatively immune to small frequency variations, particularly if the power supply includes input regulation. Motors (such as disk or tape drives) can be severely affected by frequency variation, however, which may result in system malfunctions. Ferroresonant regulators are also sensitive to frequency variations and, as a result, should not be used in situations with wide frequency variations.

4.1.2.3 Harmonic Distortion

This type of disturbance refers to the distortion of the voltage and current waveforms from a pure sine wave. Since any distortion from a pure sine wave results in harmonics, this is often referred to as **harmonic distortion**. A common parameter is **total harmonic distortion,** or **THD**, which is a measure of the residual energy of a waveform after the fundamental frequency is removed.

Harmonic distortion can be divided into two classes: voltage distortion and current distortion. Since the voltage is common to all loads in a system, any voltage distortion will result in a corresponding current distortion in even a pure resistive load. On the other hand, current distortion results in voltage distortion only to the extent that the source impedance provides a common coupling impedance. Harmonic distortion is a key concern of the power utilities, but it is usually not a serious problem for electronic equipment.

The effects of harmonic distortion upon traditional linear loads are well understood. Since the harmonics are at low frequencies (multiples of the 50 Hz, 60 Hz or 400 Hz line frequency), they can represent significant losses. The resulting harmonic currents may cause motors and transformers to heat excessively and malfunction. One journal stated that a 10 percent increase in voltage stress caused by harmonic currents typically results in a 7 percent increase in operating temperature of a capacitor bank and can reduce its life expectancy by 30 percent of normal.

The effects of harmonic currents from nonlinear loads are not so well understood at this time. Computers, for example, seem to be able to withstand low-level harmonic currents. Due to the low impedance of most power systems, the power system generally can absorb significant amounts of harmonic current without converting these to unacceptable voltage levels.

Harmonic distortion can be caused by either the utility or by the customer's equipment. Harmonics are generated by either faulty distribution equipment (voltage distortion) or by loads with nonlinear voltage/current characteristics (current distortion). An example of faulty distribution equipment might be an overloaded transformer that distorts the voltage waveform as it becomes saturated. Typical examples of nonlinear loads include arcing devices (such as arc furnaces and fluorescent lighting), ferromagnetic devices (such as regulating transformers) and silicon controlled rectifiers (SCRs) used in power supplies and electronic power converters. Figure 4.4 shows some typical waveforms due to these nonlinear loads.

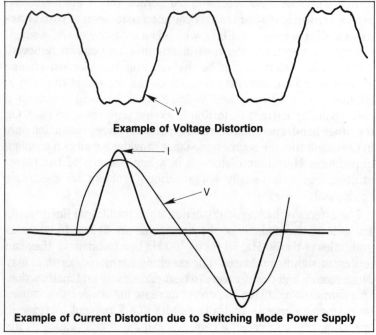

Figure 4.4—Voltage and Current Distortion

4.1.2.4 Continuous Electrical Noise

The term **electrical noise** is rather nebulous, so it may be useful to first define the term. In the most general sense, **noise** could be any variation from the desired signal, which would include the sags, surges and distortions already discussed. In this context, however, we will use **noise** to refer to energy other than directly related to the power waveform and power waveform low-frequency harmonics.

There are two subclasses of noise: continuous or steady state, and transients. Continuous noise is quite common and is due to repetitive events such as switching mode power supplies, motor brush arcing or external coupling from radio transmitters. Transients are also quite common in power distribution systems and are due to singular events such as lightning, load switching and faults. Transients will be discussed in the following section.

Typically, continuous and transient noise have little effect upon equipment such as motors and lighting. Modern electronic systems, however, are very vulnerable to both effects. That vulnerability is rapidly increasing as electronic systems increase in speed, which require faster rise times and a corresponding broader **susceptibility bandwidth**. At the same time, integrated circuits become smaller, with lower upset and damage thresholds, while coupling efficiencies increase with the higher frequencies. The net result is that the problems with electronic equipment due to electrical noise are only going to get worse.

Continuous noise is seen as continuous high-frequency energy superimposed on the power waveform. It is often referred in laymen's terms as **hash** or **radio frequency interference (RFI)**.

There are several potential sources of continuous noise. Communication transmitters are obvious sources and are becoming an increasing problem in today's society with the proliferation of both high-powered and low-powered licensed transmitters. Paging systems, portable hand-held VHF transmitters and low power unlicensed units such as portable telephones and wireless microphones are all potential sources of continuous noise on power systems.

Equipment that arcs, such as motor brushes, is also a significant source of continuous high-frequency noise due to the harmonics of the 60 Hz power. As seen in Section 4.1.1, the typical spark breakdown time of 10 ns means that significant harmonic energy is present at 30 MHz and above. These high-frequency harmonics often manifest themselves as **hash** on the power waveform.

4.1.2.5 Transients

Since transients are such a common problem in power systems, this section will explore them in some detail. We will classify transients as short-term disturbances (much less than a cycle), typically ranging from fractions of a microsecond to a few milliseconds in duration. They may instantaneously either increase (spike) or decrease (notch) the sine wave amplitude.

Key parameters for transients are amplitude, rise time, duration, oscillation and repetition rate. Understanding, observing and recording these variations can often give valuable insights into the source of the transients. Figure 4.5 illustrates several types of transient waveforms.

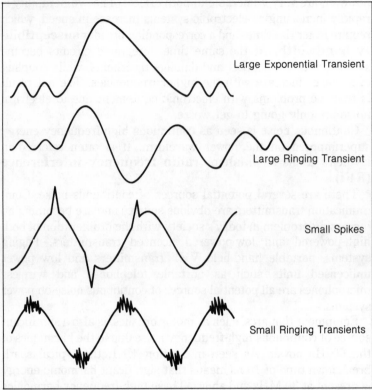

Figure 4.5—Transient Waveforms

Transient amplitudes can range from a small fraction of the operation voltage to thousands of volts. They represent the largest voltage swings of the various types of voltage disturbances. Typically, the greater the amplitude, the greater the likelihood of upset or damage to equipment.

Transient rise times can range from nanoseconds to milliseconds. The rise time is typically defined as the time between the 10 percent and 90 percent amplitude points. The shorter the duration, the more **high-frequency** the energy in the transient. The accepted conversion between rise time and frequency is $f = 1/(\pi \times t_r)$. This yields an **equivalent frequency** that defines the bandwidth of the transient. (For example, a transient with a 100 ns edge has bandwidth of 3 MHz.) Typically, the higher the frequency content, the greater the likelihood of undesired coupling around

4.12

or through protective devices such as filters, and the greater the likelihood of crosstalk and electromagnetic radiation.

Transient duration can range from nanoseconds to milliseconds and is typically defined as the time between rising and falling 50 percent amplitude points. An important measure of a transient's disturbance potential is the product of the duration and the amplitude, often referred to as the **impulse strength**. Figure 4.6 shows this as the shaded area under the curve represents the impulse strength in volt-seconds. Typically, the greater the duration, the greater the likelihood of damage due to increased energy.

Transient oscillations can be underdamped or overdamped. Underdamped oscillations result in a **ringing wave**, a damped sinusoidal waveform. Overdamped oscillations result in fast rise time and a slow damped exponential decay.

The **transient repetition rate** can vary from a single event to very high rates (falling into our other category of continuous noise). The repetition rate can be a very valuable parameter in determining the root source of the transient. For example, a repetition rate of 20 kHz would suggest a local switching mode power supply running at 20 kHz as the source.

Modern electronic systems are quite susceptible to transients. This vulnerability is rapidly increasing as electronic system speeds escalate, which requires faster logic families and a correspondingly increased **susceptibility bandwidth**. At the same time, as integrated circuits become smaller, the energy levels needed to upset or damage circuits is decreasing. The net result is that the problems

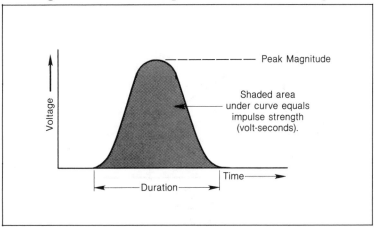

Figure 4.6—Transient Impulse Strength

with electronic equipment due to transients are only going to get worse.

Transient Sources

There are many sources of transients on both sides of the meter. Transient characteristics vary due to both the source and the distance from the source, which may give some clues to the origin.

Typical "utility-side" transient sources include lightning, power line feeder switching, power factor correction capacitor switching and distribution system faults. Typical "customer-side" transients include the turn-off of motors and other inductive loads, mechanical make and break contacts and power electronics switching.

Many transients have unique characteristics that give clues to their source. One key clue is rise time; transients with very fast rise times (in the nanosecond range) are typically located within 15 m (50 ft). The following paragraphs characterize some common transient sources.

Lightning transients can be the result of a direct lightning stroke to a conductor, magnetic field coupling or common-impedance coupling through the ground system. Amplitudes can vary up to about 6,000 V, with typical rise times of 1 to 10 μs and typical durations of 30 to 200 μs. Typical waveshapes are both the exponential decay and a "ringing" damped sine wave. Figure 4.7 shows typical lightning waveforms.

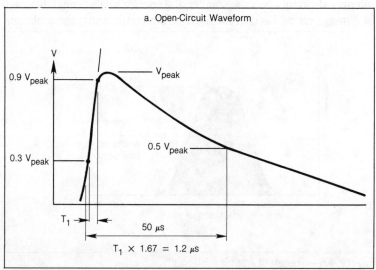

Figure 4.7—Typical Lightning Waveforms (from IEEE C62.41) (continued next page)

4.14

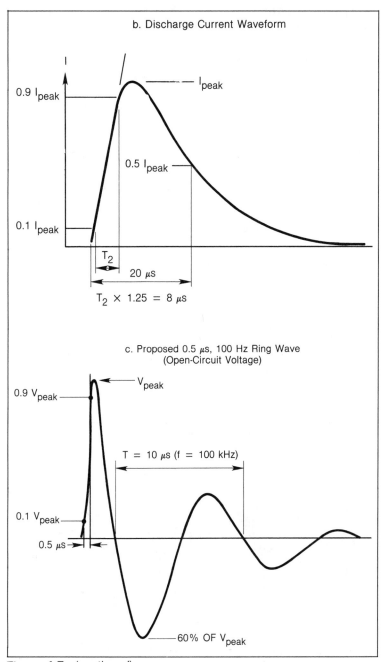

b. Discharge Current Waveform

$T_2 \times 1.25 = 8 \ \mu s$

c. Proposed 0.5 μs, 100 Hz Ring Wave
(Open-Circuit Voltage)

Figure 4.7—(continued)

Capacitor transients can be the result of energizing power correction capacitor banks. The combination of the capacitors and the parasitic line and transformer inductances often results in resonances that can "magnify" the transient. Typical amplitudes are up to several times the line voltage, with typical rise times in the range of microseconds, and damped sine waveshapes. These transients could occur one or more times per day as the power factor is corrected. Figure 4.8 shows typical capacitor energizing transient waveforms.

Power electronics switching transients often result in voltage **notches** as shown in Fig. 4.9. This is due to a brief short circuit on the system as current is being switched, or commutated. The notch characteristics are a function of the current magnitude and the power system impedance.

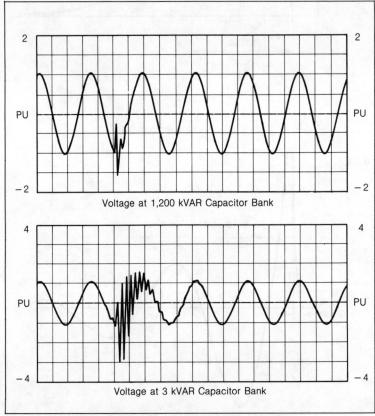

Voltage at 1,200 kVAR Capacitor Bank

Voltage at 3 kVAR Capacitor Bank

Figure 4.8—Typical Capacitor Energizing Transients

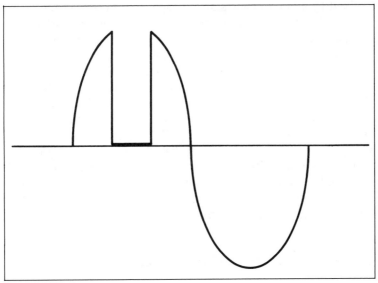

Figure 4.9—Example of Voltage Notching

4.2 Effects of Power Disturbances

This section discusses the effects of power disturbances upon modern electronic equipment.

From the earliest days, the power utilities have needed to provide power at a steady voltage and frequency. Over the years, these have resulted in increasingly strict standards. The forcing function has usually been customer demands fueled by advancing technology.

In the 1930s, the utilities were forced to devote attention to small voltage disturbances caused by customer equipment. Many people were annoyed by the visible flicker in incandescent lamps, due to voltages as small as 0.3 V on a 120 V line. These problems led to industry standards on the amount of voltage fluctuations caused by end-user equipment.

In the 1950s, a different problem arose with the early models of air conditioners. When the air conditioners were turned on, the motors demanded so much energy that the incoming line voltage was reduced to the point that the motors could not reach operating speed, often stalling. Fortunately, the problems in this case was easily fixed by adding motor starting capacitors to correct the power factor. The utilities and air conditioner manufacturers agreed on standards for motor starting capacitors, and the problems ceased.

In the 1970s, the microprocessor revolution resulted in a proliferation of electronic equipment in both the home and industry. Unfortunately, computer-based systems are very sensitive to power deviations; even a few milliseconds of low voltage is enough to cause a loss of computer memory. At the same time, **nonlinear** loads such as switching mode power supplies, SCR controls and ferroresonant voltage regulators create current distortions that cause problems on the power line. Even relatively small devices such as light dimmers and small motor speed controls can be culprits, particularly as they proliferate in use. The net result is a new set of problems plus new and evolving engineering standards.

4.2.1 Power Disturbance Studies

Due to concerns about the effects of power disturbances upon computers, numerous studies have been undertaken over the years in order to understand and quantify the phenomena. The three most comprehensive and often quoted are those by Allen and Segall of IBM, Goldstein and Speranza of Bell Labs, and Key of the U.S. Navy. This section discusses each of those studies.

Allen and Segall of IBM
This study was completed in 1974 by George Allen and Donald Segall of IBM Corporation. They monitored 49 data processing installations for a period of over three years. Their results were reported in a paper to the IEEE Power Engineering Society.

They monitored three types of voltage variations: voltage spikes due to lightning, power network switching and electrical equipment operation; oscillatory disturbances (ringing transients) due to power factor capacitor switching and load switching; and undervoltages (including outages) of greater than one-half cycle caused by fault clearing devices. Although all three types of disturbances can cause computer malfunctions, the actual faults were not correlated to actual upsets or failures.

The results are shown in Fig. 4.10. These figures show that 87 percent of the disturbances were attributed to transients, with an average of 128 incidences per month.

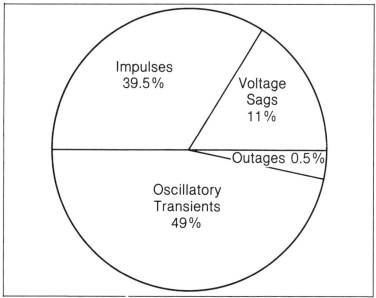

Figure 4.10—Summary of Allen-Segall Power Study

Goldstein and Speranza of Bell Labs

This study was completed in 1982 by Paul Speranza and M. Goldstein. It is based on an 11 month study of 24 Bell System locations. Their results were in the Proceedings of the IEEE Power Engineering Society in 1982.

The authors monitored four types of disturbances: voltage dips below 96 V for at least 16 ms; voltage spikes of 200 V lasting an average of 100 μs; overvoltages of over 130 V for 100 ms; and power outages.

The results of the Bell study are shown in Fig. 4.11. These figures show that 87 percent of the disturbances were due to voltage dips, with 90 percent of the sites experiencing an average of 89 disturbances per year.

The Bell study relied heavily on statistics and used a model to predict disturbances at other sites. Based on the Bell model, almost every site will experience at least one voltage dip per year, and nearly 85 percent will experience one power failure.

4.19

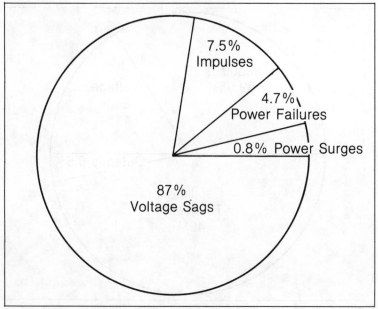

Figure 4.11—Summary of Goldstein-Speranza Power Study

Thomas Key of the U.S. Navy

This study was completed in 1978 and is based on data collected over 10 years at various U.S. Navy computer sites. The three disturbance types measured were voltage spikes and ringing transients with peak voltages of 240 V; undervoltages below 85 percent or line voltage lasting longer than 4 cycles; and power outages of over 2 s.

No specific data on rates of occurrences were presented, but undervoltages were given as the most common cause of computer failure related to power line disturbances.

Comparing and Contrasting the Studies

At a first glance, it appears that either the Allen-Segall study and the Goldstein-Speranza studies are in disagreement, or that power line disturbances changed drastically during the 1970s. Much of the discrepancy, however, can be attributed to the differences in measurements and criteria for disturbances.

For example, Goldstein-Speranza used a threshold of −4 percent for sags, while Allen-Segall used −10 percent. Oscillatory decaying disturbances were not identified in the G-S report. The G-S study used an impulse threshold of 118 percent, while the A-S report used an impulse threshold as low as 10 percent.

Nevertheless, both reports yield useful data and insights, and all three identify "long" undervoltages and "short" transients as the principal upset and failure modes for computer equipment.

4.2.2 Computer Power Requirements

Since computer equipment is more sensitive than most other electrical equipment to input power, there has been much concern within the computer industry for suitable standards. Due to this concern, several organizations have been involved in attempts to establish power requirements for computer equipment. These include the Institute of Electrical and Electronic Engineers (IEEE), Computer and Business Equipment Manufacturers Association (CBEMA) and the National Bureau of Standards (NBS). (For more information on U.S. and international standards, refer to Volumes 9 and 10, respectively, of this handbook series.)

Their efforts have resulted in the general curve shown in Fig. 4.12. This curve has appeared in the IEEE "Orange Book" (ANSI/IEEE STD 446-1987, "IEEE Recommended Practice for Emergency and Standby Power") and in FIPS PUB 94, "Federal Information Processing Standard Guideline on Electrical Power For ADP Installations." It has also been referred to as the **CBEMA Curve**, although CBEMA did not actually develop it.

This curve defines a voltage envelope within which a computer system should be designed to operate. For long-term variations, such as sags and surges greater than 2 s, the recommended voltage limits are +6 percent and −13 percent. For a nominal input voltage of 120 V, this results in 104 to 125 V. For short-term variations such as sags, surges or transients, the limits are wider, allowing for the effects of filters and transient suppressors. It should be noted that this curve allows a complete loss of power for up to one-half cycle (8.33 ms at 60 Hz), which establishes a minimal stored energy requirement.

The power utilities can not guarantee that the power they supply will always meet these guidelines. Although the power utilities typically limit steady-state voltage variations to within 5 percent, they can not guarantee outage times will be less than one-half cycle, nor can they guarantee transient levels. In addition, the utility

4.21

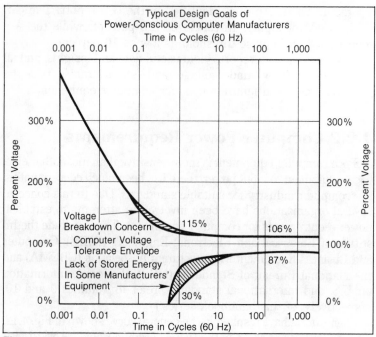

Figure 4.12—ANSI/IEEE Std 466-1987 Recommended Power Limits

voltages are "at the meter" and do not account for internal voltage drops in the wiring. Thus, it is still the responsibility of the user to maintain computer power within these limits, which often means external power conditioning units.

Nevertheless, these guidelines provide a rational set of design goals for computer systems, and this author recommends that these be used as minimal design goals in that application.

4.2.3 Lightning Transient Standards

Although the computer power requirements of the preceding section account for short-term transients, they do not include full protection from surges due to lightning. Experimental data indicate that lightning induced surges can reach amplitudes of 6,000 V and/or 3,000 A at the power input to equipment.

These levels are usually considered "damage" levels rather than "upset" levels. Thus, it is probably unrealistic to expect equipment to be operated through these transients without upset. This is a major difference from the transient levels described in the previous section, where the goal is to operate with neither upset nor damage. Nevertheless, these more extreme transient requirements may need to be considered for many computer-based systems.

The accepted specification for these transients is ANSI/IEEE C62.41-1980, "IEEE Guide for Surge Voltages in Low Voltage AC Power Circuits." This was formerly known as IEEE Std 587, a title that is still often used. This specification defines both surge amplitudes and waveshapes and is based on extensive empirical data gathered over the years. In addition, three categories of waveforms are defined, based on their location within a facility.

The prescribed waveshapes and associated values are shown in Fig. 4.13. Figure 4.14 shows the location categories. The rationale behind the **ringing** waveform for **long branch circuits** is that experimental data has shown that as wiring runs increase in length, the waveform oscillates due to resonances and reflections. Incidentally, the 6,000 V limitation is based on the fact that power wall sockets typically flash over at this voltage. Thus, the wiring and sockets establish an upper limit that will be seen by any computer equipment connected to the ac power.

Another vital parameter is the load impedance. High-impedance loads will easily allow the full voltage to be developed at the power inputs, while low-impedance circuits may limit the voltage. Transient protection devices will also present a low impedance above the breakdown voltage. Since it would be unrealistic to try to develop 6,000 V into a near short circuit, an alternate current limit is specified if the full voltage can not be developed. Again, these limits are based on empirical data.

Protection of equipment against these surge voltages is best achieved through the use of transient protective devices. There are three basic types of surge protectors: **gas tubes, metal oxide varistors (MOVs)** and **silicon avalanche devices**. Filters alone are generally not adequate for these voltage levels.

Gas tubes are **crowbar** devices, and they clamp the transient voltage to a relatively low level after the device fires. They do not dissipate much energy, but rather reflect or divert the transient energy. A disadvantage of gas tubes is that the breakdown voltage is a function of the slope of the applied voltage, so they are not suitable for extremely fast transients. Another drawback of gas devices is that they may continue to conduct after the surge has passed, since the sustaining voltage is much less than the ignition

4.23

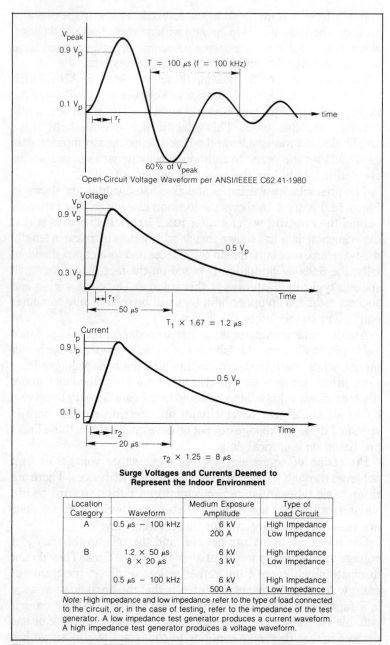

Figure 4.13—ANSI C62.41-1980 Transient Waveshapes

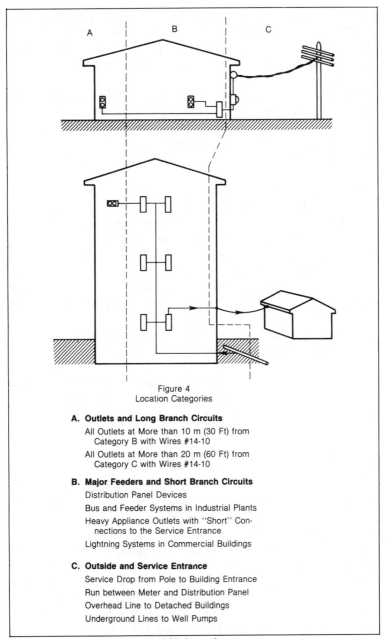

Figure 4
Location Categories

A. Outlets and Long Branch Circuits

All Outlets at More than 10 m (30 Ft) from
Category B with Wires #14-10

All Outlets at More than 20 m (60 Ft) from
Category C with Wires #14-10

B. Major Feeders and Short Branch Circuits

Distribution Panel Devices

Bus and Feeder Systems in Industrial Plants

Heavy Appliance Outlets with "Short" Connections to the Service Entrance

Lightning Systems in Commercial Buildings

C. Outside and Service Entrance

Service Drop from Pole to Building Entrance

Run between Meter and Distribution Panel

Overhead Line to Detached Buildings

Underground Lines to Well Pumps

Figure 4.14—ANSI C62.41-1987 Locations

4.25

voltage. Thus, special provisions may be needed to extinguish the arc after the surge has passed. Nevertheless, gas breakdown devices are well suited and widely used for lightning-induced transients.

Metal oxide varistors clamp, rather than crowbar, the voltage. They operate on the basis of nonlinear voltage sensitive I-V characteristics. The advantages of MOVs are their relatively low price and small size. The disadvantages are lower power dissipations than gas tubes, since they clamp, and a general degradation over time with repeated transient events. MOVs are widely used across the primary and/or secondary of power supply ac line transformers.

Silicon avalanche devices, like MOVs, also clamp transient voltages at a preset level. These are essentially special zener diodes with larger than normal junctions to dissipate transient energy. They are sold under several trade names, and probably the most well known are Transzorbs®, a trademark of General Semiconductor. The advantages of these devices are their extremely fast action and their relatively high power capabilities. The chief disadvantage is higher expense than MOVs although, as with most semiconductor devices, prices continue to decrease with time.

Given the low cost of these transient protection devices, it is probably worthwhile to include them on the ac inputs for most computer systems. And while it may not be feasible or practical to provide protection for the full voltage ranges specified by IEEE C62.41, this author recommends that at least a subset of this specification should be included in computer system design goals.

4.3 Power Line Coupling

This section discusses the third EMI element, the coupling paths for power line disturbances. Since most equipment is coupled to the power distribution system, the power wiring is a ready path for undesired energy.

There are many ways to classify the coupling of EMI energy. In fact, it is the multitude of possible paths that makes understanding EMI such a challenge. To simplify the coupling path via the power lines, the following categories will be used: conducted coupling, radiated coupling and crosstalk. In addition, two coupling modes must be discussed: common-mode and differential-mode.

Coupling Paths

Conducted coupling depends upon direct connections to **conduct** unwanted energy. Since most equipment is connected to the commercial power mains, a ready path exists for direct conduction of unwanted EMI energy throughout a system. The **safety ground** is also a path for conducted energy. Radiated coupling depends upon electromagnetic radiation to transfer energy. No direct connection is required. Crosstalk coupling is a special case of radiated coupling. It is due to the parasitic capacitances and mutual inductances that are present between wires and cables.

Figure 4.15 illustrates these coupling paths. All three paths can, and often do, act simultaneously. By understanding these different modes, however, valuable insights can be gained regarding both the source of the EMI and the solutions to the problem.

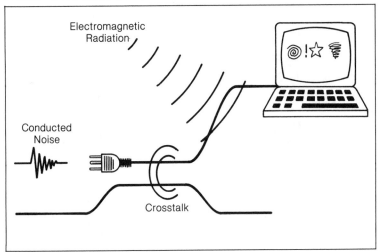

Figure 4.15—Power Line Noise Coupling Paths

Coupling Modes

In addition to the paths, the direction of current flow is an important parameter. Depending on the source and the coupling path, power line disturbances will appear in either the **common mode** or **differential mode**. These modes are illustrated in Fig. 4.16 and are defined as follows:

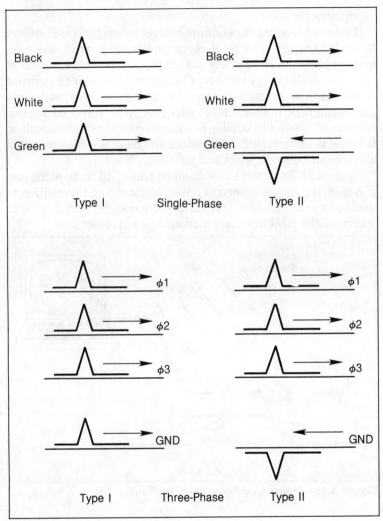

Figure 4.16—Common-Mode Coupling

Common Mode: Disturbances in which the voltage appears between the current-carrying conductors (line and neutral) and the ground. The currents on the line and neutral are in phase. This is also often referred to as **longitudinal mode**.

The common mode can be further divided into two classes, depending upon the current direction in the safety ground wiring. In "common mode I," the current in the safety ground is the same as in the conductors; in "common mode II," the current in the safety ground is in the opposite direction of the conductors. This distinction can provide important clues, as will be discussed later.

Differential Mode: Disturbances in which the voltage appears between the individual current-carrying conductors. The currents on the lines are out of phase. This is often referred to as **normal mode** or **metallic mode**.

This distinction is important for two reasons. First, some design fixes work only on one mode. For example, capacitors connected line to line are effective for differential-mode disturbances but are not effective for common-mode disturbances. Capacitors installed line to ground, on the other hand, work on both modes. Common-mode chokes work only on common-mode disturbances and are ineffective with differential-mode disturbances.

Second, the mode often gives a clue to the source and/or coupling path. For example, differential-mode currents suggest that the disturbance is purely conducted and perhaps on the same power circuit, while common-mode currents suggest radiation or crosstalk.

The easiest way to determine the mode is to use a current probe, as shown in Fig. 4.17. The probe is connected around each line individually and then around multiple lines. For example, if the current doubles with two lines, the current is all **common-mode** since it is all flowing in the same direction. If the current goes to zero with two lines, the current is all **differential-mode**, since the opposite currents cancel when measured with a current probe. Finally, if the current does not double nor cancel, it indicates the presence of both common- and differential-mode currents. As stated in the previous paragraph, this is important to know, since different strategies and component configurations are needed for the two modes.

An additional benefit of the current probe is that the waveform itself may also yield information on the source.

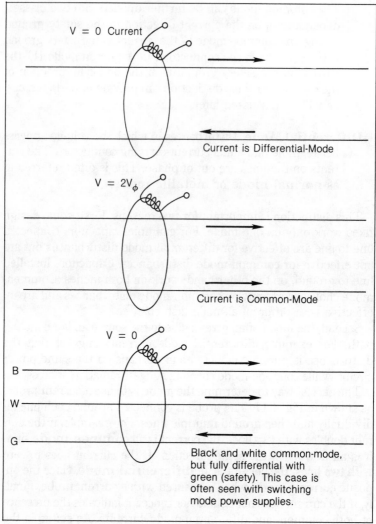

Figure 4.17—Using A Current Probe

Low, Medium and High Frequencies

When dealing with EMI issues, it is very helpful to remember that different "rules" apply, depending on the frequency range. For example, at **low frequencies**, wires exhibit resistance and components behave as predicted (capacitors are capacitors, inductors are inductors). At **medium frequencies**, wire inductance predominates, inductors and capacitors may become unpredictable due to parasitic effects, and crosstalk becomes an issue. At **high frequencies**, resonances and anti-resonances occur, and wires and components become antennas and radiate energy. Thus, it becomes very important when dealing with EMI issues to adopt a "multifrequency" approach. For each coupling path, we will clarify the frequency range(s) of interest.

4.3.1 Direct Conduction, Differential-Mode

This is a common path for low frequencies energy (typically below 100 kHz) such as power line harmonics or motor transients. In this case, the unwanted noise energy is coupled directly into a victim by the power wiring. Any equipment that derives its power from the commercial mains is connected to this unwanted noise path.

The situation is aggravated by common impedances. For example, Fig. 4.18 shows a computer and an air conditioner on a common power branch circuit. When the air conditioner turns on or off, transients from the motor are coupled into the computer due to the common impedance of the branch circuit wiring. The solution here is to use separate circuits or, as a minimum, to install the heavy load close to the distribution panel.

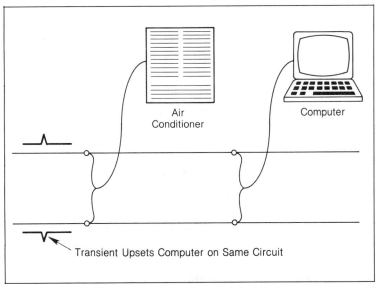

Air Conditioner

Computer

Transient Upsets Computer on Same Circuit

Figure 4.18—Computer and Air Conditioner on Common Power Branch

Another common impedance exists at the power source itself. Figure 4.19 shows two computers with switching mode power supplies connected across a ferroresonant voltage regulator. Such a configuration can result in a conducted noise problem due to the relatively high ac output impedance of the ferroresonant regulator. As each switching mode supply demands current, a common voltage is generated at the power "source," in this case the output of the regulator. For example, if each supply demands 10 A, and the ac output impedance is only 1 Ω, a 10 V voltage drop is the result. Incidentally, this example illustrates why it is not a good practice to use ferroresonant regulators (high output impedance) with switching mode power supplies (low input impedance).

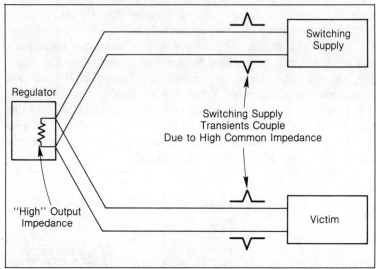

Figure 4.19—Common Impedance at Power "Source"

4.3.2 Conduction, Common-Mode

This is also a common low-frequency path, as illustrated in Fig. 4.20. In this case, the currents flow in the same direction on the current-carrying conductors. The **return** path for the current is either through the safety ground or through **earth** ground connections.

This condition is also aggravated by common impedances. The assumption that a ground system is providing an equipotential plane

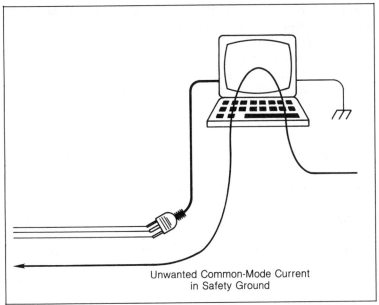

Figure 4.20—Common Low-Frequency Path

is quite often not valid. When a current is forced through a finite impedance, a finite voltage drop develops. This voltage can cause common-mode currents to flow. The forcing current can be stray return currents from other circuits, power leakage or fault currents, or lightning currents being dissipated in the earth.

The above condition is often referred to as a **ground loop**. Several solutions are possible. One can minimize the ground impedance, eliminate the common impedance paths (single-point grounding), or minimize the forcing currents. For low frequencies, the single-point ground is usually preferred, while for medium and higher frequencies, minimizing the ground impedance through reference grids is usually preferred.

Noise Conduction through the Safety Ground

Normally, the safety ground is not supposed to conduct power current. The primary purpose of a safety ground is to provide an alternate low impedance path back to the **voltage source**, so that in the event of a fault, circuit breakers or other protective devices can function to remove the voltage source from the circuit.

4.33

In accordance with the National Electric Code, any exposed metal surfaces that might become energized must be connected to the safety ground. Also in accordance with the National Electric Code, the safety ground and the power neutral are only to be connected at one point, at the power **source**. Unfortunately for EMI concerns, although only one connection exists at 60 Hz, multiple connections can and do exist at higher frequencies, due primarily to both parasitic and installed capacitors.

Switching Mode Power Supply Common-Mode Coupling

A special case of this common-mode coupling can occur with switching mode power supplies, as illustrated in Fig. 4.21. In this case, parasitic coupling from the switching circuits to the case causes a current to flow out the safety wire and to return via the current-carrying conductors. In this case, the noise appears to be common-mode on the current carrying wires, but differential with respect to the safety ground.

As switching mode supplies increase in frequency, this problem becomes more severe. In some instances, it has been the cause for equipment failing compliance regulations, such as FCC or VDE. This same energy can be effectively coupled via the power distribution system into other equipment as well.

It is relatively easy to diagnose this problem. Simply install a current probe over each wire individually, then over the current-

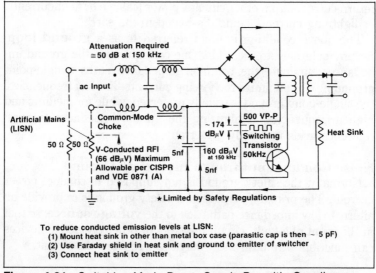

Figure 4.21—Switching Mode Power Supply Parasitic Coupling

carrying conductors, and then over the current-carrying conductors and the safety ground. If common-mode current is observed with the current-carrying conductors, and the current cancels with the safety ground included, parasitic coupling is the likely cause.

4.3.3 Radiated Coupling, Common-Mode and Differential-Mode

At higher frequencies, the power wiring acts as an antenna to efficiently collect electromagnetic radiation. Figure 4.22 illustrates this.

For the energy coupled into the **large loop**, the currents will flow in common mode; for the energy coupled into the **small loop**, the energy will flow in differential mode. In this example, both current modes will be present.

One solution is to minimize the antenna loop dimensions. For the **large loop**, this might mean simply rerouting the power lines closer to a ground plane, such as the earth or a signal reference grid. For the **small loop**, routing the wires as closely together as possible can reduce coupling. Better yet, twisting reduces **small loop**

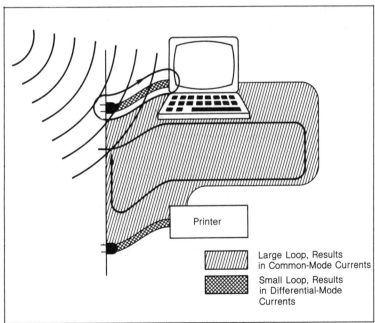

Figure 4.22—Radiated Coupling Into Power Lines

pickup by also providing cancellation due to phase reversals in adjacent twisted loops. This is illustrated in Fig. 4.23.

Another solution is to reduce the electromagnetic field at the wiring. This can be accomplished by shielding, or often by rerouting power wiring. For nearby sources, the rerouting is very effective, since the field intensity drops by a minimum of 1/r. For example, moving the wiring from 1 m to 10 m from a source will provide at least 20 dB of reduction.

Incidentally, electromagnetic radiation is generally not a problem for power wiring unless a radio transmitter is located nearby. Typically, one need not be concerned about a radio transmitter a mile or more away. On the other hand, nearby paging transmitters, land mobile transmitters and even hand-held transceivers can cause problems through pickup on the power lines.

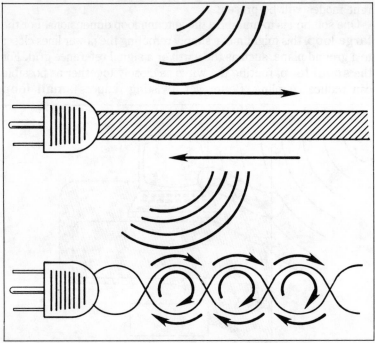

Figure 4.23—Pickup Reduced due to Cancellation Effects

4.3.4 Crosstalk

At medium and high frequencies, the parasitic capacitances and mutual inductances allow undesired coupling between cables and wires. This coupling is often referred to as **crosstalk**.

Crosstalk has two coupling modes, capacitive and inductive. In low-impedance circuits, such as power wiring, the inductive mode usually predominates. In high-impedance circuits, such as digital circuits, the capacitive mode typically predominates. Nevertheless, it is usually beneficial to determine the contribution from both coupling modes.

Models have been developed to predict crosstalk based on two parallel wires over a transmission line, as shown in Fig. 4.24. The two **wires** can represent wire pairs inside a cable (intra-cable coupling), or they can represent two cables (inter-cable coupling). For the intra-cable case, the coupling is differential-mode to the victim wire pair, while for the inter-cable coupling, the victim current would be common-mode in the victim cable.

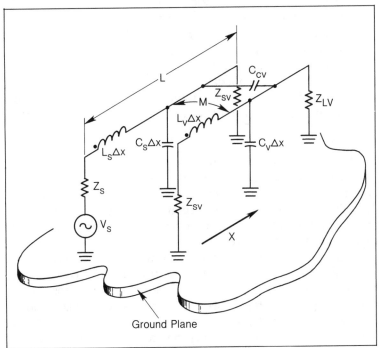

Figure 4.24—Crosstalk, Mathematical Model

Tables 4.2 and 4.3 have normalized the capacitive and inductive coupling for a 1 m length terminated in 100 Ω impedance, for numerous different wire spacings and heights above the ground plane. By using these tables, approximations can be made that are then scaled for length and impedance. Although there may be some loss of accuracy introduced in this approach, it is usually quite adequate for a first approximation of crosstalk in a power distribution system.

The steps in making such an approximation are:

1. Determine the culprit-victim wire spacing and the wire height (either wire-pair spacing or height above ground). If the heights or spacings are unequal, use the square root of the product of the two values.
2. Determine the frequency. If the crosstalk is due to a transient or digital waveform, use $1/(\pi \times$ rise time) as the frequency.
3. Use the tables to determine the capacitive and inductive crosstalk for the 1 m scaled model.
4. Discard the smaller value of the two values.
5. Using the larger value of the two, scale for length, using 20 log L. (i.e. for 10 m add 20 dB).
6. Scale for impedance. If the capacitive mode predominated, use 20 log (load impedance)/100. If the inductive mode predominated, use 20 log 100/(source impedance). As a high frequency default, 50 Ω can be used for the power system impedance.

The key variables affecting crosstalk are the common wiring distances, the spacing, the height above ground, the circuit impedances and the frequency content of the coupled energy. Generally, reducing the common distance, increasing the spacing, reducing the height above ground or reducing the frequency content will reduce the associated crosstalk.

Twisting or shielding of power wiring can also be effective in crosstalk control. Twisting should be tried first, since the inductive coupling mode is more common for power line crosstalk.

Changing circuit impedances can also affect crosstalk, although this is generally not practical with power wiring. Changing impedances will depend on whether the predominant crosstalk mode is capacitive or inductive. If predominantly inductive, raising the source impedance will reduce the crosstalk; if predominantly capacitive, reducing the culprit impedance will reduce crosstalk.

4.38

Capacitive Cable-to-Cable Coupling in dB
(Normalized to 1 m Length and AWG No. 22 Wire)

Culprit = Load = 100 Ω

Victim: $Z_{V1} = Z_{V2} = 100$ Ω

Culprit   Victim   or S_{mm} h_{mm} S_{mm} h_{mm}

Table 4.2—Capacitive Crosstalk

Frequency	h = 1 mm (0.5-3) S=1	S=3	S=10	S=30	S=100	S=300	S=1k	h = 10 mm (3-30) S=1	S=3	S=10	S=30	S=100	S=300	S=1k	h = 100 mm (30-300) S=1	S=3	S=10	S=30	S=100	S=300	S=1k
10 Hz	-144	-162	-180	-200	-220	-240	-260	-143	-153	-162	-176	-195	-215	-235	-143	-151	-157	-162	-170	-184	-203
20 Hz	-138	-156	-174	-194	-214	-234	-254	-137	-147	-156	-170	-189	-209	-229	-137	-145	-151	-156	-164	-178	-197
30 Hz	-135	-153	-171	-191	-211	-231	-251	-134	-144	-153	-167	-186	-206	-226	-134	-142	-148	-153	-161	-175	-194
50 Hz	-130	-148	-166	-186	-206	-226	-246	-129	-139	-148	-162	-181	-201	-221	-129	-137	-143	-148	-156	-170	-189
70 Hz	-127	-145	-163	-183	-203	-223	-243	-126	-136	-145	-159	-178	-198	-218	-126	-134	-140	-145	-153	-167	-186
100 Hz	-124	-142	-160	-180	-200	-220	-240	-123	-133	-142	-156	-175	-195	-215	-123	-131	-137	-142	-150	-164	-183
200 Hz	-118	-136	-154	-174	-194	-214	-234	-117	-127	-136	-150	-169	-189	-209	-117	-125	-131	-136	-144	-158	-177
300 Hz	-115	-133	-151	-171	-191	-211	-231	-114	-124	-133	-147	-166	-186	-206	-114	-122	-128	-133	-141	-155	-174
500 Hz	-110	-128	-146	-166	-186	-206	-226	-109	-119	-128	-142	-161	-181	-201	-109	-117	-123	-128	-136	-150	-169
700 Hz	-107	-125	-143	-163	-183	-203	-223	-106	-116	-125	-139	-158	-178	-198	-106	-114	-120	-125	-133	-147	-166
1 kHz	-104	-122	-140	-160	-180	-200	-220	-103	-113	-122	-136	-155	-175	-195	-103	-111	-117	-122	-130	-144	-163
2 kHz	-98	-116	-134	-154	-174	-194	-214	-97	-107	-116	-130	-149	-169	-189	-97	-105	-111	-116	-124	-138	-157
3 kHz	-95	-113	-131	-151	-171	-191	-211	-94	-104	-113	-127	-146	-166	-186	-94	-102	-108	-113	-121	-135	-154
5 kHz	-90	-108	-126	-146	-166	-186	-206	-89	-99	-108	-122	-141	-161	-181	-89	-97	-103	-108	-116	-130	-149
7 kHz	-87	-105	-123	-143	-163	-183	-203	-86	-96	-105	-119	-138	-158	-178	-86	-94	-100	-105	-113	-127	-146
10 kHz	-84	-102	-120	-140	-160	-180	-200	-83	-93	-102	-116	-135	-155	-175	-83	-91	-97	-102	-110	-124	-143
20 kHz	-78	-96	-114	-134	-154	-174	-194	-77	-87	-96	-110	-129	-149	-169	-77	-85	-91	-96	-104	-118	-137
30 kHz	-75	-93	-111	-131	-151	-171	-191	-74	-84	-93	-107	-126	-146	-166	-74	-82	-88	-93	-101	-115	-134
50 kHz	-70	-88	-106	-126	-146	-166	-186	-69	-79	-88	-102	-121	-141	-161	-69	-77	-83	-88	-96	-110	-129
70 kHz	-67	-85	-103	-123	-143	-163	-183	-66	-76	-85	-99	-118	-138	-158	-66	-74	-80	-85	-93	-107	-126
100 kHz	-64	-82	-100	-120	-140	-160	-180	-63	-73	-82	-96	-115	-135	-155	-63	-71	-77	-82	-90	-104	-123
200 kHz	-58	-76	-94	-114	-134	-154	-174	-57	-67	-76	-90	-109	-129	-149	-57	-65	-71	-76	-84	-98	-117
300 kHz	-55	-73	-91	-111	-131	-151	-171	-54	-64	-73	-87	-106	-126	-146	-54	-62	-68	-73	-81	-95	-114
500 kHz	-50	-68	-87	-106	-127	-146	-166	-49	-59	-68	-82	-101	-121	-141	-49	-57	-63	-68	-76	-90	-109
700 kHz	-47	-65	-84	-104	-124	-143	-163	-46	-56	-65	-79	-98	-118	-138	-46	-54	-60	-65	-73	-87	-106
1 MHz	-44	-62	-81	-100	-121	-140	-160	-43	-53	-62	-76	-95	-115	-135	-43	-51	-57	-62	-70	-84	-103
2 MHz	-38	-56	-75	-94	-116	-134	-154	-37	-47	-56	-70	-89	-109	-129	-37	-45	-51	-56	-64	-78	-97
3 MHz	-35	-52	-71	-91	-113	-131	-151	-34	-44	-53	-67	-86	-106	-125	-33	-42	-48	-53	-61	-74	-93
5 MHz	-31	-48	-67	-87	-110	-127	-147	-30	-40	-49	-62	-81	-101	-121	-29	-38	-43	-49	-56	-70	-89
7 MHz	-28	-45	-64	-84	-108	-124	-144	-27	-37	-46	-60	-78	-98	-118	-27	-35	-40	-46	-54	-67	-86
10 MHz	-26	-42	-61	-81	-101	-121	-141	-24	-34	-43	-57	-75	-95	-115	-24	-32	-37	-43	-51	-64	-83
20 MHz	-21	-37	-56	-76	-96	-116	-136	-20	-29	-37	-51	-70	-89	-109	-19	-27	-32	-37	-45	-58	-77
30 MHz	-19	-34	-53	-73	-90	-113	-133	-17	-26	-34	-48	-66	-86	-106	-14	-24	-29	-34	-42	-55	-74
50 MHz	-16	-31	-50	-70	-88	-110	-130	-14	-22	-30	-44	-63	-82	-102	-13	-20	-25	-30	-38	-51	-70
70 MHz	-15	-30	-48	-68	-86	-108	-128	-13	-20	-28	-42	-60	-80	-100	-12	-18	-23	-28	-35	-49	-67
100 MHz	-14	-28	-46	-66	-86	-106	-126	-12	-18	-26	-39	-58	-78	-98	-12	-16	-20	-25	-33	-46	-65

4.39

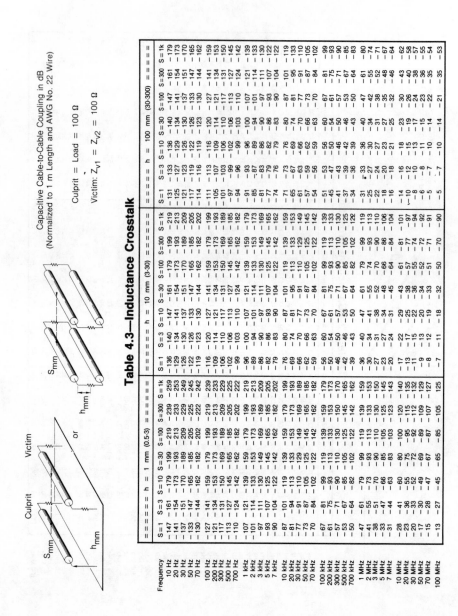

Capacitive Cable-to-Cable Coupling in dB
(Normalized to 1 m Length and AWG No. 22 Wire)

Culprit = Load = 100 Ω

Victim: $Z_{V1} = Z_{V2} = 100\ \Omega$

Culprit   Victim

Table 4.3—Inductance Crosstalk

4.4 Bibliography

This section contains additional references that may be useful for the reader interested in exploring this subject in more depth. This is by no means exhaustive, but it does represent sources for much of the information in this chapter.

Standards

ANSI/IEEE Std 141-1986, "IEEE Recommended Practice for Electrical Power Distribution for Industrial Power Plants" (IEEE Red Book) (New York: IEEE).

ANSI/IEEE Std 446-1987, "IEEE Recommended Practice for Emergency and Standby Power" (IEEE Orange Book) (New York: IEEE).

ANSI/IEEE Std 519-1981, "IEEE Guide for Harmonic Control and Reactive Compensation of Static Power Converters" (New York: IEEE).

ANSI/IEEE Std C62.41-1980, "IEEE Guide for Surge Voltages on Low Voltage AC Power Circuits" (formerly IEEE STD-587) (New York: IEEE).

ANSI/NFPA 70, "National Electrical Code 1987" (Quincy, MA: National Fire Protection Association, 1986).

FIPS PUB 94, "Guide on Electrical Power for ADP Installations" (Gaithersburg, MD: U.S. Department of Commerce, National Bureau of Standards).

Articles

Allen, G.W. and Segall, D., "Monitoring of Computer Installations for Power Line Disturbances," *IEEE PES Winter Meeting Conference Record*, paper C74-199-6, January 1974 (New York: IEEE).

Douglas, J., "Quality of Power in the Electronics Age," *EPRI (Electric Power Research Institute) Journal*, November 1985, pp 7-13.

Duell, A.W. and Roland, W.V., "Power Line Disturbances and Their Effects on Computer Designs and Performance," *Hewlett-Packard Journal*, August 1981, pp 25-32.

Edman, James, "Selecting a UPS For Today's Systems Requirements," *EMC Technology*, July-September 1985, pp 43-48.

Goldstein, M. and Speranza, P.D., "The Quality of U.S. Commercial AC Power," *IEEE/PES Transmission and Distribution Conference Record*, Paper CH1818-4/82/0000-00028 (New York: IEEE, 1982).

Gruzs, T.M., "Power Disturbances and Computer Systems: A Comparison of the Allen-Segall and the Goldstein-Speranza Power Line Monitoring Studies," application note (Columbus, OH: Liebert Corporation).

Key, T.S., "Diagnosing Power Quality Related Problems," *IEEE Transactions on Industry Applications*, Vol 1A-15, No. 4, July/August 1979, pp 381-393.

Shambrook, W., "Clean Power: Essential to Automation," *ITEM 1987*, pp 74-78.

Trenaglio, D., "Power Line Disturbances and How to Eliminate Them," *ITEM 1986*, pp 91-98.

"Understanding Power Line Disturbances" and "How To Correct Power Line Disturbances," application notes (Edison, NJ: Dranetz Technologies Inc.).

Books

Dang, G., *Electrical Noise: Causes, Effects and Solutions* (San Diego, CA: Topaz Inc., 1986).

Mardiguian, M., *Interference Control in Computers and Microprocessor Based Equipment* (Gainesville, VA: Interference Control Technologies, Inc., 1984).

Surge Protection Test Handbook (Wilmington, MA: Keytek Instrument Corp., 1986).

Violette, J.L.N.; White, D.R.J.; and Violette, M.F., *Electromagnetic Compatibility Handbook* (New York: Van Nostrand Reinhold Company Inc., 1987).

White, D.R.J. and Mardiguian, M., *EMI Control Methodology and Procedures* (Gainesville, VA: Interference Control Technologies, Inc., 1985).

Chapter 5

EMC in Power Supplies

by Robert Rynkiewicz
Onan Corporation
Power Electronics Division
Minneapolis, MN 55437

5.1 Power Supplies

Direct current sources are used nearly universally in electronic systems, dominated as they are by devices that manipulate the flow, in one net direction, of charge carriers (holes) in crystalline semiconductors (silicon). The direct current source may be a battery or power supply equipment used to convert a source of electrical energy to the required dc level. The prime source is most often the alternating current produced by the electric power utility system.

Because of the universal application of power supplies in a vast variety of electronic systems, the topic is broad. This chapter will concentrate on techniques used most widely, for applications to systems requiring relatively low dc voltages, at moderate power levels (15 to 1,500 W), with single-phase ac sources of 120 or 240 V at 50 or 60 Hz.

Practice of the art in power supplies has undergone a transition, especially in the last decade. As high-frequency conversion techniques become more widespread, power supply design has become more of a specialized practice, rather than a general one, among electronic technologists. The trend is toward specification of the power supply as a system component, manufactured by specialists. This chapter, therefore, is aimed at electronics technologists who do not practice a power electronics specialty. It assumes no prior knowledge of the art and gives generally qualitative descriptions. Those readers seeking more detail regarding a particular aspect can consult the listed references as a starting point.

Power supplies that convert ac line voltage to dc power perform most or all of the following functions:[1]

Change the ac source to a more suitable voltage
Change the ac to dc
Smooth the ripple of the rectified voltage
Control the output voltage against changes in line voltage, load current and temperature
Electrically isolate the input and output from each other

Three approaches to implementing these functions are used in power supplies known as linear, ferroresonant and switching types.

5.1.1 Linear Power Supplies

Figure 5.1 shows the block diagram of a linear power supply. The voltage transformation and isolation functions are performed by a "linear" (output proportional to input) transformer at ac mains frequency. The rectifier usually provides two pulses of current to the energy storage network per line cycle.[2] The storage network may be a pi section or "L" section filter, but it is most often a large capacitor. Regulation is provided by a series pass element, with conductance controlled by a feedback system that compares the output with a dc reference, proportional to the desired output.

Advantages of the linear approach are in its simplicity, output purity and regulation quality. Unwanted ac ripple components of

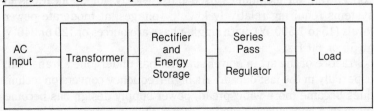

Figure 5.1—Linear Power Supply

5.2

the output voltage can readily be reduced to a few millivolts. Regulation against changes in line or load can keep output constant within 0.1 percent, typically. Also, the mild time rate of change of electrical quantities within the circuits translates into minor problems in achieving electromagnetic compatibility.

Disadvantages are in size, weight, efficiency, heat rejection, input operating range and holdup time. The transformer and storage components are bulky. The dissipative nature of the regulator and the amount of power that must be wasted to provide operating margin at low input voltages create a typical efficiency level of 45 percent, for a unit that can accommodate a ±10 percent variation of input voltage. Stored energy can typically provide protection against a temporary interruption of the input source for one-half cycle or less. These disadvantages are reducing (but not eliminating) the relative popularity of the linear type.

5.1.2 Ferroresonant (Constant-Voltage Transformer) Regulators

The **ferroresonant**, or **constant-voltage transformer (CVT)**,[3, 4] as its name implies, is a frequency-sensitive, nonlinear magnetic device that has a relatively constant output voltage over a varied input voltage range. Its use was very popular with the computer industry during most of the 1960s and part of the 1970s. It remains widely used in consumer microwave oven magnetron supplies and in battery charging for traction vehicles and telephony.

The most popular implementation has a distinctive physical structure, as shown in Fig. 5.2a. It integrates the magnetic circuits of a transformer and inductor. The inductor is connected to a capacitor to form a tank circuit that resonates at the ac mains frequency, as shown in Fig 5.2b. Tank resonance puts the magnetic circuit shared by the inductor and transformer secondary into magnetic saturation, so the magnetic characteristics of the core material effectively limit the change in magnetic flux (and output voltage) produced in the secondary coil. Secondary voltage waveform approximates a square wave with rounded corners, so rectified secondary waveform has relatively low ripple component.

Regulation against changes in line voltage is good, typically showing 0.6 percent output change for a 10 percent input change. Protection against short circuits is inherent because of the limiting nature of the magnetic circuit. The electrical circuit is simple in

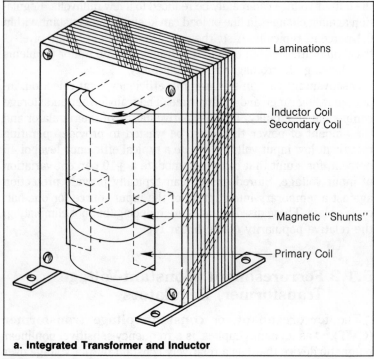

a. Integrated Transformer and Inductor

Figure 5.2—Constant Voltage (Ferroresonant) Transformer Supply (continued next page)

parts count, obtaining regulation without electronic dissipation and feedback schemes. Efficiency is reasonable, typically 75 percent, even with the relatively high core loss in the saturating magnetic circuit.

Ferroresonant transformers are inherently sensitive to input frequency, typically showing a 3 percent output variation for 1 Hz of input frequency deviation. Load regulation is limited by the resistance of the copper in the secondary coil, so the transformer is best designed for a relatively fixed load. The transformers are large in size and mass, and tend to produce an annoying audible hum.

Large operating flux densities (approximately 20 kG) tend to produce a relatively large amplitude, low frequency varying magnetic field external to the transformer. Electron beam deflection of a cathode ray tube, for example, could be upset by a nearby ferroresonant transformer. Magnetic shielding would be difficult, requiring a continuous path of high-permeability material.

5.4

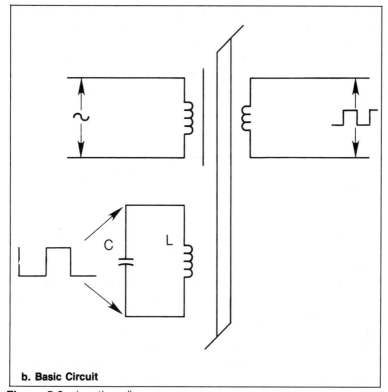

b. Basic Circuit

Figure 5.2—(continued)

5.1.3 Switching Power Supplies

Switching power supplies perform the conversion and regulation of electrical energy from one voltage level to another, using energy storage components (inductors and capacitors) and energy steering components (transistors and diodes). The regulation function is accomplished by adjusting the quantity of energy stored and released, and the processing elements dissipate energy only in through parasitic effects (conduction and switching losses in semiconductors, conduction and core losses in magnetic components, conduction and dielectric losses in capacitors). As a result, relatively high efficiencies (typically 75 to 90 percent) can be attained. Size, weight and energy storage of magnetic and capacitive components can be made relatively small by operation at high frequencies. For example, a transformer capable of processing 700 VA with a 40°C temperature rise, using ferrite magnetic materials and operating at a repetition rate of 100 kHz, can occupy approximately 170 cc and weigh 400 g. A transformer of similar power capability operating at ac mains frequency of 60 Hz, constructed with a magnetic circuit of laminated silicon steel, could occupy 4,000 cc and weigh 13 kg.

The size, weight and efficiency advantages of power supplies employing switching regulators have hastened their adoption in a wide variety of electronic systems. Unfortunately for the concern of electromagnetic compatibility, the dc-to-dc converters that form the basis of switching power supplies undergo abrupt discontinuities of voltage, current or both and are a potential source of electromagnetic energy over a broad frequency range.

The most common requirement asked of a switching power supply is the conversion of 120 or 240 Vac mains voltage to one or more regulated low-voltage dc outputs, such as +5 Vdc, +12 Vdc and −12 Vdc. There is a trend toward the use of even lower voltages in large computer systems using high-density integrated logic with low breakdown voltages.

Figure 5.3 shows the block diagram of most switching power supplies. The ac input passes through a low pass filter, is rectified and filtered to produce a dc source. A dc-to-dc converter then transforms the source to the desired output level and regulates the output to counteract changes in input voltage or load current level. Each of these functions is considered below.

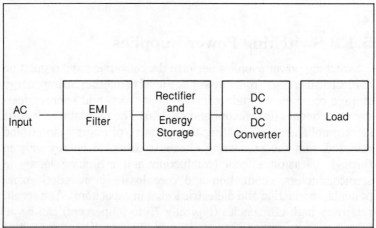

Figure 5.3—Switching Power Supply Block Diagram

5.1.3.1 AC Input Rectifier and Filter

The input section of most switching power supplies contains an input rectifier and energy storing capacitor. Chosen for simplicity, compactness and economy, the arrangement is widely used. Unfortunately, the input current characteristics cause some detrimental interactions with the ac supply.[5] For this and other reasons, three-phase supply systems are generally adopted at power levels greater than 2 or 3 kVA.

Two arrangements of input rectifier and capacitor input filter are in widespread use with a single-phase ac supply. The first, shown in Fig. 5.4a, uses a bridge rectifier and single capacitor bank. The second, shown in Fig 5.4b, uses a bridge rectifier that can be recon-

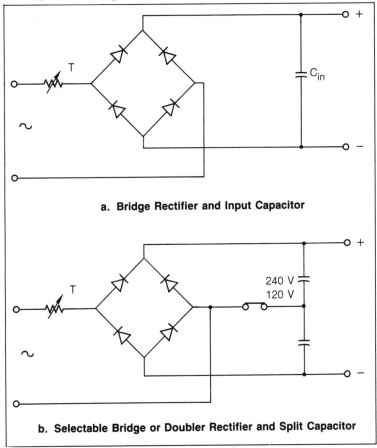

a. Bridge Rectifier and Input Capacitor

b. Selectable Bridge or Doubler Rectifier and Split Capacitor

Figure 5.4—Input Rectifier and Capacitor Circuits

figured as a voltage doubling rectifier, along with a capacitor bank split into two series sections. For operation with 220 Vac mains input, the bridge configuration is used, and for 120 Vac operation the doubler is used. Selection of bridge or doubler mode is made with a mechanical switch or jumper wire, set by the user of the equipment, or by an electronic switch, operated by a circuit that detects the magnitude of the input source. Either arrangement has a similar loading effect on the ac source.

Consider the bridge rectifier and single capacitor arrangement shown in Fig. 5.4a. The capacitor C_{in} serves as dc link between the input rectifier and dc-to-dc converter sections. C_{in} is charged to the peak ac input voltage each half cycle of the ac mains, as shown in Figure 5.5b. This capacitor charging current appears on the input circuit as pulses of roughly rectangular waveshape, as shown in Fig. 5.5c. The dc-to-dc converter discharges C_{in}, with repetitive

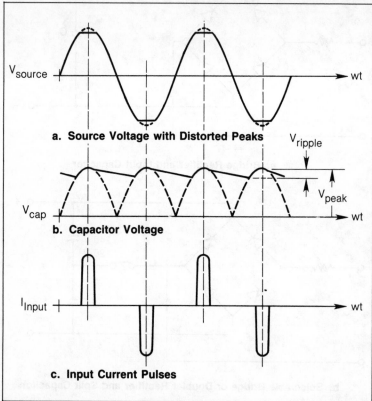

a. **Source Voltage with Distorted Peaks**

b. **Capacitor Voltage**

c. **Input Current Pulses**

Figure 5.5—Input Circuit Waveforms

pulses of higher repetition rate (typically 20 to 300 kHz). The conduction angle of the input diodes, and hence the width of the input current pulses, is determined by the charge to voltage ratio (capacitance) of C_{in}, and the loading provided by the dc-to-dc converter.

The size of C_{in} is determined as a compromise. If C_{in} is too small, the dc link will operate with a large ripple voltage, with low minimum value. The dc-to-dc converter will need to operate over a greater duty cycle range, and the control loop will need greater gain to maintain the proper output. Transformer utilization, peak transistor voltage and peak rectifier reverse voltage will all suffer.

A larger capacitance reduces operating range required of the dc-to-dc converter but uses a larger, costlier capacitor. The recharging current pulses become narrower, and larger in amplitude, with detrimental effects. The high peak amplitude of the input current pulses causes large stresses in the rectifiers, and high peak ripple currents in transferring charge to the input capacitor. The finite source impedance of the ac source, together with the large peak-to-rms ratio of the input current, can lead to a distortion of the ac input waveform: the voltage waveshape is partially reduced, or "flat topped" during the conduction period of the input diodes, because distribution line voltage drops are especially severe during the current pulse. This is shown in Fig. 5.5a. This waveform distortion can lead to problems if other loads on the distribution system are especially sensitive to the peak voltage presented to them.

The input current pulse also has high harmonic content, principally third harmonic, which leads to other problems placed upon the ac distribution system. The power factor is degraded, decreasing the effective utilization of utility power generation and distribution equipment. Many electric utilities charge large industrial customers a price premium for utilization below 90 percent power factor. Also, the third harmonic content, which is typically of comparable magnitude to the fundamental frequency component, can cause large, unwanted currents circulating on the neutral of three-phase distribution systems.

A general expression for power factor, PF, presented to a source is:

$$PF = \cos \phi \left(\frac{I1}{I} \right)$$

where,

ϕ = the "displacement" angle, or phase angle between the fundamental frequency components of line voltage and current

I1 = the rms value of the fundamental frequency component of supply current

I = the rms value of the total supply current

The cos ϕ term represents power factor degradation due to reactive energy storage. This term alone is often presented as a definition of power factor, but such a definition is accurate only in the special case of perfectly sinusoidal line voltage and current. The I1/I factor represents the power factor degradation due to harmonic frequency components of the line current. The harmonic current component is the major mechanism of power factor degradation, for the input circuit arrangements commonly used in switching power supplies.

In a typical switching power supply, the input capacitor is sized to allow a periodic ripple voltage variation on the input capacitor of 25 to 30 percent at full load.[6] The diode conduction period is then less than 2 ms, out of each half-cycle period of 8.33 ms. The input current form factor then has a peak-to-rms ratio greater than two. Power factor degradation due to the displacement angle term in the above definition is minor, since the current peak leads the voltage peak by 1 ms or less. Harmonic content severely degrades the power factor, yielding a typical total power factor of 65 percent at full load.

Severe as 65 percent power factor may seem, this is often a best-case value. At partial load, the input capacitor ripple voltage and diode conduction period are smaller, increasing peak-to-rms ratio and relative harmonic content of the input current and degrading the input power factor. The only compensating factor is decreased total throughput power.

As switching power supplies become more widespread in application, and as systems scale to higher absolute power levels, users become more acutely aware (and less tolerant of) poor power factor and high line harmonic content. Power factors above 90 percent can be obtained by drawing input current proportional to voltage, during the middle 2/3 portion of each half cycle. The interested reader can demonstrate this result numerically, by making the observation that a linear (resistive) load, with voltage proportional to current, has an energy transfer rate (power) proportional to voltage squared. The definite integral of the sine squared energy function, over the first 30°, has 3 percent of the total energy, integrated over the full 180°. Several alternative methods are available to improve input current form factors and reduce the burden on the distribution system.

Choke Input Filter

Replacing the single input capacitor, common to many power supplies, with a choke input, "L" section filter, is perhaps the most straightforward method to improve input current form factor.[7] Above a minimum "critical" current, the diode conduction becomes continuous and more nearly proportional to input voltage. This option has not been widely adopted in practice, partly because such a filter would require substantial inductive energy storage at the ac mains frequency. The added filter inductor would substantially increase the size and weight of a power subsystem.

Active Power Factor Correction

Another approach to improving power factor[8, 9] involves an additional dc-to-dc converter subsection between the input rectifier and input capacitor of the "boost" or "buck-boost" configuration (see Section 5.1.3.4). The duty cycle and/or repetition rate controlling functions of this converter are manipulated by one or more feedback loops to draw an average current proportional to voltage during most or all of each input half cycle. This approach does not have as severe an impact on size and weight, compared to the passive choke input filter, but complexity is greatly increased.

5.1.3.2 DC-to-DC Converters

Dc-to-dc converters form the basis of switching power supplies, whether the input source is ac or dc. Many arrangements, or **topologies**, of energy storage and steering components are possible, but all can be derived from one or more of four fundamental topologies: buck, boost, buck-boost and Ćuk. Each of the elemental topologies can be represented as a three-port network containing four internal elements: an inductor, capacitor, diode and transistor. The inductor most often is the main element used to store energy from the source and transfer it to the load, with the capacitor also involved in this function. The diode acts as a switching element, controlled by the polarity of applied voltage. The transistor performs a regulation function by having its conduction state controlled, usually with a fixed frequency, variable ON time, pulse width modulation (PWM) method.

Other control schemes, using frequency modulation techniques, are possible. One method uses a fixed ON time for the switch, and a variable OFF time. Another method uses a fixed OFF time, and modulates the on time. A third method fixes neither ON time nor OFF time, but instead fixes the amplitude of inductor ripple current: switch state is changed when the difference between minimum and maximum inductor current reaches a preset level. This method is sometimes called **hysteretic control**.[10, 11]

Operation of the fundamental dc-to-ac converters, and several of the commonly used derived configurations, is discussed below. Operation under a fixed frequency, variable ON time, pulse width modulation (PWM) scheme is assumed. Also assumed, unless otherwise stated, is operation with continuous inductor current. This means that the inductor is sized, relative to the input and output voltages, operating frequency and load, so that the inductor current never falls to zero but has a finite value at the beginning and end of each cycle. Input-to-output voltage transfer ratio, component stresses relative to throughput power and dynamic properties such as phase delay from duty cycle control function to output are all distinctly different for operation in discontinuous inductor current mode.

In the accompanying figures, time period of the pulse width modulation is denoted as T. Beginning of a cycle is noted as time t_0, the time at which the transistor switch begins conduction. At time denoted t_1, switch current is interrupted.

Duty cycle, D, is defined as the ratio of switch ON time to the total period:

$$D = \frac{(t_1 - t_0)}{T_s}$$

Input-to-output dc transfer ratio, M, is defined as the ratio of output voltage to input voltage:

$$M = \frac{V_o}{V_i}$$

The dc transfer ratio can be derived as a function of converter topology and duty cycle. Results are shown neglecting switch and conductor losses.

5.1.3.3 Buck Converter

The **buck converter**, also sometimes referred to as **step-down** or **chopper converter**, is so named because the output voltage is always less than or equal to **(bucking)** the input voltage. Configurations derived from the buck converter are among the most popular in common use.

The fundamental circuit of the buck converter is shown in Fig.5.6a, with idealized waveforms in Fig. 5.6b summarized below.

At time t_0, the switch is closed, and inductor L is impressed with the difference between source and output voltages. Current in the inductor increases at the rate shown by:

$$\frac{d_i}{d_t} = \frac{(V_s - V_o)}{L}$$

During the switch ON interval, energy stored in the inductor increases. Diode D is reverse biased.

At time $t = t_1$, the switch turned OFF, and the input current is abruptly interrupted. Voltage at the input side of the inductor abruptly decreases from a value near the input voltage until it is clamped by the forward biasing of diode D. The diode then carries the "freewheeling" current of inductor L, which decreases in magnitude as the energy stored in the inductor feeds the load. Another period begins as the switch is again turned ON.

In principle, periodic variations (ripple) in output amplitude can be eliminated by making the inductor indefinitely large. In practice, the output ripple is reduced, with an inductor of finite size, by placing a capacitor in parallel with the load. The capacitor experiences a ripple current that is complementary to the ripple current in the inductor to produce a nearly constant load current. Output voltage ripple alleviation by the capacitor is generally limited by the parasitic resistance (equivalent series resistance, ESR) and/or inductance (equivalent series inductance, ESL) of the element.

The switching period is usually much shorter than the LC time constant of the output filter elements, so current waveforms of the

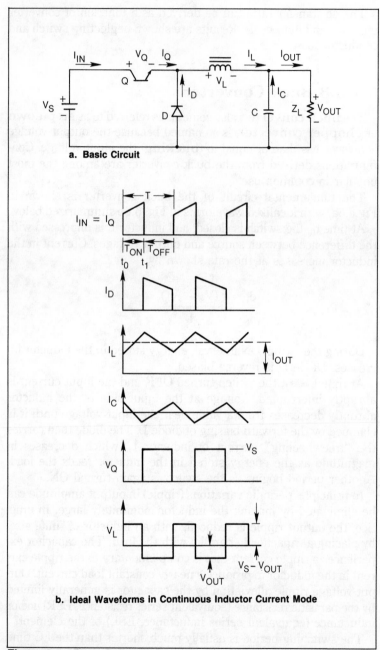

a. Basic Circuit

b. Ideal Waveforms in Continuous Inductor Current Mode

Figure 5.6—Buck Converter

inductor and capacitor, between switch transitions, are very nearly straight line segments composing a sawtooth. This establishes a minimum output current, equal to half the peak inductor current ripple amplitude, for which the minimum inductor current stays just above zero. This minimum current is known as the critical current for continuous conduction of the inductor.

The buck converter, operated with at least the minimum load required for continuous inductor current, has an input-to-output voltage transfer ratio equal to the duty cycle, or:

$$M = D$$

Contrasting the continuous current of the output filter is the chopped input current, which periodically transfers between the input source and switch, and diode. This interrupted input current can contain harmonic energy over a broad spectrum, and it constitutes the major disadvantage of the buck converter and all derived configurations.

The advantages of the buck converter and its derivatives are many, and they usually preclude its elimination solely for the sake of EMC. Output voltage less than input is required for compatibility between most source and load types used in electronic systems. Protection against a short circuit of the load can be attained by disabling the switching element. Voltage transfer ratio, and dynamic properties such as phase delay through the power circuit, are well behaved functions, simplifying the closure of feedback loops used to control the output.

5.1.3.4 Boost Converter

The boost converter, shown schematically in Fig. 5.7a, has an input voltage that is always greater than (**boosted**) or equal to the input voltage. In many regards, it may be considered to be in mirror image, in structure and properties, to the buck converter. Operation during a switching cycle is described below, with waveforms in as shown in Fig 5.7b.

At the portion of the cycle initiated by the closure of the switch at time $t = t_0$, inductor L is impressed with the input source voltage. Current in the inductor increases linearly during the switch ON time. Diode D is reverse biased, effectively isolating the output circuit. The load is fed by energy stored in the output capacitor

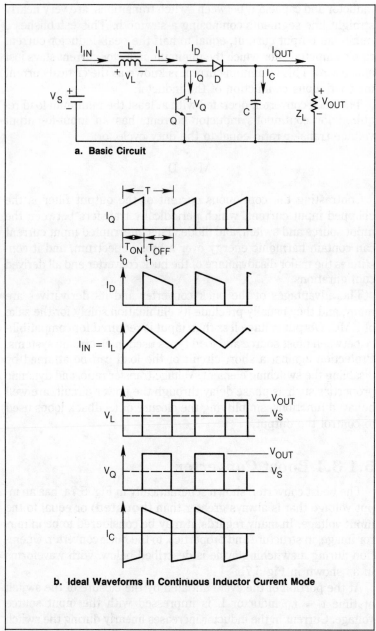

a. Basic Circuit

b. Ideal Waveforms in Continuous Inductor Current Mode

Figure 5.7—Boost Converter

during the previous cycle.

Upon interruption of the switch current at time $t = t_1$, voltage at the load end of the inductor abruptly increases until it is clamped by the forward biasing of diode D. The inductor releases stored energy into the capacitor and load, through the diode. As the inductor releases its stored energy, the inductor current magnitude deceases with time. If the next cycle starts before the inductor current has decreased to zero, the converter is said to be operating in **continuous inductor current mode**. Input-to-output voltage transfer ratio for this mode of operation is:

$$M = \frac{1}{(1 - D)}$$

where,

D = the duty cycle, or ratio of ON time to the total period

Because the inductor is in the input circuit, the boost converter can draw continuous input current with relatively smooth undulations. It has found some use in power factor correction schemes, primarily in single-phase ac input applications, but it is not in the mainstream of use in power conversion systems, for a number of reasons.

The input supply circuit is relieved of impulsive currents, but they are now imposed on the output capacitor and diode. Continuous mode voltage transfer ratio is quite nonlinear and affected by relatively small values of parasitic resistance in the inductor. This limits practical operation to duty ratios below about 0.7 and can even lead to the control circuit latching into an inoperative condition during startup transient. No protection can be provided against an output short circuit without auxiliary measures because the load is always presented with at least the input voltage, limited only by source, inductor and diode parasitic impedances. The dynamic response of the power circuit can be relatively difficult to put under control of a feedback loop, characteristic of a system with a right half-plane zero in its control variable (duty cycle) to output (voltage) response function.

5.1.3.5 Buck-Boost Converter

This configuration can have an output amplitude less than or greater than the input, and in its basic form, diagramed in Fig. 5.8a,

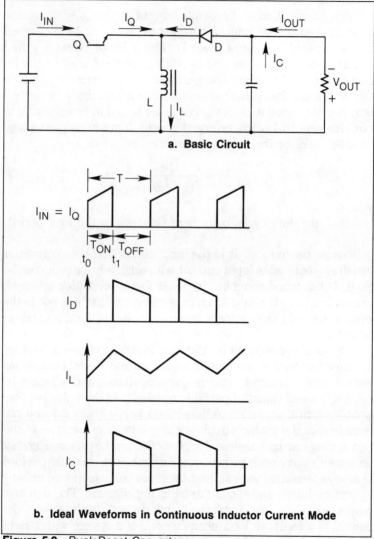

a. Basic Circuit

b. Ideal Waveforms in Continuous Inductor Current Mode

Figure 5.8—Buck-Boost Converter

provides an output polarity inversion. Derived configurations are popular in application where relatively low power and/or multiple outputs are involved.

Although at least one set of authors[12] considers the buck-boost configuration to be derived from the cascaded combination of buck and boost type converters, many present it as a fundamental configuration.

In operation, closure of switch Q presents the input source to the inductor L. Inductor current and energy storage increased during the switch ON time, while the capacitor, isolated by reverse-biased diode D, feeds the load.

Opening of switch Q interrupts the inductor current in the input circuit. Inductor voltage rapidly decrease until clamped by the forward biasing of diode D. The inductor then releases stored energy into the capacitor and load.

The ideal voltage gain of the buck-boost configuration is given by:

$$M = (-1) \times \frac{D}{(1 - D)}$$

Often, the inductor current is allowed to decrease to zero during the OFF time of the switch (discontinuous inductor current mode), because the energy storage and size of the inductor are reduced. Also, the continuous inductor current mode has a minimum load current, required to keep the inductor current continuous. Dynamic characteristics are distinctly different above and below this critical current, imposing great constraints on a feedback control loop that must operate in either mode. Changes in operating mode can most readily be avoided by operating in discontinuous mode only.

A configuration derived from the buck-boost converter, known as the **flyback**, or **ringing choke converter**, is extremely popular in use below approximately 100 W, especially when multiple outputs are required. The drawbacks of the approach, however, limit its application to relatively low power levels.

The buck-boost converter suffers from both the impulsive input current of the buck converter and the pulsating output circuit current of the boost converter, which increases the size of input and output filters added for EMI reduction. Current stresses on the semiconductors, for a given power level, are higher than either the buck or boost converters. Like the boost converter, the control to output expression has a right half-plane zero, complicating the closure of a feedback control loop.

Presence of a right half-plane zero in the control (duty cycle) to output (voltage) function can be thought of as a result of the impulsive transfer of energy to the output capacitor and load, in either the boost or buck-boost converter. If a change in input voltage or load current requires an increase in the output level to compensate, the control circuit will command an increase in duty cycle, i.e., an increase in the fraction of the cycle spent increasing energy storage in the inductor. This also, however, increases the fraction of the cycle during which the capacitor alone feeds the load. As a result, the output voltage will temporarily dip, until the average current and energy storage in the inductor increases, to meet the increased demand. Thus, an incremental change in duty cycle produces a temporary change in output that is opposite to the commanded steady state value.

5.1.3.6 Ćuk Converter

The basic form of the Ćuk (pronounced "chook") converter, also known as **boost-buck converter**, is shown schematically in Fig. 5.9a. Invented during the late 1970s by Dr. Slobodan Ćuk, of the California Institute of Technology,[13, 14] the configuration is the result of an effort to synthesize a converter with as many desirable features as possible. In particular, both the input and output current are continuous. Extensions to the topology can actually reduce the amplitude of ac ripple components of input and/or output currents to zero.[15] The ability to eliminate the ac ripple currents offers the possibility of constant power flow, approaching the ideal of a true "dc transformer," without additional filtering components added to reduce EMI. This ideal remains to be approached as a general practice.

Like the buck-boost converter, the Ćuk converter, in its basic form, produces an output greater than or less than the input in amplitude, with an inversion in polarity. The configuration is notable in that it has an inductor in both the input and output circuits, shown in the figure as L_1 and L_2, respectively. A centrally located capacitor, shown as C_1, serves as the main energy transferring link between input and output circuits. Operation during a switching cycle is summarized below, with waveforms shown in Fig. 5.9b.

During the conduction interval of switch Q, the source voltage is impressed upon input inductor L_1, and the current through it increases. At the same time, charge stored in capacitor C_1 during the previous half cycle is transferred to the load and output capacitor C_2 via output inductor L_2. Diode D is reversed biased and carries no current, while switch Q carries both the input inductor current (storing energy in L_1), and the capacitor current (transferring energy to the output).

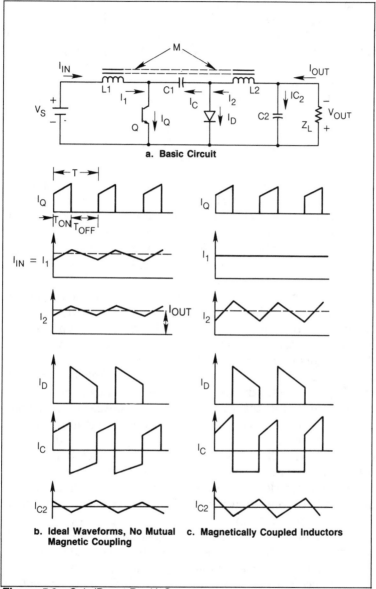

a. Basic Circuit

b. Ideal Waveforms, No Mutual Magnetic Coupling

c. Magnetically Coupled Inductors

Figure 5.9—Cuk (Boost-Buck) Converter

When the switch is turned OFF, the diode D becomes forward biased. The input source and energy stored in L_1 charge capacitor C_1, through diode D. The load is fed from energy previously stored in output inductor L_2, circulating through diode D.

The output capacitor C_2 is similar in function to the output capacitor in the buck converter. It provided reduction of the output voltage ripple by experiencing a current that mirrors the changes in output inductor current. The output capacitor can be eliminated, in principle, by making L_2 arbitrarily large.

The ideal input-to-output voltage transfer ratio, for the condition of continuous current in both inductors, is:

$$M = (-1) \times \frac{D}{(1 - D)}$$

Several features are notable in the operation of the Cuk converter. Capacitor C1 serves a central function in the transfer of energy from input to output. In fact, all the power processed by the Ćuk converter flows through the central capacitor. In the other basic topologies, the capacitor is incidental to the main flow of power (in the buck converter) or shares power transfer with the diode (in the boost and buck-boost arrangements).

Also noteworthy is the observation that the input and output current ripples are in phase with each other. This property allows an extension of the topology to completely cancel the ripple component of the input or the output current by magnetically coupling the inductors on a common magnetic core.

Magnetic coupling between the inductors is indicated schematically in Fig. 5.9c, by the dashed lines between the inductors. With the proper degree of mutual magnetic coupling between input and output inductors, the ac current component of the input current can be completely cancelled by effectively steering it into the output circuit. This result will be exact only for one operating point of voltage transfer ratio and duty cycle. At other operating points, the ac current component reappears. Similarly, mutual coupling can be arranged to cancel output current ripple at a given operating point by steering it to the input.

In fact, a further extension of the topology is possible that ideally eliminates the ac component of both the input and output currents (see Ref. 15). Such an arrangement requires a fairly complicated magnetic component that integrates the input and output inductors with a transformer that shares magnetic flux paths with both inductors. The ac components of both input and output currents are then effectively steered into the inner transformer portion.

Several factors have slowed the widespread adoption of the Ćuk converter. Semiconductor stresses are relatively high, with both semiconductors effectively carrying a portion of both the input and output current. Severe stresses are placed upon the central link capacitor, which must handle high ripple currents and withstand large ac voltage swings. This creates perhaps the most severe component selection problem at high power levels. The topology is relatively new, and designers do not have as large a body of experience and literature to draw upon. Techniques to cancel ripple currents using magnetic integration, while not unique to the Ćuk converter in possible application, are also relatively new and unknown. Versions of the Cuk converter with magnetic coupling between input and output inductors can be subject to a transient reversal in output voltage polarity during startup. Finally, the Ćuk converter is under patent protection, and potential users may be deterred by the possible need of a licensing agreement. At this writing, the invention of the Ćuk converter is approximately 10 years in the past. Perhaps by the time the original patents expire, the general state of analytical knowledge and supporting electronic component technologies will have advanced the Ćuk converter to general and economical application.

5.1.3.7 Derived Converters

Most electronic systems place requirements on the power supply that cannot be met without augmentation of the basic dc-to-dc conversion blocks presented above. Complete isolation between the input source return and output return is usually required. Conversion from a rectified ac source of 170 or 340 Vdc peak amplitude to an output of 5 Vdc is beyond the practical range of pulse width for the basic converters. Many systems also require multiple dc output voltage levels. Such additional requirements are met by augmenting a basic converter with a high-frequency isolation transformer. Insulation between windings provides the isolation function, and the turns ratio provides voltage and duty cycle scaling. Multiple transformer secondary windings can provide additional dc outputs. Of note for its effect on electromagnetic compatibility is turns ratio scaling of the rates of change of circuit quantities. The primary circuit generally has the largest operating voltage range and maximum dv/dt during transitions. The secondary circuit generally has the largest currents, and hence the largest di/dt values.

Hundreds of modifications to the basic converters are possible, and several are popular. The method chosen is a compromise based on power level, complexity, semiconductor stresses, magnetic component size and complexity, regulation, dc level and ripple required, efficiency, cost and other factors.

5.1.3.8 Buck Derived Converters

Most popular are derivatives of the buck converter. One of these is known as the **forward converter**, diagramed in Fig. 5.10a. It is most often applied to power levels of 100 to 300 W. To derive the forward converter, a transformer and rectifier diode are added to the basic buck converter of Fig. 5.6a, between the input chopping transistor and circulating current diode. The transistor is relocated to the negative supply leg to simplify drive circuits. (Needed, but

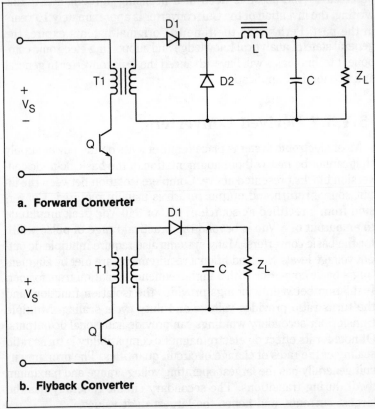

Figure 5.10—Derived Converters

not shown, are means to remove energy stored in the magnetic core of the transformer, during the OFF time of the switch. Otherwise, successive cycles of operation will be at more extreme portions of the B-H loop describing the transformer magnetic material, driving the transformer into destructive magnetic saturation.) Multiple outputs can be obtained by winding the transformer with multiple secondaries and providing each secondary output winding with its own rectifier, circulating current ("freewheeling") diode, filter inductor and capacitor.

The single-ended forward converter has a disadvantage in scaling to high power levels because the transformer magnetic material is excited in only one quadrant of its B-H loop. To obtain better transformer utilization, circuits are used that excite the transformer core in opposite polarities during alternate pulses.

5.1.3.9 Flyback Converter

A buck-boost derived converter known as the **flyback** or **ringing choke converter** is probably the most popular arrangement for multiple isolated outputs below about 50 W. Shown in Fig. 5.10b, the flyback converter combines voltage isolation, turns ratio and energy storage functions into one magnetic component. Often called a flyback "transformer," the component is more accurately referred to as a **coupled inductor**.

The schematic diagram for the flyback converter looks similar to a forward converter, but the operation is different. During the ON time of the primary switch, current and energy storage in the primary winding increase. The secondary winding does not conduct, the secondary diode is reverse biased and the capacitor feeds the load from energy stored during the previous half cycle. When the primary switch opens, and primary current discontinues, the stored inductive energy is transferred to the secondary winding and, through the diode, to the capacitor and load. Note the polarity reversal between primary and secondary windings that cancels the output polarity inversion of the parent buck-boost converter.

Multiple outputs are accommodated by adding, for each additional output, a secondary winding, diode and capacitor. This is the chief advantage of the configuration: multiple isolated outputs are attained sharing only one magnetic component. Several disadvantages, including adverse impact on EMC, limit the flyback to economical use at relatively low power levels.

5.25

The peak currents per unit of power processed are higher in a flyback converter than the buck or boost converters. This not only increases the normalized semiconductor stresses but also the peak rate of change of current (di/dt) in the current carrying loops, increasing the potential of problems due to electromagnetic radiation. The magnetic core, designed to store substantial amounts of energy, has an air gap. Flux fringing about the gap can lead to external radiation and increased eddy current losses in the portion of the windings immediately adjacent to the gap.

5.1.3.10 Quasi-Resonant Converters

All the switching power conversion approaches share a basic drawback: the semiconductors are forced to rapidly interrupt large currents and immediately block large voltages. This places large stresses on the semiconductors during the transitions, during which they must simultaneously handle appreciable fractions of both the full voltage and current, with high peak power dissipation. It also leads to the basic mechanism generating electromagnetic interference: the large values of dv/dt can lead to unwanted high frequency displacement (capacitively coupled) currents, and the large di/dt values can cause radiation from current-carrying loops.

Quasi-resonant approaches to power conversion are being researched in an effort to reduce these problems. In such an approach, the semiconductor switches steer energy into an inductor and capacitor to shape the voltage and current much like a sine wave. The semiconductor can then either interrupt the current when there is nearly zero voltage across it or go into voltage blocking mode near zero current. Rate of change of voltage and current is determined by the reactive circuit, and they can be much more moderate than the rectangular wave approaches now prevalent. Energy transfer is basically fixed energy per pulse, and pulse repetition rate rather than duty cycle is the main control variable.

The use of resonant circuits in power electronics is not new. SCR-based inverters, commutated by resonant or underdamped loads, have been around for decades. What is new is the attempt to go beyond the present component and system limitations to provide new levels of power density, efficiency, operating frequency, transient response and electromagnetic compatibility.

Much of the academic research has been at Virginia Polytechnic Institute and State University and at the California Institute of

Technology. The chief commercial application thus far has been in the product offerings of a Massachusetts company, Vicor, Inc. The company produces a number of dc-to-dc converter modules that use a secondary circuit capacitor, with transformer "leakage" inductance, to shape the pulses. (**Leakage** is jargon for ordinarily undesired magnetic flux that does not couple to both the primary and secondary circuits. See Ref. 15.)

Like the Ćuk converter, quasi-resonant approaches are worthy of mention but are likely to be several years away from common practice.

5.2 Noise Sources and Coupling Paths

We have observed that switching power supplies can have adverse effects on the source of supply at the ac mains frequency due to the nonlinear nature of the input rectifying circuit. More widely noted are interactions between the dc-to-dc converter and other equipment in the radio frequency range. Radio frequency energy can be coupled from the power supply through conducted or radiated paths.

Conducted energy is transferred chiefly by capacitive coupling to ground of circuit nodes that have a high time rate of change of voltage (dv/dt). Control of conducted EMI therefore involves minimization or shielding of circuit components and nodes that have high dv/dt from capacitance to ground. Control of radiated EMI is through minimization of rate of change of current (di/dt) and area of current-carrying loops. Several important noise sources and coupling paths[16, 17] are considered in the following sections.

5.2.1 Time To Frequency Domain Transformation

Circuit quantities in preceding sections were shown as periodic functions of time. Representation of time-domain functions can be made with the Fourier transformation. Figure 5.11 shows the envelope containing solution to the Fourier series expansion of an important group of periodic functions: aperiodically repeating pulse train of height A, pulse duration τ, and repetition period T.

Values within the envelope are at integer multiples of the

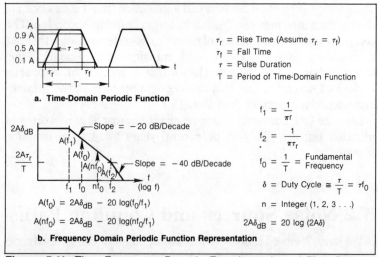

a. **Time-Domain Periodic Function**

τ_r = Rise Time (Assume $\tau_r = \tau_f$)
τ_f = Fall Time
τ = Pulse Duration
T = Period of Time-Domain Function

$$f_1 = \frac{1}{\pi\tau}$$

$$f_2 = \frac{1}{\pi\tau_r}$$

$$f_0 = \frac{1}{T} = \text{Fundamental Frequency}$$

$$\delta = \text{Duty Cycle} \cong \frac{\tau}{T} = \tau f_0$$

$$n = \text{Integer } (1, 2, 3 \ldots)$$

$$2A\delta_{dB} = 20 \log (2A\delta)$$

$A(f_0) = 2A\delta_{dB} - 20 \log(f_0/f_1)$

$A(nf_0) = 2A\delta_{dB} - 20 \log(nf_0/f_1)$

b. **Frequency Domain Periodic Function Representation**

Figure 5.11—Time-Frequency Domain Transformation of Time-Domain Periodic Function

fundamental frequency $f_0 = 1/T$. The maximum value is a constant proportional to the product of the amplitude and duty cycle to a first corner frequency $f_1 = 1/(\pi \times \tau)$. Above the first corner frequency, the envelope decays at a rate of 20 dB/decade. Above a second corner frequency, determined by the risetime of the pulses, the envelope decays at a rate of 40 db/decade. The input current to a buck-derived converter can be represented by a trapezoidal pulse train. The rise and fall times are constrained to small values by efficiency considerations, to reduce switching losses. The product of pulse height and duty cycle will be proportional to power throughput. The pulse repetition rate is usually fixed. The pulse period, and therefore the first corner frequency, will be proportional to duty cycle, which is the main control variable used to regulate against changes in input voltage.

Thus, the broader the voltage range a converter is designed to regulate against, the greater will be the range of operating duty cycle, adversely broadening the frequency range for high input voltage. This is especially pronounced in "wide input range" supplies, designed to operate from 120 or 240 Vac mains without using a mode selection between doubler and bridge rectifier input circuits.

5.2.2 Conducted Noise Paths

Case terminals of power semiconductors (drain or emitter of transistors, cathode terminal of rectifier or freewheeling diodes) are usually nodes of high dv/dt. The power semiconductor case must be thermally (and capacitively) coupled to a heat sink to keep junction temperatures within safe limits. The heat sink may be grounded, or it may have considerable capacitive coupling to ground if left floating.

Capacitive coupling from the case of the primary circuit power transistor is generally the most troublesome source of common-mode conducted noise in the input power conductors. The path of common-mode conduction forms a loop, beginning at the high dv/dt transistor case node, flowing through the grounded heat sink and earth safety wire, and returning through the high-frequency admittance of the ac source and input power leads (both line and neutral). The origin of this input common-mode noise current is shown in Fig 5.12a.

A brief example can show the magnitude of primary circuit dv/dt and the magnitude of the capacitively coupled current. Primary circuits of converters often work from a nominal source amplitude of 340 Vdc, from rectified ac mains. Modern standard MOSFET power transistors readily achieve 100 ns rise and fall times with simple gate driving circuits. This gives an available dv/dt of 340 V/100 ns = 3,400 V/μs. A power transistor insulated from the heat sink with a silicon-coated Kapton® (polyamide material) spacer, can have

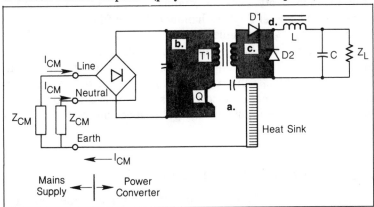

Figure 5.12—Noise Sources and Coupling Paths (a) Common Mode Conduction from High dv/dt Node (b) High di/dt Primary Loop (c) High di/dt Secondary Loop (d) Diode Recovery Induced Ringing

50 pF capacitance from the high dv/dt drain node to heat sink. Maximum current ($I = C \times dv/dt$) then would be $I = 50 \text{ pF} \times 3 \times 400 \text{ V}/\mu s = 170 \text{ mA}$. In practice, measures would be taken to reduce this magnitude.

Cathode terminals of output rectifying and freewheeling diodes are also often nodes of large dv/dt and coupling to ground through heat sinks. A similar common-mode conducted noise pathway is possible in the output circuit. With the magnitude of the output voltage generally much less than that in the primary circuit, and transition times similar in both primary and secondary circuits, the resultant secondary circuit dv/dt is generally less. Also, the secondary circuit can be more readily rearranged to put the diode cathodes at a dc potential rather than a rapidly changing ac potential.

5.3 Conducted Noise Control

Several techniques can be exercised in the design, construction and installation of the power supply to reduce the severity of conducted noise. These are summarized below.

5.3.1 Input Filtering

Most switching power supplies incorporate a lowpass filter in the ac input circuit to attenuate the conduction paths for high-frequency current (see Chapter 7 of this handbook). The filter acts to reduce the transfer of high-frequency energy by providing a mismatch between the relatively high source impedance of the noise sources in the supply and the low impedance of the ac distribution line. The filter not only blocks the conduction pathway of the capacitively coupled common-mode noise but also attenuates the difference mode noise of the input current pulse spectrum of the dc-to-dc converter.

5.3.2 Transition Time Control

Spectra of both differential-mode and common-mode noise are related to the rise and fall time transitions of the transistor. Slowing the transitions by controlling the rate of charge transfer in the gate or base circuit has some effect, but it is extremely detrimental in the power wasted in switching loss and resultant temperature stress. It is therefore a method of low improvement or flexibility.

5.3.3 Transistor Snubbers

Networks known in the jargon as **snubbers**, or **switching aid networks**,[18] are usually added to the primary transistor switch or switches to gain some control over the rate of change of voltage, independent of the current transition. The most basic form, shown in Fig. 5.13a, is a series resistor capacitor combination. The diode polarized snubber of Fig. 5.13b has its greatest effect in reducing dv/dt during the turn-off portion of the transistor pulse, as shown in Fig. 5.13c.

Snubbers are also used for other measures. By delaying the transistor turn-off voltage rise, current in the external circuit can decay before the transistor has to block large voltages. This reduces the switching stress and power dissipation in the transistor. In some circuits this measure is mandatory for safe operation of the device. Snubbers are also used as damping networks in transistor and diode

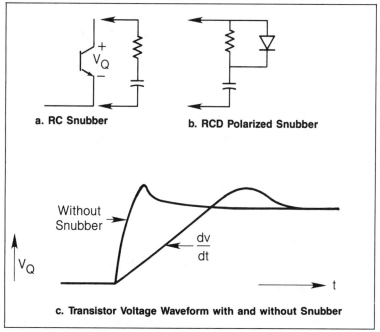

a. RC Snubber   b. RCD Polarized Snubber

c. Transistor Voltage Waveform with and without Snubber

Figure 5.13—Transistor Snubber

circuits to reduce circuit ringing and voltage overshoot that result from parasitic reactances.

The basic snubbers shown in Fig. 5.13 share a common drawback in that dv/dt control is attained at the cost of power dissipation in the resistor, which is often the limiting factor. More sophisticated circuits[19] use reactive elements and diodes to return energy to the dc source.

5.3.4 Relocation of High Dv/dt Nodes

Some topologies can be modified to place power semiconductor case terminals at a dc or slowly changing potential. The common cathode terminals of secondary circuit diodes can be common with a dc output potential by relocating the output averaging inductor in the negative output conductor. The disadvantage is that a transformer terminal is then at ac potential instead of fixed potential. This can be a net improvement, since capacitances to heat sinks are considerable.

Likewise, a primary circuit transistor can be arranged to have the source or emitter terminal switch the transformer node. This usually requires a magnetically isolated transistor driving circuit, considerably increasing complication and expense. Also, the conducted noise pathway is relocated to the transformer, where it may be no easier to control.

5.4 Radiated Sources

Current-carrying conductors with rapidly changing currents are sources of radiation proportional to:

$$I \times A \times f^2$$

where,

I = intensity of current

A = area enclosed by the conductors carrying the current

f = frequency

The most important frequency component is the one associated with the maximum rate of change of current, di/dt (max).

Both the primary and secondary circuits have areas of high di/dt, as shown in Fig. 5.12b and 5.12c. The primary circuit has the most rapidly changing currents in the path from the input dc capacitors through the transformer primary and switch. The secondary circuit has a loop of rapidly changing current that transfers between the rectifying diode D1 of Fig. 5.12 and the circulating current (freewheeling) diode D2. Other topologies, with center tapped secondary circuits, use the same diodes in both rectifying and freewheeling modes. Each diode conduction pulse then has four high di/dt transitions, rather than two, because of transitions between rectifying and circulating current modes. Each transition, however, changes approximately half the output current.

Secondary circuits generally have the larger di/dt and radiation problems, partly because the secondary currents are larger, and also because of the non-ideal turn-off characteristics of the diodes, known as **reverse recovery.**

5.4.1 Loop Area Minimization

Of the contributions to radiation, loop area is the quantity under most direct control of the power supply designer. The intensity of current is determined by required power output. Efficiency constraints hinder control of di/dt by limiting transistor current rise and fall times. Loop area is determined by a printed wiring board geometry.

Placement of circuit elements in close physical proximity helps reduce the area of the conducting loops. In primary circuits, the input capacitor, transistor and transformer should be close to each other. In the secondary circuit, the diodes should be proximal to each other and the transformer and output capacitor in flyback and boost circuits.

5.4.2 Flux-Cancelling Geometries

By closely paralleling conductors carrying high current with a complementary conductor carrying current in the opposite direction, external magnetic fields tend to cancel each other. One effective arrangement is "positive" and "return" conductors parallel to each other, on opposing sides of a printed wiring board. Not only are the conductors separated in space by only the thickness of the board (typically 1.6 mm), but the higher dielectric constant of the board constrains the electric field lines. Another effective geometry uses "+" and "−" conductors next to each other on the same side of the printed wiring board, with the opposite side a single "ground" plane or other constant potential surface. Image currents are induced in the ground plane and tend to cancel the distant magnetic field.

5.4.3 Rectifier Reverse Recovery

The non-ideal turn-off characteristics of silicon rectifiers strongly affect di/dt in secondary circuits and can provoke ringing responses in circuit parasitic reactances. Figure 5.14 shows the changes in diode voltage and current during the turn-off interval.

At time $t = t_0$, forward current through the conducting diode starts to decrease at a rate (−dIf/dt) determined by the transistor current fall time, the leakage inductance of the transformer and the series inductance in the diode circuit. At time t_1, the forward current has decreased to zero, but the diode is still in conduction due to minority charge carriers in the junction. The quantity of stored minority charge carriers is the product of the forward current at which the diode is operated and the lifetime of the charge carriers.

After time t_1, a current flows in the reverse direction, which con-

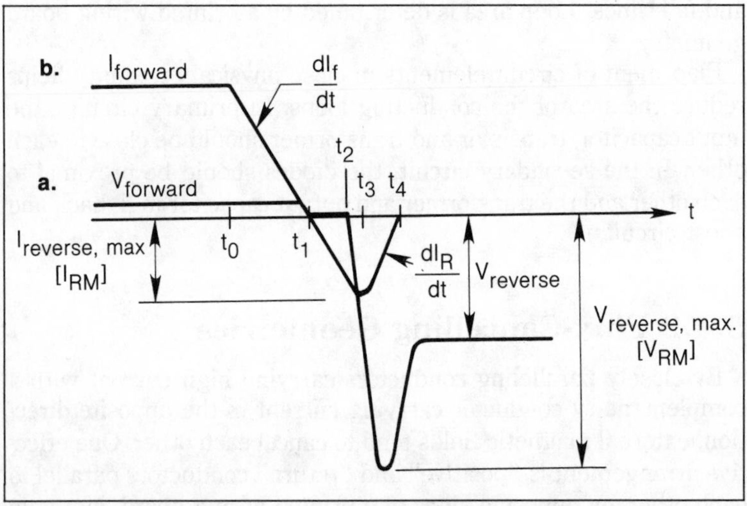

Figure 5.14—Rectifier Recovery. (a) Ideal Voltage Waveform, (b) Ideal Current Waveform

tinues until the minority carriers are removed from the junction by two mechanisms:

1. Recombination with imperfection sites in the crystal
2. Being swept out by the reverse current (charge = current × time)

Between t_2 and t_3, the diode begins to block voltage. The rate of decrease of reverse current between t_3 and t_4 (dI_r/dt) is determined by the diode and not under influence by the external circuit, as is dI_f/dt.

Diode manufacturers intentionally introduce crystal defects to act as charge carrier recombination sites and to reduce the charge carrier lifetime and stored charge. This is done by doping with gold or platinum.

Equally important to a small stored charge is the rate of change of current during the interval t_3 to t_4 of Fig. 5.14. An abrupt "snap off" can excite the resonant circuit, formed by junction capacitance and series inductance, into a ringing response.

5.4.4 Effect of Layout on Output Noise

As an example of how circuit layout of conductors affects radiated and conducted output noise, Fig. 5.15 shows diode turn-off waveforms from two similar power supplies. Both units delivered similar power levels (12.5 Vdc at 45 A) with similar secondary di/dt values of approximately 200 A/μs. Both used diodes from the same manufacturer, with similar recovered charge. The main difference that effected the change shown here is in the relative shape and position of the conductors in the secondary circuit.

The unit of Fig. 5.15b was in volume production, but it suffered from excess radiated interference with television reception. The secondary circuit between the transformer and rectifiers was formed from standard insulated wire of round cross section, with each wire approximately 10 cm long and 4 cm from the other. Resulting loop area was approximately 400 cm^2.

The unit of Fig. 5.15a resulted from an effort to reduce the magnetic moment of the secondary circuit of the original design. Terminations of the transformer and rectifiers were integrated with a printed wiring board using flat conductors and the flux-cancelling ground plane geometry mentioned earlier. Area enclosed by the

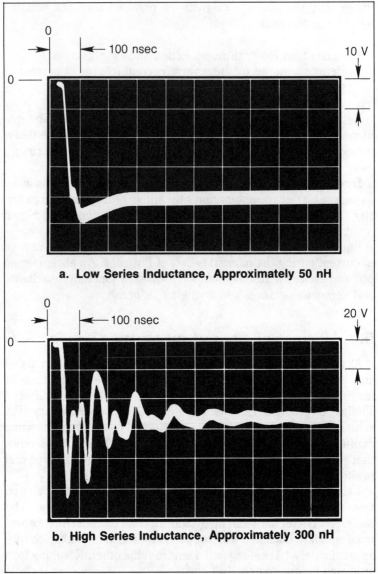

Figure 5.15—Measured Rectifier Recovery Voltages

mean path length of the secondary loop was approximately 2 cm^2. Note that the diode measured in Fig. 5.15b is subjected to an extra reverse voltage stress of 50 V, and that the circuit shows underdamped ringing for 5 cycles. The diode of Fig. 5.15a is subjected to an overvoltage of 10 V, and ringing decays within 1 cycle.

5.4.5 Effect of Parasitics in Output Filter

Figure 5.16a shows that the output inductor is effectively shunted by a capacitance, the effect of capacitance between individual turns, and to the magnetic core. The output capacitor has an effective series inductance and effective series resistance. Figure 5.16b shows the resultant effect on the output waveform. The sawtooth-shaped ripple voltage appearing in the output is due chiefly to the ESR of the capacitor, leading to imperfection in how closely the capacitor current can mirror the inductor ripple current. The spike voltage that appears at each inflection point is from the diode recovery induced ringing (as in Fig. 5.15b), through the parasitic parallel capacitance of the inductor.

The magnitude of the spike can most effectively be reduced by preventing ringing, as in Fig. 5.15a. Further reduction can be had by adding a second stage of filtering, as shown by L2 and C2 of Fig. 5.16c. Inductor L2 is made with a few percent of the inductance of L1, but the "interwinding" capacitance can be orders of magnitude smaller. In high current outputs, L2 is often a "one-turn" inductor, made by surrounding a bus bar with a magnetic core. Likewise, C2 has low capacitance and inductance, so the combination has filtering effect at the spike frequency.

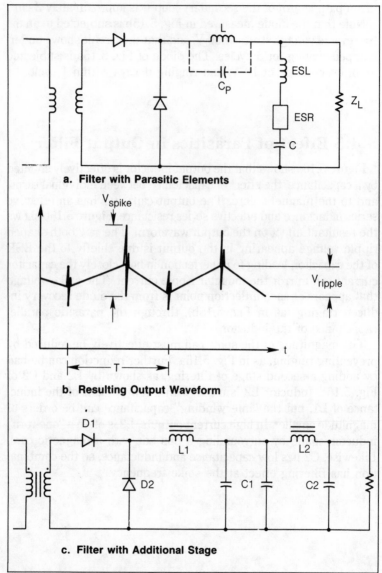

a. Filter with Parasitic Elements

b. Resulting Output Waveform

c. Filter with Additional Stage

Figure 5.16—Output Filter Effects

5.5 References

1. *Power Supply Engineering Handbook* (Computer Products Company, 1987).
2. Dewan, S.B. and Straughen, A., *Power Semiconductor Circuits*, Chapter 2 (New York: John Wiley and Sons, 1975).
3. McLyman, Col. W.T., *Transformer and Inductor Design Handbook*, Chapter IX (New York: Marcel Decker Inc., 1978).
4. Spangler, J.J., "A Power Factor Corrected, MOSFET, Multiple Output, Flyback Switching Power Supply," (Schaumburg, Illinois: Motorola Semiconductor Products Inc.).
5. Hendriks, J.H., "A Simple But Accurate Analysis of Capacitor Input Rectifier Circuits," *Powerconversion International*, July 1985, p. 32.K
6. *Power Supply Application Manual* (SGS Semiconductor Co., July 1985) p. 39.
7. Kamm, E., "Design Techniques to Limit EMI From Switching Mode Converters," *Proceedings of the Sixth National Solid State Power Conversion Conference (Powercon 6)* (Power Concepts Inc., 1979) p. A3.
8. Bucher, J., U.S. Patent 4,683,529, Power Factor Correction Circuit, assigned to Zytec Inc., July 28, 1987.
9. Chambers, D. and Wang, D., "Dynamic Power Factor Correction in Capacitor Off-Line Converters," *Proceedings of the Sixth National Solid State Power Conversion Conference (Powercon 6)* (Power Concepts Inc., 1979) p. B3.
10. Froeschle, T.A., U.S. Patent 4,456,872, assigned to Bose Corporation, Framingham, Mass., 01701.
11. Redl, R. and Sokal, N.O., "Current Mode Control, Five Different Types...," *Power Electronics Specialists Conference 1985 Record*, pp. 379-401.
12. Severens, R.P. and Bloom, G.E., *Modern Switchmode DC-to-DC Converter Circuits*, (New York: Van Nostrand Reinhold, 1985) p. 159.
13. Ćuk, S. and Middlebrook, R.D., DC-to-DC Switching Converter, U.S. Patent Application S.N. 837,532, filed Sept. 28, 1977.
14. Middlebrook, R.D., "Modeling and Design of the Ćuk Converter," *Proceedings of the Sixth National Solid State Power Conversion Conference (Powercon 6)*, May 1979.

15. Ćuk, S. and Polivka, W.M., "Analysis of Integrated Magnetics to Eliminate Current Ripple in Switching Converters," *Proceedings of the Tenth National Solid State Power Conversion Conference (Powercon 10),* April 1983.
16. Nave, Mark, "Noise In Switched Mode Power Supplies," Training course noted Rev. IX, (Seminole, Fla.: Electromagnetic Consulting Services, May 1987).
17. Carsten, Bruce W., "Design Techniques for the Inherent Reduction of Power Converter EMI," *Proceedings of the Eleventh National Solid State Power Conversion Conference (Powercon 11),* April 1984.
18. PETER, Jean-Marie, "Reliable Switching: Safety Areas and Overvoltage Limiting," Transistors and Diodes in Power Processing, (Aix-en-Provence, France: Thomson Semiconducteurs, 1984), p. 97.
19. Whitcomb, E.C., "Designing Non-Dissipative Snubbers for Switched-Mode Converters," *Proceedings of the Sixth National Solid State Power Conversion Conference (Powercon 6),* May 1979.

Chapter 6

Equipment Power Line EMI Filters

by Lon Schneider
Corcom Inc.
Libertyville, IL 60048

Power line EMI filters are employed at the power mains input of electronic devices and equipment to attenuate EMI. These passive devices are composed of inductors and capacitors arranged to form lowpass filters. Originally, they were intended to protect computing devices from interference which might be present on the power lines. This EMI was found to be the cause of random errors and program execution problems. Adding a power line filter to the computer often eliminated these errors.

Computing devices, however, also generated significant EMI. As the EMI environment degraded, regulatory agencies such as the West German FTZ and, more recently, the U.S. Federal Communications Commission imposed limits on the levels of EMI that a marketed computing device may produce. Complying with these limits has become the primary criterion for selecting a power line EMI filter.

6.1 Unique Characteristics of Power Line EMI Filters

The application of RF filters to the power input terminals (port) of electronic devices results in their having several unique requirements. First and most obviously, these filters must be capable of handling significant supply voltage and current. The requirement to support several amperes or more without a significant drop in supply voltage precludes the use of resistive elements. Thus, power line filters provide attenuation through reflection of the undesired energy rather than through dissipation.

Additionally, filters which are applied to the ac line generally must meet the safety criteria of agencies such as Underwriters Laboratories (UL), the Canadian Standards Association (CSA) and the West German Verband Deutscher Electrotechniker (VDE). These requirements include temperature rise, voltage withstand capability, component durability and safe failure mechanisms. The logic behind applying these requirements to products which are connected to utility ac power is that this power source represents potentially lethal voltages and extremely high available energy under fault conditions. For these reasons, special attention is directed toward minimizing the risk of injury as a result of component failure. This will be discussed in greater detail later in this chapter.

6.1.1 Nonspecified Termination Impedances

Filters applied to communication circuits generally operate into tightly controlled terminating impedances. Indeed, filter performance cannot be determined unless the terminations are specified. Power line filters, however, do not enjoy such a controlled environment. The ac power input port of an electronic device is not characterized by its impedance versus frequency characteristic. Neither is the ac line (although standardized networks have been defined to represent an average ac line impedance during emission testing). In this environment, only a qualitative understanding of the device's input impedance characteristic is developed.

Recall that maximum available power is transferred when source and load are impedance matched. Since the objective for the power line filter is to minimize the transfer of noise power, the approach is to mismatch its terminations to the extent that this is practical. Thus, the configuration of an appropriate filter is one which provides a mismatch to the range of anticipated termination impedance. High-impedance sources are generally mismatched with terminations of shunt capacitance, as practical values may be selected which provide adequate mismatch down to the lowest frequency of interest. Similarly, low-impedance sources are mismatched by series inductance. Examples are shown in Fig. 6.1.

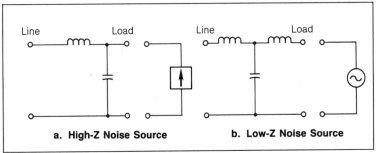

a. **High-Z Noise Source**   b. **Low-Z Noise Source**

Figure 6.1—The Concept of EMI Filter Mismatch

Switch-mode power supplies (SMPSs) permit a more analytical approach to be used. These supplies may be represented by simple equivalent circuits, thus permitting a more quantitative filter analysis. This will be discussed later in this chapter.

6.1.2 Four-Port (Six-Terminal) Network

Figure 6.2 is an example of the schematic diagram of a single-phase power line filter. Note that single-phase power is generally provided via three terminals: line (hot), neutral and ground. Thus the ac power terminations include two ports, (line-to-ground and neutral-to-ground). As the filter provides two ports at both its line and its load side terminals, it is a four-port network.

Four-port networks are much more cumbersome to analyze than two-port networks. It is therefore useful to reduce the four-port to two independent two-port networks. One approach would be to treat the line and neutral sides as independent networks. However, the filter includes significant capacitive and inductive coupling between lines, making them quite interdependent.

The solution is to separate the four-port into its common-mode

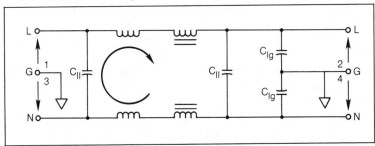

Figure 6.2—Commercial Power Line EMI Filter

(CM) and differential-mode (DM) equivalent circuits, each of which is an independent two-port. These modes may be defined through the use of Fig. 6.3. Common-mode currents (represented by I_{CM}) are those which appear on the line and neutral conductors at the same potential and phase with respect to ground. They behave as if line and neutral were connected in parallel, circulating between this pair and the ground conductor. Thus, the CM equivalent circuit of a network treats the line and neutral conductors as though they were a single conductor referenced to ground.

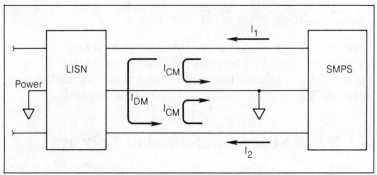

Figure 6.3—Common- and Differential-Mode Currents

Differential-mode current (represented by I_{DM}) appears on the line and neutral leads at the same magnitude but 180° out of phase. Thus DM current circulates only between the line and neutral conductors. As a result, the DM equivalent circuit of a network includes only the line and neutral conductors.

By inspection of Fig. 6.3 it is apparent that I_1 and I_2 may be completely represented by the vector sums of I_{CM} and I_{DM}. Thus, any response characteristic of a linear single phase (four-port) network may be completely represented by its CM and DM components.

The selection of CM and DM components to represent four-port networks is more than an artificial convention. In the power line environment, noise can behave as if it were derived from independent CM and DM sources. Power line filters also behave as if they were composed of independent CM and DM filters, where some components and characteristics function only for CM purposes while others only function for DM. Therefore, the analysis of a power line filter involves the separate analysis of its CM and DM components. This will be discussed later in this chapter.

6.4

6.2 Elements of a Power Line EMI Filter

Filters designed to operate on the power line must meet power handling and safety requirements in addition to providing the desired attenuation characteristic over frequency. To meet these requirements, special components have been developed for use in power line filter applications. One such element is the CM inductor.

To discuss inductors, some terms first must be defined. Permeability, μ, is the ratio of magnetic flux density, B, to field intensity, H; i.e.:

$$B = \mu H \qquad (6.1)$$

Relative permeability, μ_r, is a factor which is applied to μ_o, the permeability of free space, to describe permeability in a medium. That is:

$$\mu = \mu_o \mu_r \qquad (6.2)$$

All things being equal, increased μ_r in the core of an inductor corresponds to increased inductance.

Another term is **incremental permeability**, $\Delta\mu$. This is the permeability experienced by a small signal alternating magnetic field in the presence of a large bias field. In the context of power line filters, it represents the permeability which a core presents to fields generated by RFI currents while simultaneously undergoing large, slowly varying bias fields due to the presence of current on the 60 Hz power line. Note that it is not necessarily equal to the permeability experienced by the large field.

Inductors employed in power line EMI filters generally are fabricated on cores made of ferrite or powdered iron materials. These high-permeability materials permit compact structures which provide high values of inductance. However, they exhibit nonlinear behavior. Their incremental and large signal permeabilities are functions of magnetic flux density. Above low levels of excitation, incremental permeability (and thus incremental inductance) decreases with instantaneous flux density, i.e., as flux density increases, the core saturates. The maximum field, and consequently the flux density in the core, are related to the peak current in the

6.5

winding. Thus, the current which an inductor may support while providing its intended inductance is limited.

This limitation is most significant in the common mode. Inductance values must be much larger in CM than in DM because the allowable values of CM capacitance are restricted by considerations of safety. Effective CM filters require values in the range of several tenths to several tens of millihenries. Ferrite cores can provide compact structures in this range; however, they would saturate at currents below a few tenths of an ampere. Fortunately the ability to separate noise and filter performance into CM and DM components permits a convenient solution, the CM inductor.

6.2.1 Common-Mode Inductor

Common-mode inductors are those for which high values of CM inductance and operating current are achieved at the expense of DM inductance. This is accomplished by providing identical windings on a common core for all current-carrying lines to be filtered. A single-phase example is shown in Fig. 6.4; however, the technique may also be applied to multiphase filters.

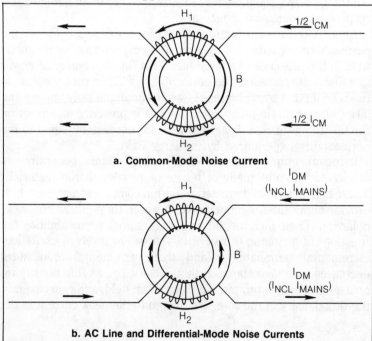

Figure 6.4—Common-Mode Inductor

Identical line and neutral side windings are arranged on a core such that the flux developed in the core cancels when currents in the windings are equal but of opposite phase. Such currents are DM and include the current on the ac power line. Thus, ideally, this current does not generate flux which might saturate the core. CM currents, which are in phase on the L and N windings, generate flux which is additive.

Because the flux in the core, and thus the resulting inductance, cancels for DM currents, the full inductance value is realized only for CM currents. In practice, the cancellation is not perfect. Some flux generated by one winding leaks out of the core before it can cancel that of the other winding. This is called **leakage flux**. The inductance corresponding to this leakage flux is called **leakage inductance**. It is the value of inductance achieved for DM currents and is generally less than a few percent of the CM value.

Again, because the flux cancellation is not perfect, the core does support some flux as a result of the operating current. Thus, avoidance of core saturation still places a limit on the usable operating current of a given CM inductor.

As described above, this technique permits the design of compact large-value CM inductors which tolerate much larger values of ac line current than would a comparable inductor with only one winding. Its effectiveness may be shown by example. Table 6.1 below describes two typical CM inductors and lists values of CM and DM inductance measured under zero-current conditions. Both inductors are wound on toroidal cores of ferrite with nominal μ_r = 10,000. Additionally, the results of saturation measurements are shown. The value of peak current, which instantaneously reduces the CM inductance to one half its initial value, is recorded. This is compared to the saturation current measured when the inductor is configured as an independent rather than a CM structure.

Table 6.1—Common-Mode Inductor

| Core Dimensions in mm | | | No. Turns | Inductance in mH | | $I_{pk\ (sat)}$ | |
O.D.	I.D.	Ht.		CM	DM	CM	Independent
22.1	13.7	12.7	54	27.7	0.065	11 A	0.012 A
36.0	23.0	15.1	24	6.5	0.027	30 A	0.070 A

6.2.2 Independent Inductors

Filters which must provide high DM performance often require more DM inductance than that provided by leakage of the CM inductor. In these cases, independent DM inductors are added. These generally employ single windings on cores of moderate permeability. Closed magnetic structures (those in which a core provides an uninterrupted magnetic circuit, such as a toroid) may be made of powdered iron or related alloys. Rods or bars of ferrite, powdered iron or alloys are also employed. These structures are lower in cost than toroids and much easier to wind. However, their effective permeability is much lower than that of the core material used because the magnetic circuit includes a significant air path. As a result, these open structures provide much less inductance than a toroidal core with comparable turns. However, core saturation may be avoided at higher levels of operating current than that for a comparable toroidal structure.

Other structures are used to provide DM inductance. Gapped structures may be made of higher-permeability materials than closed structures. Additionally, L and N windings may be applied on either structure such that the flux is additive for these DM currents.

An effect of open-core structures is worth noting. Because their magnetic circuit includes significant space outside the core, these devices may pick up noise from stray magnetic fields and couple it into the filter. Additionally, the fields that they generate may also become coupled into other structures.

Finally, magnetic fields generated by current on the ac power line flowing in these elements may cause problems. When used inside steel enclosures, they may cause nearby walls to hum at the power line frequency. Additionally, the steel enclosure can become part of the rod's magnetic circuit, thus increasing the structure's inductance at low frequencies. This has the effect of aggravating core saturation due to the current on the ac power line. Because the enclosure walls are generally too thick to prevent eddy current losses at the filter's RF operating frequencies, this coupling usually degrades rather than improves filter performance in the stopband. A comparison of saturation and inductance at power and signal frequencies is shown in Table 6.2.

Table 6.2—Enclosure Effects upon Rod Inductance and Saturation

	L(120 Hz)	L(100 kHz)	I_{pk} (sat)
In Air	47 μH	46 μH	9.5 A
Near 0.024" Steel Wall	68 μH	36 μH	6.4 A

6.2.3 Line-to-Ground Capacitors

Capacitors applied in filters between the power mains and ground are different from other capacitors in that they must endure production testing of their high-voltage withstand capability. All internationally approved ac power line filters rated at 250 Vac must withstand line-to-ground high potential (hipot) of 1,500 V rms for 60 s. The requirement for filters which are recognized by UL alone is 1,000 V rms.

The values of line-to-ground capacitors are limited by safety agency restrictions on the amount of ac current which may flow on the ground conductor (safety or "green" wire). Maximum values are in the range of 0.022 μF for products sold only in North America and 0.005 μF for those intended to be marketed throughout the world.

Such capacitors are constructed by one of two basic methods. First, a ceramic dielectric may be employed with metalized electrodes. Generally, ceramic capacitors used on the ac power line are single-layer structures of high dielectric-constant material. Alternatively, a paper or plastic film may be employed as the dielectric, with metal foil or deposited metal electrodes. The dielectric constants of available ceramics approach 10,000 while those of paper or plastic films are typically less than 5. In order to provide sufficient capacitance, these low-dielectric materials are provided in long, thin strips which are then tightly wound. Multiple layers may be employed, and impregnation (for paper) may be added to increase endurance.

6.2.4 Line-to-Line Capacitors

Line-to-line capacitors are constructed by methods similar to those used on line-to-ground capacitors. As part of a power line filter, they must withstand high-voltage breakdown testing at 1,000 V rms or 1,414 Vdc (1,075 Vdc for Europe only). Thus they are designed with less dielectric breakdown withstand capability than line-to-ground capacitors.

Unlike-line-to ground capacitors, the values of line-to-line capacitors are not restricted by safety agencies. Thus values range from several nanofarads to several microfarads.

6.3 Filter Equivalent Circuits

Having described the major components of a power line EMI filter, it is now appropriate to combine them to form equivalent circuit models. These models illustrate the effects of components in the filter upon its CM and DM performance and provide the basis for quantitative analysis.

6.3.1 Common-Mode Equivalent Circuit for Filter

A representative filter schematic was shown in Fig. 6.2. This filter employs independent inductors as well as a CM inductor. The CM equivalent circuit for this filter is shown in Fig. 6.5. The CM inductor appears in the model as its total self-inductance. This is the value measured with both windings in parallel and is essentially identical to that measured on one winding alone.

Because the line and neutral leads are essentially in parallel, the line-to ground capacitors (C_{lg}) and the independent inductors appear in the model in parallel, while line-to-line capacitors (C_{ll}) do not appear in the model. Parasitic elements (R_p, C_p, L and r) are also shown for each individual component (windings in parallel for the CM inductor).

These parasitic elements prevent the performance of the filter from reaching that of an ideal filter. First, C_p causes the inductors to appear capacitive at moderate to high frequencies. In this range C_p and C_{lg} form a capacitive divider with constant attenuation over frequency. At higher frequencies, L causes C_{lg} to series resonate and then turn inductive. The effect of both elements having resonated is to reverse the attenuation slope of the filter above this point (i.e., the lowpass filter is turned into a highpass filter).

The effects of parasitics are graphically demonstrated in Fig. 6.6.

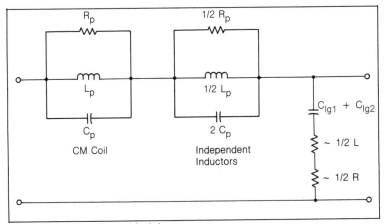

Figure 6.5—CM Filter Model

In this figure the CM insertion loss (IL) of an actual filter is compared to that which would be calculated with ideal elements of the same value. In Region I, the actual and ideal filters are in good agreement. In Region II, the actual filter diverges from the ideal, forming a notch in the response. This is the region of parallel resonance of the CM inductor. The insertion loss is constant with frequency in Region III. Its value is determined by the ratio of C_p to C_{lg}. Another notch is visible in Region IV, where C_{lg} has become series resonant. Finally, the actual filter has a positive IL slope in Region V.

It is important that a power line filter maintains high performance at high frequencies. Conducted emission performance limits extend to 30 MHz (commercial) or 50 MHz (military). Also, some radiated emission problems are due to high-frequency noise which is conducted out of the electronic device via the power cable. Finally, high-frequency EMI may be radiated onto the power cable and thereby enter the equipment. Thus it is useful to extend the effective stopband frequency range of the filter by controlling these parasitic problems.

The effects which degrade high-frequency performance may be controlled by winding techniques which minimize C_p (see Fig. 6.5) and by assembly and construction techniques which limit L. The value of C_p may be minimized by either minimizing the capacitance per turn or by restricting the number of turns which are shunted by a single interwinding capacitance. Techniques which

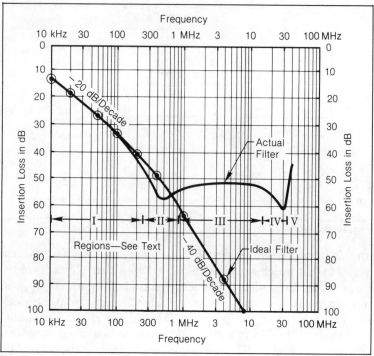

Figure 6.6—CM Insertion Loss of Actual and Ideal Filters

address the former are not plentiful in the power line filter environment because constraints are added by the need for compact structures which handle power and control heat rise. Opportunities do exist, however, for the latter approach. An example will be used to illustrate the point as shown in Fig. 6.7.

An inductor with N + 1 turns applied in a single layer on a core of low electrical conductivity may be seen to include capacitance, c, between each pair of adjacent turns. Then C_p is composed of N capacitances of value c in series and is thus equal to c/N. Multiple layer winding causes C_p to increase for two reasons. First, multiple layers result in each turn coming into contact with additional turns. Thus many more capacitances of value c are generated. Additionally, many of these capacitances involve turns which are not sequential. This coupling bypasses some fraction of the total inductor. In the extreme case, the first and last turns would be adjacent. Then C_p would be larger than c.

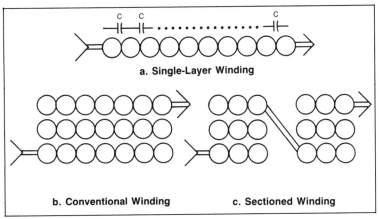

a. Single-Layer Winding

b. Conventional Winding   c. Sectioned Winding

Figure 6.7—Interwinding Capacitance

The solution, therefore, is to place turns together which are as close as possible to being sequential. Where layer winding is necessary, odd numbers of layers are preferable to even numbers. Additionally, the winding may be divided lengthwise into sections (as in Fig. 6.7c) so that turns which are above others are sequentially closer together than they would be if layers traversed the full winding length before a new layer was formed (Fig. 6.7b).

Generally, to minimize L, the lengths of capacitor leads are kept as short as practical. A technique for further reducing L is to provide separate input and output leads on the capacitor, thus turning it into a three-terminal device (Fig. 6.8). The ground connection, of course, must be kept extremely short. This technique removes the inductance of each long lead from the shunt branch. It thereby greatly increases the series resonant frequency of the C_{lg} structure.

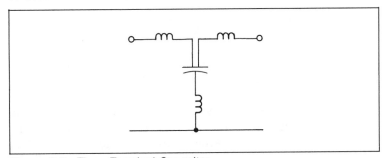

Figure 6.8—Three-Terminal Capacitor

While these techniques for extending high-frequency performance are quite effective, they alone are often inadequate for military or TEMPEST applications, which extend performance requirements to 1 GHz or higher. These filters generally require additional elements. The most significant example of a 1 GHz component is the feedthrough capacitor. This is a three-terminal capacitor with the ground inductance minimized by the way the device is packaged. The capacitor is applied by mounting it through an electrically conductive wall or bulkhead which serves as either the enclosure of the filter or an internal separator. Thus the capacitor is used to feed current through this barrier. The capacitor electrode which is intended to be grounded is connected to the mounting element of the device through a short-length, wide-area connection. Thus the inductance in the ground leg is kept very low. The result is an element usable at high frequencies which also serves to provide a means for passing desired power or signals through an enclosure or bulkhead. A typical mounting application is shown in Fig. 6.9.

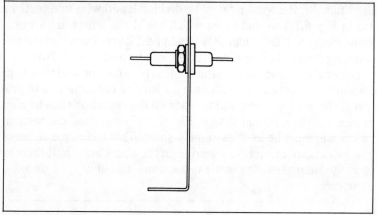

Figure 6.9—Application of Feedthrough Capacitor

Feedthrough capacitors are constructed in three different styles: tubular ceramic, discoidal ceramic or wound plastic film and metallic foil. These styles are shown in Fig. 6.10. In the case of the tubular capacitor, metallic electrodes are applied to the inner and outer surfaces of a ceramic tube to form a coaxial capacitor. An electrically conductive rod or wire is attached to the inner electrode such that it extends beyond the ceramic tube at both ends. An eyelet or bushing is then attached to the outer electrode.

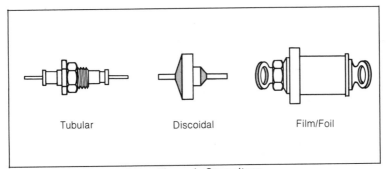

Figure 6.10—Types of Feedthrough Capacitors

Discoidal feedthrough capacitors employ a ceramic disk with a hole in the center. Electrodes are applied to both surfaces; however, the electrode, which is intended to be grounded, is physically isolated from the center hole. A wire or rod is passed through the hole and soldered to the electrode which meets the center. This device then may be attached via the ground electrode either directly to the bulkhead or to a metallic package which will be attached to a bulkhead.

Film foil construction is quite different from the above. Layers of aluminum foil and plastic film are wound over an insulating tube. Foils are arranged to extend beyond the film on one side each. Thus the foil extending beyond the rolled film on each end forms a terminal. The insulating tube is provided to extend beyond the roll of foil and film on one side. This provides an insulated path through the bulkhead for the brass screw which is used to mount the capacitor and to provide a feedthrough conductor through it. An appropriate insulating washer, metallic washer and nut complete the assembly.

6.3.2 Differential-Mode Equivalent Circuit for Filter

The DM equivalent circuit for the filter of Fig. 6.2 is shown in Fig. 6.11. Here the line and neutral leads are in series, and the signal current flows through these leads in opposite directions. Thus the independent inductors are in series for the DM model, and the CM coil appears as its leakage inductance and the associated parasitics. These elements, L'_p, C'_p and R'_p are those measured on a CM coil with the windings connected series opposed (i.e., in DM).

6.15

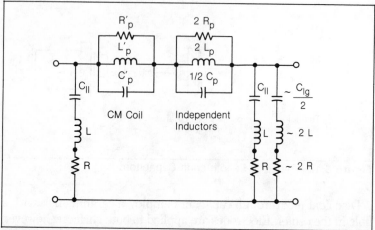

Figure 6.11—DM Filter Model

Capacitors for this model are only those which appear between line and neutral, i.e., the line-to-line capacitors (C_{ll}'s) and the series combination of the line-to-ground capacitors (C_{lg}'s). Due to their relative magnitudes, C_{lg} is often ignored when it is in parallel with C_{ll}. However, this simplification ignores the higher-frequency effects of series resonance of the C_{lg} arm and the parallel resonance of the combination of C_{ll} and C_{lg}.

6.4 Insertion Loss

An earlier discussion indicated that EMI filters applied to the power line do not enjoy specified termination impedances. Thus, filter manufacturers cannot specify the actual in-circuit attenuation performance of their products. To permit a standardized method for comparison, the attenuation of a filter in a 50 Ω environment is usually specified. This measurement is termed **insertion loss** (IL). It is defined as the ratio, expressed in dB, of the power transferred to the load with no filter connected to that which is transferred when a filter is inserted between source and load. Circuits representing these two conditions are shown in Fig. 6.12.

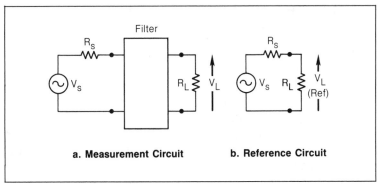

Figure 6.12—Insertion Loss

$$IL = 10 \log(P_{L\ (Ref)}/P_L)$$

$$IL = 20 \log(V_{L\ (Ref)}/V_L)$$

The primary purpose of insertion loss measurement is to provide a convenient means for describing the performance of an approved filter so that subsequent samples may be compared for consistency. Test circuits are shown below.

6.4.1 Common-Mode Insertion Loss Measurement

The CM IL test circuit is shown in Fig. 6.13 with the applicable reference circuit. It is apparent that the CM source and load impedances are 50 Ω.

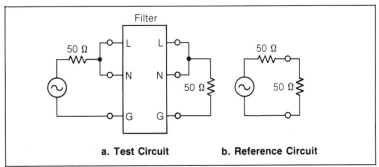

Figure 6.13—Common-Mode Insertion Loss Measurement

6.4.2 Differential-Mode Insertion Loss Test Circuit

The DM IL test circuit is shown in Fig. 6.14. Because the filter line and neutral are balanced with respect to ground while the test instrumentation (spectrum analyzer and tracking generator) are unbalanced, this measurement employs 50 Ω, 180° power splitters. These divide input power equally between the two 50 Ω output ports while maintaining 180° phase difference between them. When used as combiners, these devices provide output which is the difference of the signals on the two input ports. As line and neutral each see 50 Ω to ground, the DM IL termination impedance is 100 Ω. Note that some manufacturers use other devices to convert from unbalanced to balanced lines. Their termination impedances may be different.

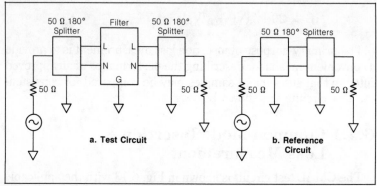

Figure 6.14—Differential-Mode Insertion Loss Measurement

6.5 Filter Performance

Equipment power line EMI filters are available with a wide variety of performance characteristics. These will be organized in terms of application and relative IL. Filters designed to reduce equipment susceptibility to RF energy on the power line will be discussed first. This will be followed by emission filters, which will be divided into discussions of filters for linear powered equipment and those for equipment which is powered by a switch-mode power supply. These applications are quite different, both in the method by which EMI becomes coupled onto the power line and in the type of filtering needed to attenuate it.

6.5.1 Filters to Reduce Equipment Susceptibility to EMI

Problems of susceptibility to conducted RFI are often caused by RF energy entering an electronic device via the power cable and propagating via stray coupling into sensitive circuits. Sources of this EMI include radio transmitters, oscillators, computers, switching devices, etc. This phenomenon typically has been found to be the cause of erratic operation of computing devices and consequently was the primary reason for including an EMI filter in computers. As this stray coupling mechanism was typically a CM phenomenon and was most significant at moderate to high frequencies, susceptibility filters were generally CM filters with significant attenuation beginning in the vicinity of 0.5 to 1 MHz.

The earliest versions resembled the circuit of Fig. 6.15a. It includes a two-element CM filter and a three-element DM filter, where one of the DM elements is the series combination of the C'_{lg}s. Higher DM performance was provided by the circuit of Fig. 6.15b, which employed larger values of C_{ll} as well as one on each end. Increased performance in both modes was provided by the circuit of Fig. 6.15c, a three-element CM filter (best for relatively low-impedance CM sources) and a five-element DM filter. Representative values of advertised minimum IL are shown in Fig. 6.16 for each of these three filters.

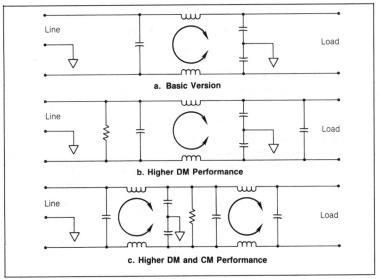

a. Basic Version

b. Higher DM Performance

c. Higher DM and CM Performance

Figure 6.15—Typical Filters for Susceptibility Control

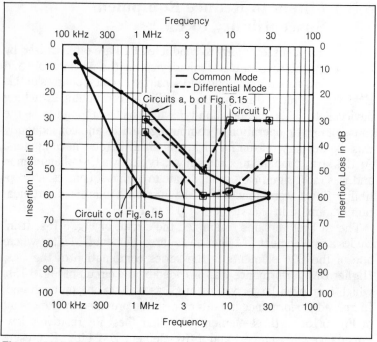

Figure 6.16—Representative IL for Susceptibility Filters

6.5.2 Emission Filters for Linear Powered Equipment

Conducted emission problems on linear powered computing devices generally involve clock or logic signals which appear on the power line through stray coupling or as a result of inadequate isolation in the supply. This phenomenon is very similar to that which affects susceptibility. Thus, the emissions of devices with linear power supplies, especially in the context of FCC limits, are often addressed by the higher-performance susceptibility filters or the like. Filters with additional performance were developed as standard products to address equipment with higher levels of emissions or those which were intended to meet more stringent emission limits. In addition to the employment of larger element values, filters were developed which included additional elements or poles to provide steeper attenuation slopes.

The family of filter circuits shown in Fig. 6.17 may be used to control emissions on linear as well as SMPS powered equipment. At a given rated current level, all variations employ the same inductors. The circuit of Fig. 6.17a is intended for high-impedance CM sources. The circuit of Fig. 617b moves the C_{lg}s to the center of the filter. This permits the rod inductors to represent an additional CM pole. Additionally, an additional C_{ll} in the center provides an additional DM pole. A second set of C_{lg}s is provided in Fig. 6.17c. This further increases the slope and maximum value of its CM IL. Values for the minimum IL values of 3 through 10 A models are shown in Fig. 6.18.

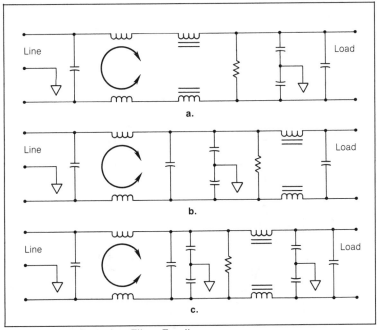

Figure 6.17—Emission Filter Family

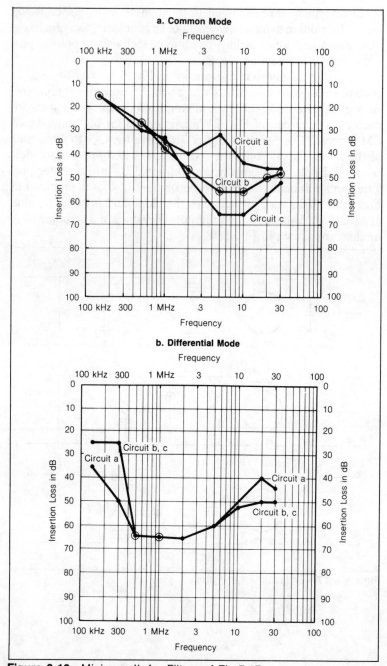

Figure 6.18—Minimum IL for Filters of Fig 7.17

6.5.3 Filters for Switch-Mode Powered Equipment

Unlike filters for linear powered devices, the performance of an emission filter for equipment powered by a switch-mode power supply is generally dictated by the noise that the SMPS itself generates. These supplies usually produce a wideband series of harmonics of the switching frequency, beginning with the fundamental. This may be as low as 20 kHz. Both CM and DM components are usually significant. Thus, an effective SMPS emission filter must provide significant CM and DM attenuation in-circuit, at frequencies within the spectrum specified by the applicable regulatory agency and coinciding with the emissions of the SMPS. This translates to 450 kHz through 30 MHz for FCC Class A or B, 150 kHz through 30 MHz for VDE Class A level and 10 kHz (or the SMPS switching frequency) through 30 MHz for VDE Class B level.

From the above it is apparent that SMPS emission filters represent the highest performance class of commercial, equipment power line filters. Fortunately, they permit a much more analytical design approach than do their lower-performance relatives. Models have been developed to represent SMPSs as their first-order equivalent CM and DM noise sources.

6.5.3.1 Common-Mode Model for SMPS Noise Source

The CM noise source is essentially a current source with shunt capacitance and resistance. The source is generally much more capacitive than resistive. This capacitance is that which exists between the collectors of the SMPS switching devices and ground. Values for the capacitance range from near zero through 3,000 pF, depending upon power level and construction. Typical capacitance values for SMPSs at 300 W or less are under 1,000 pF.

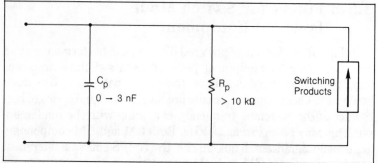

Figure 6.19—CM Noise Source

6.5.3.2 Differential-Mode Model for SMPS Noise Source

The DM noise source is composed of two sources: a high-impedance source and a low-impedance source which is periodically connected across it. This dual nature is the result of the rectifier and storage capacitor(s) which are at the input of all offline SMPSs. When the rectifier bridge is conducting, the capacitor is coupled across the ac line. In this condition, the source includes the capacitor (generally inductive at the switching frequency), the diodes, any soft-start or protection circuitry and any additional inductance between the capacitor and the ac input. Thus, so long as the bridge is conducting, the DM source impedance is very low. For the purpose of this chapter, this source will be called **low-Z DM**.

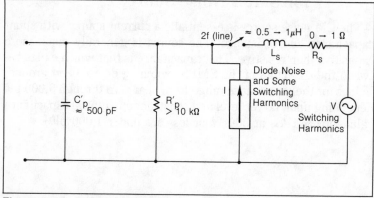

Figure 6.20—DM Noise Source

When the rectifier bridge is not conducting, the source impedance is high. In this condition, switching harmonics still may be coupled to the line via several stray-path mechanisms. This phenomenon is called **high-Z DM noise**. The magnitude of this part of the DM noise source is highly dependent upon the layout and configuration of the supply. Wideband high-Z DM noise also results from the turn-off pulse of the rectifier bridge.

6.5.3.3 Application of Models to SMPS Emission Filters

The above shows that a power line EMI filter actually includes three filters: CM, low-Z DM and high-Z DM. The CM circuits of SMPS emission filters generally employ C_{lg} at or electrically close to the load. This is especially true for VDE filters, as the small source capacitance would resonate in-band with reasonable values of L_{CM}. The number of poles is dictated by the needed attenuation slope and the level required in the middle to upper frequency range. Filter elements for low-Z DM present DM inductance to the load. Additionally, C_{ll} is often added for high-Z DM.

A wide range of SMPS emission filters are available commercially. Typical filter schematics are shown in Fig. 6.21. Advertised

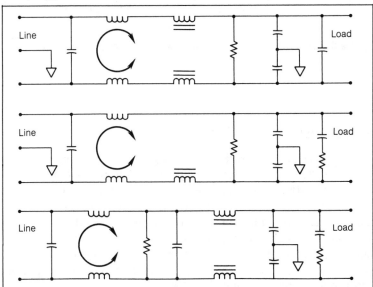

Figure 6.21—Typical SMPS Emission Filter Circuits

values of minimum IL for 3 and 6 A SMPS emission filters rated for VDE Class B are shown in Fig. 6.22. Note that the IL curves do not describe in-circuit attenuation and are shown only for comparison with the lower-performance filters above.

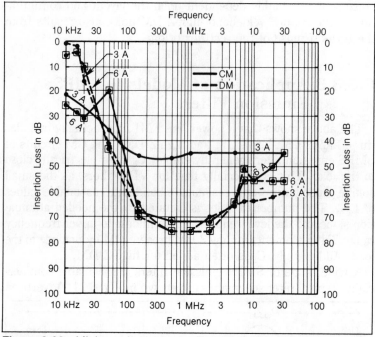

Figure 6.22—Minimum IL Values for Two VDE Class B SMPS Emission Filters

6.5.4 TEMPEST Filters

TEMPEST is a U.S. National Security Agency program designed to provide standards for computing devices and peripherals which protect sensitive data from electronic eavesdropping. Filters developed for these applications often must provide high performance over the range of 10 kHz through 1 GHz. This is accomplished at the low-frequency end of the range by providing high-performance elements in conventional filter designs. Performance at the high end of the range is supplemented by the use of feedthrough capacitors and the like.

To realize this high performance in the actual application, TEMPEST filter enclosures generally employ features which permit bulkhead mounting with very high RF isolation. This is aided by the use of RF gaskets, controlled flat surfaces and multiple fastening points. Some suppliers offer such filters as standard products. Custom versions are also provided by these and other suppliers.

6.5.5 Military Filters

Equipment power line EMI filters for military applications employ the same techniques as those employed in the commercial sector. The characteristics which differentiate military filters from commercial filters are the additional documentation, environmental testing and standardized marking requirements which they must meet.

The specification defining EMC requirements for military equipment is MIL-STD-461C. This specifies conducted emission and susceptibility performance for various types of equipment, applications and branches of service. Emission limits generally apply in the range of 15 kHz through 50 MHz and with limited applicability may extend all the way down to 30 Hz or the ac power frequency. Additionally, radiated emission control may dictate that filter performance extend to 1 GHz or more. Performance in these ranges is accomplished using the approaches described above. However, the element values required to meet the most stringent attenuation requirements may not comply with commercial standards for line-to-ground leakage current or filter economy.

Another difference between military filters and commercial filters is that the former generally employ the IL test method of MIL-STD-220A. This specification provides for IL measurements in a 50 Ω environment wherein the filter may be tested while supporting full rated current or under no-load conditions. Figure 6.23 depicts one of several similar test circuits for MIL-STD-220A measurement.

MIL-STD-220A applies only to two-port filters or those which contain independent two-port networks. As the document was issued in December, 1959, before the widespread use of common-mode inductors and line-to-line capacitors in power line filters, it does not specify how these filters should be measured. Some manufacturers ground the terminals which are not connected to the IL fixture, but others leave them unterminated. Neither test alone fully describes the IL performance of the filter. Some effort is being applied to revise this aspect of the document.

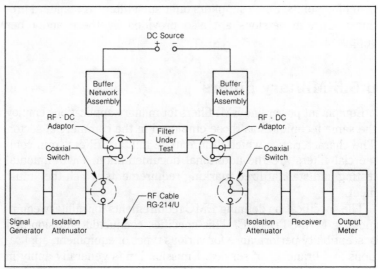

Figure 6.23—MIL-STD-220A Test Circuit

6.6 Filters for Commercial Equipment

A wide range of standard filters are available from several suppliers (see Fig. 6.24). When standard products cannot meet the customer's need, most manufacturers will perform custom designs. This section describes the range of available standard products and provides a listing of commercial suppliers of equipment filters. Additionally, information is offered to aid the designer in selecting a filter, both in terms of its attenuation performance and safety requirements.

6.6.1 Available Products

The discussion of filter performance resulted in the development of three general classifications of EMI filters: (1) susceptibility filters, (2) emission filters for linear powered equipment and (3) SMPS emission filters. Suppliers of standard or catalog products provide many examples in each category. In addition to ranges of IL, a variety of packages and terminations is available.

The most typical package is a fully enclosed metal can. Terminal choices include solder lugs, quick-connect terminals, wire leads and screw or stud terminals. These apply to all three catagories of filters. Temperature-rise restrictions on quick-connect terminals limit the current levels for which they may be used. Single-blade terminals may be replaced at higher currents with double-blade versions or stud terminals.

Additionally, many products are available which employ a standard CEE 22 appliance inlet receptacle. This internationally recognized connector permits the filter to be mounted on a bulkhead so that the line-side wiring is fully outside the equipment. Again, filters in all three performance categories are available with these receptacles. As another benefit, ac line cords compatible with the receptacles of most countries are available with the CEE 22 connector on the other end. Thus, this feature facilitates marketing an electronic device internationally.

Filters intended for mounting on printed wiring boards are also available. Standard versions are not usually enclosed in a metallic housing; pins are provided for insertion into the circuit board. Several versions of susceptibility filters are available. Also, a few manufacturers offer linear and SMPS emission filters for this application.

Extending the CEE 22 receptacle idea, many suppliers offer filters which combine these receptacles with additional features such as fuse holders, primary voltage selection and power switches. By including these functions in the filter, the user may avoid most of the effort associated with purchasing, wiring and approving a design employing individual components. Filter performance offered in these packages includes all three catagories, but with fewer selections.

Several manufacturers offer standard filters for three-phase applications. Rated current values up to 80 or 100 A are available as standard products. These employ metal enclosures and stud terminals. Some include shrouds for enclosing the terminations. At these high current levels, attenuation performance is in the range of high-performance susceptibility filters. These three-phase filters are often used as systems filters in conjunction with lower-current, higher-performance filters located in individual subsystems.

Figure 6.24—Typical Equipment Power Line EMI Filters

6.6.2 Filter Selection

Whether a filter is intended to meet specific emission or susceptibility requirements, its performance must be verified by testing
in the intended equipment. Insertion loss does not predict the attenuation which will be provided by the filter in-circuit. Nor is the

recommended application published for an SMPS emission filter a guarantee that a given system is compliant.

Techniques and criteria for performing conducted emissions and susceptibility are described in other volumes of this handbook series. The selection of a filter to use in initial tests should be based upon experience, relative IL performance or, for SMPS emission filters, manufacturers' recommendations. The objective is to select a filter that provides a reasonable but not excessive margin to the desired criterion. When this criterion is not met in initial testing, the results should direct the selection of further iterations. Note that the EMI performance of the system may be compromised by the way it is constructed or by the way the filter is installed. This is addressed at the end of this chapter.

Given that the attenuation performance is verified by in-circuit testing, other considerations in the selection of a filter should include safety approvals in the countries in which the end product is to be marketed. Additionally, the availability of features such as receptacles, fuse holders, voltage selection and power switching may influence the selection. Obviously, cost and size are important parameters. Finally, measures of durability beyond specific safety agency requirements may enter into the selection process. Examples include overload current rating, insulation resistance and environmental ratings.

6.6.3 Commercial Regulations for Safety

The major safety agencies regulating equipment power line EMI filters are Underwriters Laboratories (UL), which applies in the U.S.A., the Canadian Standards Association (CSA) and the West German Verband Deutscher Electrotechniker (VDE). Specifications for equipment filters are UL 1283, CSA C22.2 No. 8-M1986 and VDE 0565 part 3. Some filter requirements for these and other agencies are shown in Table 6.3. While it is not mandatory that equipment filters carry these approvals, they greatly facilitate the approval process of the end-use equipment. In the absence of a filter approval, all the applicable tests must be performed on the filter during systems approval testing. Then the equipment manufacturer, rather than the filter manufacturer, becomes responsible for assuring that future production lots of the filter will remain in compliance with agency requirements. For these reasons, safety approvals for filters are extremely useful.

Table 6.3—Interference Filter Requirements and Specifications

Country	Leakage Current Equip. Requirement* Maximum 1 mA	@ V	Hz	Qualification Hipot Rating (1 minute)	Insulation Resistance Minimum $\Omega \times 10^9$	@ V	High Voltage Pulse Test	Current Overload Test	Approving Organization Name	City	Specifications Applicable to Filters
United Kingdom	0.5^1	250	50	2,250 Vdc or 1,500 Vac^3 4.3 × Vr, Vdc^4	$6,000^{3,4}$	100	—	—	BEAB (BSI)	London	BS2135
	$0.25/5^2$	250	50		20^4	100					BS613
Switzerland	0.5^1	250	50	2,250 Vdc or 1,500 Vac^3 2,000 Vac^9 4.3 × Vr, Vdc^4	$3,000^{3,4}$	100	Yes Par 5.6	—	SEV	Zurich	1016/1017 1055,1022
	$0.25/5^2$	150	50								
Sweden	0.5^1	250	50	1,500 Vac^3	$6,000^{3,4}$	100	—	—	SEMKO	Stockholm	SEN432901
	$0.25/5^4$	250	50								
Canada	5	120	60	1,000 + 2 Vr, Vac^3 1,414 Vdc Min. 500 + 2 Vr, Vdc^4			Yes Per 6.8	—	CSA	Rexdale	C22.2 No. 0.8 No. 0.4 No. 08
Germany	$0.75/3.5^{1,5}$	250	50	1,500 Vac^3 4.3 × Vr, Vdc^4	$6,000^{3,4}$	100	—	75 × I rated for 2.5 cycles	VDE	Offenbach	0565-1,0565-2 0565-3^3
	$0.25/3.5^2$	250	50		$2,000^3$ $1,500^4$	100 100	Yes Par 5.419				
France	—	—	—	—	—		—	—	UTE	Paris	—
United States	5	125	60	1,000 Vac or 1,414 Vdc^3 1,000 Vac or 1,414 Vdc^4 1,500 Vac or 2,121 Vdc^{10}			—	—	UL	Various	UL1283,544

*General Equipment Values, Applicable Equipment Values May Take Precedence
[1]—Class,1 Equipment/Ground Wire
[2]—Class II Equipment/Double Insulated (Lower Value Applies to User-Accessible Metal Parts)
[3]—Line-to-Ground/Case
[4]—Line-to-Line
[5]—Lower Value Applies to Portable Equipment
[6]—Proposed
[7]—At Upper Temperature
[8]—At Room Temperature
[9]—Line-to-Ungrounded or Non-Metallic Case
[10]—Line-to-Ground/Case and Line-to-Line for Patient Care Equipment
Vr—Rated Line Voltage

The criteria for UL include flammability, lead wire durability, spacings between conductors of opposite polarity, ground circuit conductors, dielectric withstand capability, line-to-ground leakage current (in the equipment specification), maximum internal operating temperatures and marking. CSA adds endurance tests, insulation resistance, humidity, voltage-surge withstand and resistance to flame.

In addition to the above, VDE also limits component tolerances, tests mechanical durability and durability of regenerative capacitors and specifies maximum capacitance change with temperature. All three agencies require 100 percent testing of dielectric withstand capability during production.

6.7 Filters for Military Equipment

The features which make military filters different from commercial versions involve their environmental performance, testing requirements and nomenclature. The general requirements for military EMI filters are contained in MIL-F-15733G. This number is part of the military part number of approved filters and filter capacitors. Note, however, that the requirements of an individual filter specification supercede the general requirements when a conflict exists. Thus, MIL-F-15733G may be used as a guide rather that a rigid requirement. Type designations are used to describe filters that meet standardized values for style, rated current (0.1 through 500 A), IL, terminals, temperature range and vibration rating. Additional federal and military specifications are referenced for insulation, hardware, enclosures, metal plating, test methods, etc.

Criteria specified in the document include creepage and clearance distances, hermeticity, dielectric withstand (including tests at reduced barometric pressure), insulation resistance, voltage drop under load, flammability, mechanical shock and vibration, environmental criteria, endurance, terminal solderability and marking, etc. The inspection procedure for qualification is described, as is the plan for production lot verification. Test methods for the environmental, physical and electrical criteria are found in MIL-STD-202F. The production lot sampling plan is in accordance with MIL-STD-105.

6.8 Suppliers of Equipment Power Line EMI Filters

Suppliers of equipment power line EMI filters include the following manufacturers:

Atlas Engineering Co.
10 Cheney St.
Dorchester MA, 02121
(617) 445-7100

Captor Corp.
5040 S. County Rd. 25A
Tipp City, OH, 45371
(513) 667-8484

Control Concepts Corp
P.O. Box 1380
328 Water St.
Binghamton, NY 13902-1380
(607) 724-2484

Corcom Inc.
1600 Winchester Rd.
Libertyville, IL 60048
(312) 680-7400

Curtis Industries Inc.
7400 W. Douglas Ave
P.O. Box 18699
Milwaukee, IL 53218-0699
(414) 535-1500

Emission Control Ltd.
P.O. Box 797
Cedarburg, WI 53012
(414) 375-4775

Filter Concepts Inc.
2624 S. Rousselle St.
Santa Ana, CA 92707
(714) 545-7003

Filtron Co. Inc.
148 Sweet Hollow Rd.
Old Bethpage, NY 11804
(516) 752-1144

Genisco Technology Corp.
14930 E. Alondra
La Mirada, CA 90638-5754
(714) 523-7001

Hopkins Engineering Co.
12900 Foothill Blvd.
San Fernando, CA 91342
(818) 361-8691

Potter
North Hwy 51
Wesson MI 39191
(619) 268-2513

RFI Corp.
100 Pine Air Dr.
Bay Shore, NY 11706
(516) 231-6400

RTE Aerovox
740 Belleville Ave.
New Bedford, MA 02745
(617) 994-9661

Schaffner EMC Inc.
825 Lehigh Ave.
Union, NJ 07083
(201) 851-0644

Schurter Inc.
1016 Clegg Ct.
Petaluma CA 92121
(707) 778-6311

Siemens Components Inc.
186 Wood Ave. South
Iselin NJ 08830
(201) 321-3477

Spectrum Control
2185 W. 8th St.
Erie PA, 16505
(814) 455-0966

Sprague Electric Co.
92 Hayden Ave.
Lexington, MA 02173
(617) 862-5500

TDK Corp. of America
1600 Feehanville Dr.
Mount Prospect, IL 60056
(312) 803-6100

Tycor Electronic Products Ltd.
Jacqui Lane 6107-6 St. SE
Calgary, Alberta
Canada T2H 1L9
(403) 259-3200

6.9 Filter Installation Practices

Well designed filters are meant to provide isolation between their line-side and load-side terminations. However, this isolation can be degraded by the way in which the filter is installed. This section will discuss the effects of the installation upon performance, methods by which EMI may couple around a filter and techniques for recognizing these modes of EMI coupling.

6.9.1 Effects of Installation upon Filter Performance

The method by which a filter is installed may seriously compromise its performance. Noise on either the line-side or load-side wiring to the filter can radiate and be picked up by leads on the opposite side. Shielded equipment cabinets do not prevent radiation within the enclosure. To prevent this degradation, the line-side and load-side wiring must be kept separate. Long line-side leads inside the equipment can also pick up noise radiated by power or logic components. The reverse is also possible. This effect is controlled by minimizing the length of line-side wiring inside the equipment and dressing it away from noisy areas. The optimum solution is to employ a filter with an ac connector and mount it directly on a metal panel so that the power line exits the equipment directly at the filter. Examples are shown in Fig. 6.25.

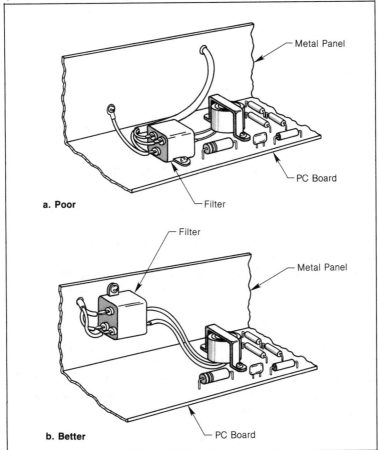

Figure 6.25—Filter Installation Practices (continued nex page)

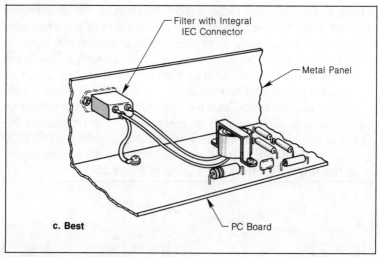

c. Best

Figure 6.25—(continued)

6.9.2 EMI Coupling Mechanisms

One EMI coupling mechanism to avoid is that resulting from a filter ground return impedance which is common to both the line and load circuits. This phenomenon can compromise the protection provided by a filter for either susceptibility or emission control. An example of a common ground return is shown in Fig. 6.26a. Here the resultant V_o is the sum of $V_{(filt)}$, the actual filter output voltage and V_g, the voltage drop in the ground impedance.

$$V_o = V_{(filt)} + (I_{in} - I_{out})\, Z_g$$

The second term shows the effect of the input current returning through the common impedance. Even though Z_o may be small, I_{in} is large compared to I_{out}. Thus the resultant voltage drop ($I_{in}\, Z_g$) is significant. The correct method is to separate the input and output ground connections as shown in Fig. 6.26b. In this way,

$$V_o = V_{(filt)} - I_{out}\, Z_g$$

This is best accomplished by connecting the ground lead of the power cord directly to the ground terminal of the filter.

Another coupling mechanism results from EMI radiation. Radiation in unshielded equipment may return on the line cord as if it and the radiation source were a dipole antenna. In this case, noise current imposed only onto the ground lead of the line cord at the filter end appears as CM noise at the other (line impedance stabilization network, or LISN) end. Thus, conducted emission problems appear over which the filter has little control. This phenomenon generally occurs above 15 MHz and is affected by shielding the equipment. Once identified, the solution to this problem is to reduce radiation by employing a shielded enclosure or by reducing differences in RF potential between various parts of the equipment ground system. Where radiation is due to a limited number of individual components or circuits, these may be individually shielded.

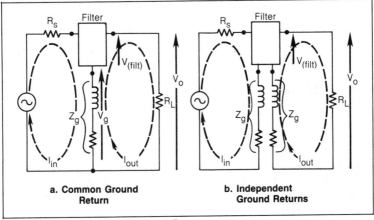

a. Common Ground Return

b. Independent Ground Returns

Figure 6.26—Common Ground Return

6.9.3 Test Method to Identify the Coupling Mechanism of Problem EMI

One may apply a simple test to determine the degree to which EMI is being stray coupled around the EMI filter. The technique involves disconnecting the L and N leads of the filter under evaluation and powering the equipment from a separate, filtered ac source. This is called the **separate power test** (Fig. 6.27). Since the elec-

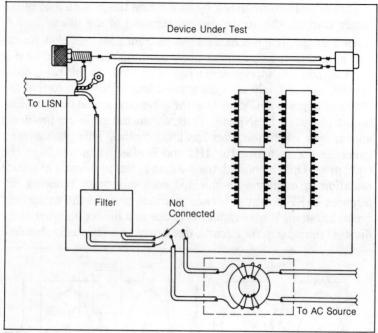

Figure 6.27—Separate Power Test

tronics are not connected to the filter under test, any emission or susceptibility problems encountered are not limited by filter performance but are the result of other means of coupling.

Note that the ground of the subject filter is still connected normally. To test for the coupling mechanism by which radiation returning on the ground lead gives rise to apparent conducted EMI, it is necessary to preserve the normal ground circuit. This requires that the ground of the separate power source be disconnected so that the only ground return is through the LISN. Additionally, the separate power source should be supplied through a high impedance so that its influence on ground currents is minimized. This may be accomplished by using a common-mode inductor with a small value of C_p.

While using the separate power test, EMI radiating into the line-side wiring may be readily identified. EMI measured above 15 MHz, which is barely affected when the line side L and N leads are removed from the filter, is a good candidate for radiation-induced ground currents. This may be further investigated by providing a low-impedance braid or strap between the filter and the LISN grounds. Diverting ground currents away from the line cord will significantly affect (reduce) this form of coupling.

6.10 Bibliography

1. Schneider, L.M., "New Techniques Make Power Line Emissions Filter Selection Easy," *ITEM 1987, Interference Technology Engineers' Master.*
2. Schneider, L.M, "Noise Source Equivalent Circuit Model for Off Line Converters and its Use in Input Filter Design," IEEE Symposium on Electromagnetic Compatibility, Arlington, VA, August 1983.
3. Neufeldt, D., "Radiation Masks Conducted RFI Power Line Filter Testing," *EMC Technology and Interference Control News,* May-June 1984.
4. Schneider, L.M., "Take the Guesswork Out of Emissions Filter Design," *EMC Technology and Interference Control News,* May-June, 1984.
5. Schneider, L.M., "Power Line EMI Filter Insertion Loss," IEEE EMC Symposium, Sept 1982.
6. *ITEM 1987, Interference Technology Engineers' Master.*
7. *Compliance Engineering 1987,* Dash, Straus and Goodhue, Inc.
8. MIL-STD-220A, "Method of Insertion Loss Measurement."
9. MIL-F-15733G, "Filters and Capacitors, Radio Frequency Interference, General Specification for."
10. MIL-STD-202F, "Test Methods for Electronic and Electrical Component Parts."
11. UL 1283, "Standard for Safety," Underwriters Laboratories Inc.
12. C22.2, No. 8-M1986, "Electromagnetic Interference (EMI) Filters," Canadian Standards Association.
13. DIN 57 565 Part 3: VDE 0565 Part 3/9.81, "VDE Specification for Radio Frequency Interference Suppression Devices, Part 3: RFI Filters, 16 Amperes Maximum," translated by Emaco Inc., San Diego CA.
14. Corcom Catalog 871G, "RFI Power Line Filters" Corcom Inc., Libertyville, IL.
15. Corcom Tech Tips, "Installation of Power Line Filters," Tech Tip No. 113A, Nov. 1984, Corcom Inc., Libertyville, IL.

Chapter 7

Facility Power Line Filters

by William H. Parker, P.E.
Genisco Technology Corp.
La Mirada, CA 90638-5754

7.1 Basics of High-Current (>20 Ampere) Filters

Facility power line EMI filters are used to provide radio frequency isolation between a dedicated power distribution service and the local general power distribution system. Facility filters differ from individual equipment-level filters in that the latter are typically much smaller, carry less current and are designed to isolate a single item of equipment from its power source. Facility filters are commonly rated at currents as high as 250 A for single-filter units, with several manufacturers recently beginning production of individual filters in the 400 to 600 A range. Above that range, single-filter units are paralleled for current sharing to give effective line current ratings in excess of 1,000 A continuous duty.

7.1.1 Insertion Loss Requirements

The ultimate purpose of any electromagnetic interference power line filter is to provide a substantial degree of higher frequency (i.e., much greater than the power frequency) isolation between power source and load while not overtly disturbing the efficient delivery of electrical power from the power source to the load. Power line filters are among the very few items of electrical hardware with performance specifications over more than eight frequency decades (≈ 50 Hz to 10 GHz). Filters are constrained to provide high levels of attenuation for signals in the stopband (typically 14 kHz to 10 GHz), while not causing excessive deleterious effects in the passband (i.e., at and near the power frequency).

Perhaps the two most common applications of facility filters are for shielded enclosures and nonshielded computer rooms, although filters can be used to help provide clean power for any installation with sensitive electronic apparatus. The filters can also serve to prevent conducted emanations from noisy electronic gear or electronic data processing equipment from appearing on the incoming facility power conductors.

For shielded enclosure applications, the most widely seen filter insertion loss requirement is a minimum of 100 dB from 14 kHz through 10 GHz. This requirement is probably an "overkill" in many situations and may not be justifiable by detailed analysis of potential EMI problems.

A commonly invoked requirement for nonshielded facilities is 60 dB from 14 kHz through 10 GHz. Some nonshielded facility specifications have been seen to erroneously require 100 dB of insertion loss; the shielding effectiveness offered by the facility mounting wall may be much less than 100 dB, allowing radiated coupling around the filter, for a resultant path loss of a mere 30 to 60 dB. Although there is not a simple one-to-one correlation between filter insertion loss and wall shielding effectiveness, it is clear that, in many events, an excessive level of insertion loss is specified, i.e., excessive compared to the level of power input to power output isolation actually supported by the installation.

7.1.2 Component Value Limitations

As can be seen in Fig. 7.1, a typical high-current power line filter is a single-circuit ladder network of successive capacitive and inductive elements. The range of values of the components is restricted due to both power frequency and insertion loss requirements.

To prevent excessive power frequency voltage drop and to pre-

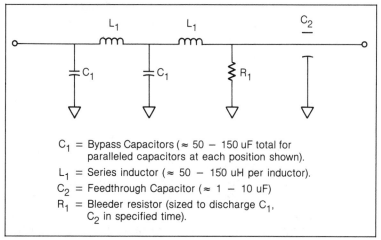

C₁ = Bypass Capacitors ($\approx$ 50 – 150 uF total for paralleled capacitors at each position shown).
L₁ = Series inductor ($\approx$ 50 – 150 uH per inductor).
C₂ = Feedthrough Capacitor ($\approx$ 1 – 10 uF)
R₁ = Bleeder resistor (sized to discharge C₁, C₂ in specified time).

Figure 7.1—Typical Facility EMI Filter Schematic

vent excessive temperature rise due to copper and core losses, high-current filter inductors are generally limited to 100 μH maximum, depending upon rated current, with 50 μH being more common for ratings on the order of 100 A or greater. To achieve as much as 60 to 100 dB of attenuation at 14 kHz, the bypass capacitors and feedthrough capacitor must be rather large to compensate for the severely restricted inductor values.

7.1.3 General Design Considerations

An EMI filter is somewhat of an anomaly for design purposes: it must be essentially "invisible" at the power frequency (causing minimal disturbance to effective power transmission), it must attenuate strongly in the radio frequency spectrum with "real-world" source and load impedances, and it must pass a typical insertion loss requirement of 100 dB from 14 kHz through 10 GHz when terminated at source and load (respectively) with 50 Ω, resistive. The latter requirement is perhaps the least significant, but is often the most emphasized aspect of filter performance and, therefore, filter design. In actuality, no electrical power source/load combinations can be represented accurately by 50 Ω, but the widespread use of MIL-STD-220 has caused overt emphasis on its impedance system, originally chosen only as a convenient measurement standard.

The proper way to achieve an acceptable EMI filter design for power line usage can be summarized as follows:

7.3

1. Determine or approximate the source and load impedances with respect to frequency. Two frequencies are critical: the intended power frequency, and the intended *in situ* filter cutoff frequency (i.e., the 3 dB attenuation point).

2. Using the Z_{source} and Z_{load} values appropriate for the cutoff frequency, design a passive series L, shunt C network capable of providing adequate attenuation. The actual design method can utilize classical filter design tables and frequency/impedance scaling (for which see White, Donald R.J., in the bibliography), modern network synthesis or existing circuit duplication/modification techniques.

3. Check the performance of the design at the power frequency. A common error made by power line filter design novices is to use series filter inductors which are much too large to allow unimpeded power current flow. For example, a 1 mH inductor at 400 Hz would have an inductive reactance of 2.5 Ω. At an intended current of 100 A, implying a load impedance of 1.2 Ω for a 120 Vac power source, that single filter inductor would be effective in "filtering out" some of the 400 Hz power itself, which is hardly a desirable phenomenon.

4. Iterate steps 2 and 3 above until a satisfactory filter design is produced. Build a prototype and check in-circuit performance.

5. Measure the performance of the prototype filter per MIL-STD-220A. Use the measured data to produce a filter quality assurance specification, along with filter schematic and component values. (Caution: Errors at this point can cause a design to be non-manufacturable due to conflicting requirements).

7.2 High-Current Filter Specification and Acquisition

As mentioned in Section 7.1.3, determination of the MIL-STD-220A performance of a filter should be the last step in the filter design and specification process; all too often, the MIL-STD-220A performance is improperly used as the initial and primary filter design criteria. The insertion loss characteristics of a given filter in the actual circuit application may bear little resemblance to its performance per MIL-STD-220A. It must be kept in mind that the military standard should serve only as a quality assurance tool, not as a design requirement.

7.2.1 MIL-STD-220A

Published in 1959, MIL-STD-220A, "Method of Insertion Loss Test Measurement," was intended to provide a convenient test methodology to ensure that the RF performance of procured filters met specified minimum requirements. As will be explained in Section 7.3.2 below, the measured total inductance and capacitance of a filter can be correct, but if component construction and layout are poor, the high-frequency filter insertion loss may be deficient. The prescribed insertion loss test methods of MIL-STD-220A serve to check the stopband adequacy of not only the filter components, but the layout and lead dress of those components.

7.2.1.1 Requirements

MIL-STD-220A sets specific setup and procedural requirements for the insertion loss testing of EMI filters. Chief among those requirements are:

1. The use of 50 Ω test instruments
2. A test frequency range up to 1 GHz
3. Testing from 100 kHz through 20 MHz with dc equivalent of full load current (up to 100 A)
4. Pertinent miscellaneous setup details, calibrated standard attenuators and general procedures
5. The use of a standardized test fixture

7.2.1.2 Limitations

MIL-STD-220A falls short of an ideal filter performance specification for the main reasons described below.

First, the test fixture described in the specification is of limited utility because it can handle only smaller filter sizes. Alternate test fixtures have been constructed, however, so the size limitations of the specified fixture are a non-problem if the procuring agency allows reasonable latitude in test setup. Historically, the military has not required mindless compliance with the physical test setup fixture of MIL-STD-220A.

The main, and continuing, problem with MIL-STD-220A is its gross misapplication by filter specifiers. The original intent of the document was to provide a convenient and consistent RF quality

7.5

assurance test method for filters. As used, however, the specification's intent has been distorted, and filters have been essentially both specified and designed for high insertion loss in a 50 Ω system, with little recognition of the fact that 50 Ω system performance may bear little relation to filtering performance as installed in an actual power system, especially at frequencies below 1 MHz, where filter source and load impedances are often furthest from 50 Ω. Specifically, since EMI filters can be thought of as functioning by creating maximum mismatch between the source impedance and filter input impedance, and the filter output impedance and load impedance, it is easily seen that such mismatch can be achieved in a 50 Ω system with capacitive filter input and output elements. Such a filter could show superior insertion loss in a 50 Ω system. In an actual application, however, a low source impedance and low load impedance would render the filter's input and output capacitors ineffective at filtering.

In other words, MIL-STD-220A has been misapplied and used as a "performance prediction" specification instead of merely a convenient quality assurance tool. For its intended purpose, MIL-STD-220A is still a valid and needed specification; it does serve to provide a basis for expeditious and efficient checking of the higher-frequency performance of power line filters, albeit in an arbitrary impedance system, which gives results not directly related to actual filter usage.

Another problem with MIL-STD-220A for equipment-level filters is that it does not distinguish between common-mode and differential-mode insertion loss, although the two performance curves for a given filter may differ greatly. Specifically, common-mode inductors are primarily effective in suppression of common-mode noise only, and line-to-line capacitors are effective against differential-mode noise only. A comprehensive filter test specification must address both types of noise suppression. Equipment-level filters commonly use components with EMI mode-sensitive components (i.e., common-mode inductors and line-to-line, or differential-mode, capacitors). The common-mode versus differential-mode performance problem largely does not affect common facility power line filters, however, as these filters are single-circuit filters with no common-mode chokes or differential capacitors.

7.2.2 SAE ARP 4244 (Proposed)

To remedy the shortcomings of MIL-STD-220A, the AE-4 committee of the Society of Automotive Engineers (SAE) has been working to produce a filter insertion loss test specification which would build upon the solid foundation laid by MIL-STD-220A for quality assurance testing, while adding more realistic termination impedances to produce performance prediction results, for both common-mode and differential-mode characteristics. Also, an improved specification would address common-mode quality assurance (QA) testing as contrasted to differential-mode QA testing.

7.2.2.1 ARP 4244 as an Addition to MIL-STD-220A

The present intent of ARP 4244 is to replace some portions of MIL-STD-220A while retaining necessary parts of the specification where appropriate. The specific (proposed) test methods are as follows:

1. 50 Ω/50 Ω differential-mode QA Testing, from 10 kHz to 1 MHz, with and without load current
2. 50 Ω/50 Ω common-mode QA testing, from 10 kHz to 30 MHz, with and without load current
3. Differential-mode performance prediction testing, from 10 kHz to 30 MHz, with and without load current
4. High-frequency QA and performance prediction testing, 30 MHz to 10 GHz, no load only, per general MIL-STD-220A methods

7.2.2.2 Recommended Test Procedures

The four test methods in the preceding paragraph expand the scope of MIL-STD-220A to allow not only efficient quality assurance testing at high frequencies but also to allow low-frequency QA and performance prediction testing for both common-mode and differential-mode filter circuits.

The following test procedure descriptions explain test setups, rationale, applicability and procedures.

7.2.2.2.1 50 Ω/50 Ω Differential-Mode QA Testing

Test Setup

See Fig. 7.2.

Frequency Range

The frequency range is 10 kHz to 1 MHz, with and without load current.

Rationale

This test uses line impedance stabilization networks (LISNs) to present more realistic source and load impedances than the 50 Ω resistive terminations of MIL-STD-220A while still maintaining a straightforward test setup. The 1:1 baluns are the only "new" test components required. Their purpose is to couple the EMI test signal into and out of the filter circuits differentially to measure the actual differential-mode rejection. The LISNs are intended to provide a 50 Ω higher frequency impedance ($\approx$ 1 MHz), while displaying a lower impedance at lower frequencies. For Army purposes, the LISN would be as described in Figs. 9 and 10 of MIL-STD-462, Notice 3. For FCC, VDE, CSA or CISPR applications, appropriate commercial LISNs should be used.

Applicability

This test should be performed on a sample basis or on 100 percent of manufactured power line filters in a lot, as required by purchase agreement. This test replaces MIL-STD-220A testing, for differential-mode purposes, from 10 kHz to 1 MHz.

Procedure

Set up per Fig. 7.2, without the filter (i.e., attach incoming power leads from input LISNs directly to output LISNs). Adjust output of 50 Ω signal generator to be $A_{required}$ + 10 dB over the EMI meter (or spectrum analyzer) background noise level, where

$A_{required}$ is the attenuation in decibels required at the first test frequency. Without changing the signal generator output, insert the filter(s) as shown. The decrease in decibels in received level at the EMI meter constitutes the filter differential-mode insertion loss at that frequency. Repeat at all filter test frequencies up to 1 MHz.

Swept RF response techniques (scalar network analyzer or spectrum analyzer with tracking generator) can be used for this test. The same general test procedure applies. Note that two filters will be required for this test if single circuit filters are being tested. For multi-circuit filters, use two circuits at a time.

For no-load testing, the 10 μF feedthrough capacitors (per SAE ARP 936) and the 30,000 μF electrolytic capacitor will supply an

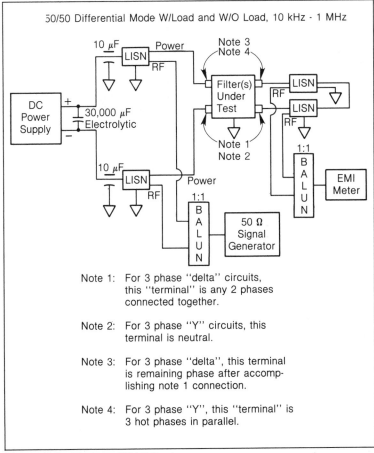

Figure 7.2—Test 1 - "QA" Test

adequate AF/RF short across the dc power source terminals, so it may be left out of the setup. For full-load testing, the dc equivalent of peak current should be applied up to the maximum rating of the 10 μF capacitors and LISNs (typically 100 A maximum). For example, a 50 A ac filter should have 50 $\times$ 1.414 = 70.7 A dc applied. Caution should be exercised to prevent overheating of filters.

7.2.2.2.2 50 Ω/50 Ω Common-Mode QA Testing

Test Setup

See Fig. 7.3a.

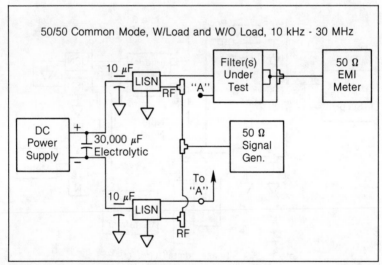

Figure 7.3a—Test 2 - "QA" Test

Frequency Range

The frequency range is 10 kHz to 30 MHz, with and without load current.

Rationale

This test uses LISNs as source impedances and a 50 Ω receiver as the load impedance. The EMI signal from the 50 Ω signal generator is directly coupled into the two LISNs through a coaxial tee fitting for common noise injection. LISNs would be per Paragraph 7.2.2.2.1 herein. The test setup is again identical for load and no-load purposes, except for the insertion and deletion of the dc power supply.

Applicability

This test should be performed on a sample basis, or on 100 percent of manufactured power line filters in a lot, as required by purchase agreement. This test replaces MIL-STD-220A testing, for common-mode purposes, from 10 kHz to 30 MHz.

Procedure

Set up per Fig. 7.3a, without the filter. Adjust output of 50 Ω signal generator to be $A_{required}$ + 10 dB over the EMI meter (or spectrum analyzer) background noise level at the test frequency. Without changing the signal generator output, insert the filter(s) as shown, with the output of two filter circuits shorted together as shown. The decibel decrease in received level at the EMI meter is the filter common-mode insertion loss at that frequency. Repeat at all test frequencies through 30 MHz.

Again, this setup is also appropriate for swept RF test equipment.

7.2.2.2.3 Common-Mode Performance Prediction Testing

Test Setup

See Fig. 7.3b.

Frequency Range

The frequency range is 10 kHz to 30 MHz, with and without load current.

Rationale

This test uses realistic source impedances ($\approx 0 \, \Omega$ at low frequencies, rising to $\approx 50 \, \Omega$ at higher frequencies). LISNs are per Paragraph 7.2.2.2.1 herein. The setup is identical for load and no-load deletion of the dc power supply.

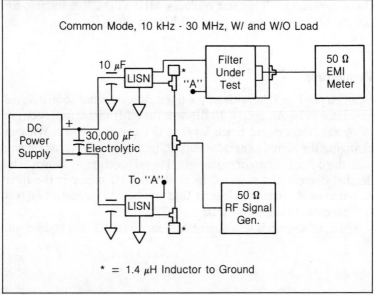

Figure 7.3b—Test 4 - Performance Prediction

Applicability

This test should be performed on only the first unit of a new filter design. The intent is to gain nominal insertion loss prediction curves for a new filter model, with realistic power line impedances. The data can then be used to check whether the filter would be appropriate for a given real requirement. This test is thus **not** intended as a QA test on quantities of manufactured filters.

Procedure

Set up per Fig. 7.3b, without the filter. Adjust the output of the 50 Ω signal generator to be $A_{required}$ + 10 dB over the EMI meter background noise level at the test frequency. Without changing the signal generator output, insert the filter(s) as shown, with the load terminals of two filter circuits shorted together as shown. The decibel decrease in received level at the EMI meter is the filter common-mode insertion loss at that frequency. Repeat at all test frequencies through 30 MHz.

7.2.2.2.4 Differential-Mode Performance Prediction Testing

Test Setups

See Figs. 7.4a and 7.4b.

Frequency Range

The frequency range is 10 kHz to 1 MHz, with and without load current.

Rationale

This test determines the low-frequency differential-mode performance of power line filters, for either very low impedance sources (Fig. 7.4a) or source impedances which increase with frequency (Fig. 7.4b). The two setups use differential-mode EMI signal injection and pickup via RF current probes on the input and output sides of the filter circuits under test. As on previously listed tests, two

7.13

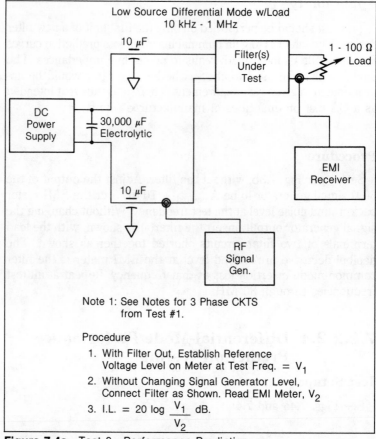

Figure 7.4a—Test 3 - Performance Prediction

filter circuits are required, whether in two filter cases or two separate circuits within the same case. The dc power supply voltage and resistive load are varied to achieve dc equivalent of peak load current simultaneously with the proper magnitude load impedance.

Applicability

One of these two setups should be used on only the first unit of a new filter design. The intent is to gain nominal insertion loss prediction curves for a filter type. That data can be used by an intended filter user to check whether the filter in question will be

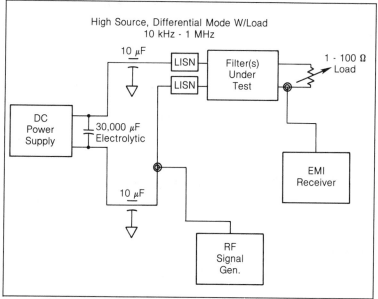

Figure 7.4b—Test 3 - Performance Prediction

likely to satisfy his real-world insertion loss needs. This test then, is **not** intended to be performed as a QA test on large numbers of identical manufactured filter units.

Procedure

Using the setup of Fig. 7.4a (for low-impedance source) or Fig. 7.4b (for higher-impedance source), except with the filter out of the circuit, the output of the RF signal source at a test frequency is adjusted to $A_{required}$ + 10 dB over the EMI meter noise level. The filter is then inserted into the circuit. The resultant signal loss in decibels at the EMI meter is the filter insertion loss at the test frequency. Swept methods can also be used. As before, two filter circuits at a time are needed for this test.

Testing is performed both with and without dc equivalent of peak rated filter load current.

Note: see notes for three-phase circuits from test #1

Procedure:
1. With Filter out, establish reference voltage level on meter at test frequency, V_1.
2. Without changing signal generator level, connect filter as shown. Read EMI meter, V_2.
3. Insertion loss = 20 log (V_1/V_2) dB.

7.2.2.2.5 High-Frequency Quality Assurance and Performance Prediction Testing

Test Setup

The test setup is per MIL-STD-220A.

Frequency Range

The frequency range is 30 MHz to 10 GHz, no load current.

Rationale

All typical power line filter inductors self-resonate well below 30 MHz due to parasitic turn-to-turn and winding-to-case capacitances. Load versus no-load testing serves only to identify inductor core saturation differences. With the inductors bypassed by the lumped parasitic capacitance, there is no rationale to support loaded condition testing of filters above 30 MHz. In the author's experience, no power line filter inductors have resonated above 10 MHz; 30 MHz is a conservative break frequency to ensure load testing to previously described methods somewhat past the actual resonance point. Note that MIL-STD-220A stopped load testing at 20 MHz, which was only slightly less conservative than the 30 MHz dividing frequency recommended herein.

Above 30 MHz, almost all common EMI conducted emission or susceptibility problems have been seen to be common-mode in nature; thus the recommendation herein is to test only common-mode characteristics above 30 MHz.

Procedure

To determine common-mode insertion loss characteristics above 30 MHz, use the general test setups and procedures of MIL-STD-220A without applying load current. For single-circuit filters, test the filters singly. For multi-circuit filters, test each circuit singly, with all circuits not under test open (not sequentially open and shorted per the original procedures of MIL-STD-220A). With line-to-line capacitors of multiple-circuit filters not grounded to test ground, they will not contribute to the insertion loss readings. This is proper, as those capacitors only attenuate differential-mode noise, not common-mode. The common-mode inductors, discrete (i.e., single-winding) inductors, and line-to-case capacitors which contribute to common-mode insertion loss will be properly measured with this procedure.

7.3 Filter Design Considerations

As EMI power line filters are lowpass filters, the critical performance elements are the cutoff frequency (i.e., the frequency above which significant attenuation occurs), the slope of the attenuation curve above the cutoff frequency, and the frequency spectrum over which the filter maintains significant attenuation. The filter operates within a larger circuit, so the interactions with that circuit partially determine filter performance. Termination impedances and other electrical, mechanical and environmental constraints of the circuit to be filtered affect the total filter system results.

7.3.1 Filter Cutoff Frequency

As traditionally defined, a filter's cutoff frequency is the transition frequency between stopband and passband. Since a filter's attenuation versus frequency curve will not be vertical, but will have a finite slope, a set amount of attenuation must be specified to define the passband/stopband transition frequency. Figure 7.5 displays a typical power line filter response and the fundamental definition of terms.

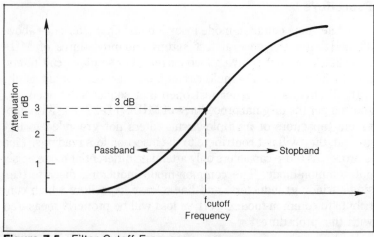

Figure 7.5—Filter Cutoff Frequency

The restrictions on the location of the cutoff frequency for a facility power line filter are that it be adequately far above the power line frequency to avoid overt voltage drop or voltage rise difficulties, and that it be sufficiently low to allow the natural slope of the filter attenuation curve to provide adequate filter attenuation at the lowest system EMI frequency. The location of the cutoff frequency is thus a compromise. In practice, the cutoff frequency is usually much above the power frequency, mainly because excessively large component values are required to filter at very low frequencies.

7.3.2 Limitations of Filter Components

The concept of electrical filter design is not new. Indeed, sufficient normalized filter tables have been published to fulfill all requirements, assuming that the filters designed per those tables actually perform as intended. Over a narrow frequency spread, elements can be constructed to perform in a near-ideal fashion. For power line filters, however, which typically must perform predictably from the power frequency through at least 10 GHz, the actual effective filter circuit performance depends upon the frequency at which we observe performance. Actually, not only the filter performance varies, but the effective component values and even the effective components list (!) varies with frequency. To understand why this is so, we must examine the limitations of the two functional reactive components of EMI filters: inductors and capacitors.

7.3.2.1 Inductor Current Rating and Saturation

To the uninitiated, power line filter inductor design would seem to be elementary; determine the filter series impedance at a given frequency needed to suppress EMI at that frequency, and solve X_L = $2\pi fL$ for the value of L. The effective inductance of a real inductive component, however, is variable, depending not only upon effective inductor core permeability change with frequency (which is a valid concern, but will not be further discussed here), but also depending greatly upon the level of magnetizing force on the core. As the magnetizing force increases, due to increasing current through the windings around the inductor's ferrous core, the magnetic flux in the core increases. Beyond a point dependent upon core material, however, the flux cannot be further increased, a flux saturation level has been reached, and the effective permeability of the core material decreases. At that point, the inductor effectively loses inductance value. As an example, a nominally 5 mH inductor can decrease to 1 nH with 100 A of power line current. Even if such a drastic decrease in inductance were permissible for filtering purposes, the swinging inductance value could cause the generation of power frequency harmonics.

A measure of conservatism in inductor design is thus practiced. A general goal is to have the no-load value of inductance decrease by less than 20 percent under full load current. Size, weight and volume constraints often preclude meeting that goal, and a value between 20 and 50 percent must be accepted. General good engineering practice is to avoid saturation in excess of 50 percent. To prevent saturation, inductors are made small in value, generally less than 100 μH for representative 100 A filters.

In addition to inductor saturation levels, power dissipation concerns must be addressed. The total power dissipation at the power frequency (power dissipation due to EMI current can normally be safely ignored) can be presented as:

$$P_{core} = I^2(R_{core} + R_{wire})$$

where,

R_{core} = the resistive equivalent of core loss
R_{wire} = the dc resistance of the windings

Decreasing cross-sectional wire area and thereby increased ac resistance can be ignored at the power frequency.

7.3.2.2 Inductor Self-Resonance

To further compound filter inductor design, it is necessary to consider the effect of parasitic element values at higher frequencies. At very low frequencies, the effective model of an inductor is as shown in Fig. 7.6.

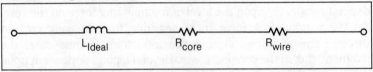

Figure 7.6—Inductor Model, Low Frequency

At higher frequencies, however, the relatively small winding-to-winding and winding-to-core parasitic capacitances must be considered. Figure 7.7 shows a higher-frequency inductor model.

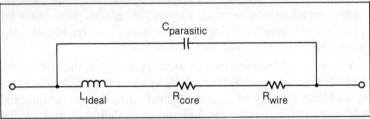

Figure 7.7—Inductor Model, High Frequency

As can be seen from Fig. 7.7, a "real" inductor can be understood by modeling it as a somewhat lossy parallel resonant circuit. The resonant frequency can be found by:

$$f_R = \frac{1}{2\pi\sqrt{L_{ideal} \times C_{parasitic}}}$$

Most power line filter inductors self-resonate in the region from 100 kHz to 5 MHz, with the largest population in the 500 kHz to 2 MHz area.

Below self-resonance, the filter inductor performs as a somewhat lossy (small R_{core} and R_{wire}) inductor, at resonance it looks like a resistor, and above resonance it performs as a capacitor, with the associated finite capacitive reactance decreasing with increasing frequency.

7.3.2.3 Capacitor Dielectric Rating

Capacitors are typified as metal foil plates separated by an insulating, or dielectric, material. Such a dielectric material has a limit to the voltage gradient (volts per meter) it can tolerate without suffering a voltage breakdown. Higher-voltage capacitors are designed with adequate thickness of voltage punch-through resistant dielectric material. Quite often, a margin of safety factor of two will be used; e.g., a 1,000 V rated capacitor would be designed, built and tested to meet 2,000 V.

As a capacitor is used as a line-to-case shunt element in power line filters, each capacitor must withstand the full peak power line voltage. A common practice to achieve a higher voltage rating is to series two lower-voltage rated capacitors while accepting the resultant increase in size and decreased capacitance value.

7.3.2.4 Capacitor Self-Resonance

As was true of inductors, real capacitors do not behave as simply as ideal capacitors. Figure 7.8 depicts the actual impedance components of a real capacitor.

As can be seen from the simplified model, the actual capacitor will look capacitive until $|X_{C\ ideal}| = |X_{L\ leads}|$, after which the impedance will rise due to increasing X_L. The resonant frequency is given by:

$$f_R = \frac{1}{2\pi \sqrt{L_{leads} \times C_{ideal}}}$$

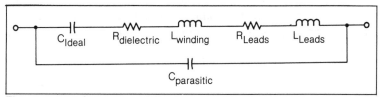

Figure 7.8a—Capacitor Model

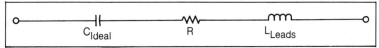

Figure 7.8b—Simplified Capacitor Model (High-Frequency Construction)

The above assumes that the capacitive is noninductively wound and $L_{winding} \ll L_{leads}$. Capacitors are used in power line filters to provide low shunt impedance to case ground; they can obviously not function as very low impedances much above f_R. Capacitor design, construction and installation methods, then, must absolutely minimize $L_{winding}$, L_{leads} and, to a lesser degree, $R_{dielectric}$ and R_{leads}, which are normally negligible.

7.3.2.4.1 Bypass Capacitors

As used herein, bypass capacitors are simply capacitors having wire leads. Assuming an essentially noninductively wound capacitor body construction ($L_{winding} \approx 0\ \mu H$), L_{leads} must be minimized. The lead inductance can be kept small mainly by keeping capacitor leads extremely short. The same effect could be achieved by modifying the lead self-inductance through form factor (i.e., flat, wide straps rather than round cross-sectional wire leads).

7.3.2.4.2 Feedthrough Capacitors

To absolutely maximize the performance of capacitors, the leads can simply be eliminated. A capacitor without leads is termed a **feedthrough capacitor** for reasons apparent in Fig. 7.9.

In such a capacitor, the grounded plate is attached to a metal shielding bulkhead. The capacitance exists between hot line and ground (filter case) with no intervening lead inductance. The primary limitations to filtering/shielding performance of a feed-through capacitor are proper noninductive construction and proper 100 percent sealing of the mounting bulkhead. The bulkhead and auxiliary compartment covers provide RF compartmentization of a power line filter.

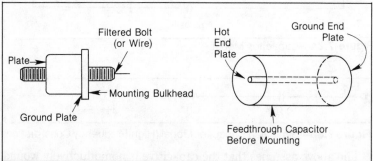

Figure 7.9—A Feedthrough Capacitor

Feedthrough capacitors in the 0.05 to 5 μF range used for power line filters can perform well into the gigahertz region. More than 100 dB of feedthrough capacitor insertion loss has been recorded (in a 50 Ω/50 Ω system per MIL-STD-220) to 18 GHz.

7.3.2.5 How Can A Filter Perform Above Resonance?

Rather than considering an EMI power line filter as having a single resonant frequency above which the filter does not provide RF isolation, it is more instructive to consider the resonances of each of the three types of filter components and the resultant contributions to total filter insertion loss.

To achieve filtering at relatively low frequencies ($\approx$5 kHz to 50 kHz), large component values are mandated. Adequately large inductor values are not feasible, so very large values of capacitors are used ($\approx$15 to 200 μF). These capacitors are needed only up to a frequency at which other components can assume the majority of the filtering performance, so relatively inexpensive bulk capacitors are used. The capacitors may resonate as low as 10 to 50 kHz, after which they still perform as relatively low impedances to filter case ground for perhaps two frequency decades. That is, the above resonance impedance does not increase as a step function but in a linear fashion based upon capacitor (unintentional) inductance. Normally, 4 to 20 capacitors are paralleled for total capacitance value, and the undesired inductive components are also paralleled, decreasing total inductance.

In the medium- to high-frequency range ($\approx$50 kHz to 50 MHz), the bulk low-frequency capacitors described above will be decreasingly effective, and higher-frequency components will be needed. Modest valued, well-designed inductors can serve here. With typical values of 10 to 100 μH, and self-resonances in the 100 kHz to 5 MHz region, these inductors can generally offer relatively high series impedance as desired for proper filter action, for nominally two frequency decades above the resonant frequency.

Above the effective range of the in-line inductors, an even better RF quality component is needed. With the use of relatively modest valued, high-quality (i.e., noninductively wound, feedthrough construction) capacitors, the high to very high frequency region can be effectively filtered. Typical feedthrough capacitor values are 1 to 5 μF, offering 100 dB of attenuation (MIL-STD-220A 50 Ω

system) at about 600+ MHz (for 1 μF) down to about 100+ MHz (for 5 μF). Thus, by the frequency at which the filter inductors are ineffective ($\approx$ 10 MHz to 500 MHz), the feedthrough capacitors are becoming very effective. The table below summarizes the relative characteristics and performance of the three types of power line filter components.

Table 7.1

Component Type	Typical Construction	Relative RF Quality	Typical Value per Component	Resonant Frequency Range	Most Effective Freq. Range
Bypass "Bulk" Capacitor	"Tab-Wound" (High self-inductance.) Perhaps supplemented by noninductively wound capacitors of small vlaue, for filter "performance tweaking."	Poor	5 - 15 μF	10 - 50 kHz	5 kHz - 500 kHz
Inductor	Random Wound, Ferrous Core	Fair	5 - 100 μH	100 kHz - 5 MHz	50 kHz - 100 MHz
Feedthrough Capacitor	Noninductive, metal container, for bulkhead mounting.	Good to Very Good	1 - 5 μF	1 GHz +	100 MHz - 10 GHz

In summary, we should not think in terms of the performance above resonance of a filter as a whole, but rather the performance limitations and resonances of individual filter components. Except that there is some overlap of the respective effective frequency ranges of the various components, we could almost categorize power line filters as containing three separate filters: low-frequency (bulk bypass capacitance), mid-frequency (inductors) and high-frequency (feedthrough capacitors).

7.3.3 Impedance Effects

Although an EMI power line filter is intended to have certain specified performance characteristics, its behavior must be viewed in terms of the total circuit into which it is inserted.

7.3.3.1 Source Impedance

Power line source impedance is commonly considered to be so low as to be negligible. Such is ordinarily the case, at or near the power frequency. At higher frequencies, the inductance and resistance of the power source and distribution system cause the effective source impedance to rise to a value as high as 50 to 150 Ω. The EMI filter performance will vary as the source impedance increases; if the first element in the filter on the power source end is a capacitor, the insertion loss of the filter will tend to increase with frequency due to the increasing impedance mismatch between high-impedance source and low capacitive reactance. If the first filter element is inductive, the increasing inductive reactance due to the source and that of the filter will present a lesser impedance mismatch, giving less insertion loss increase with frequency compared to that of the capacitive input.

Reasonable approximations of power line source impedance magnitudes versus frequency are the U.S. Army low-frequency and high-frequency line impedance stabilization network curves shown as Figs. 7.10 and 7.11 (from Figs. 10 and 8, respectively, of MIL-STD-462, Notice 3).

For filter design purposes, an adequate first approximation of power line source impedance would be to use the low-frequency LISN's impedance at the intended filter's in-circuit cutoff frequency. For example, at 14 kHz, that design impedance would be a nominal 4 Ω (refer to Fig. 7.10). Similarly, the filter theoretical performance at 100 kHz would be predicated upon a source impedance of between 6 Ω (if following Fig. 7.11) and 26 Ω (if using Fig. 7.10). Due to the disagreement between the two LISN impedance curves, a suggested table of convenient compromise impedance values follows:

Table 7.2

Frequency	Z of Low-Frequency LISN (in Ohms)	Z of High Frequency LISN (in Ohms)	Suggested Design Source Impedance (in Ohms)
14 kHz	4	-	5
50 kHz	13	-	10
100 kHz	26	≈ 6	20
200 kHz	38	8	25
500 kHz	46	16	30
1 MHz	48	27	40
2 MHz	48	39	45
5 MHz	48	47	50
10 MHz	48	49	50
20 MHz	-	49	50
50 MHz	-	49	50

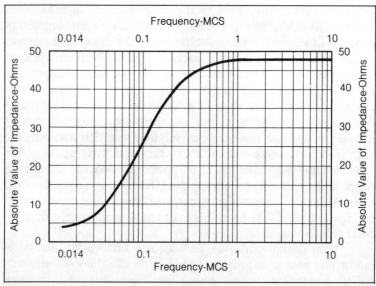

Figure 7.10—Approximation of Nominal Power Line Impedance at Low Frequencies (From Fig. 10, MIL-STD-462, Notice 3.)

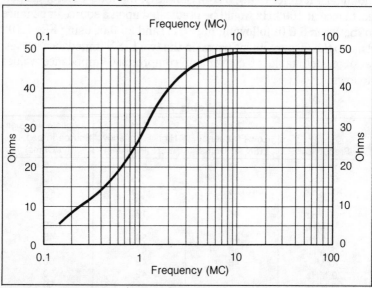

Figure 7.11—Approximation of Nominal Power Line Impedance at High Frequencies. (From Figure 8, MIL-STD-462, Notice 3.)

For most applications, the precise source impedance at a given frequency will be complex as well as indeterminate. The impedances suggested above will lend speed to the design process while remaining adequately close to realistically expected source impedances. As a further simplification for initial design work, the source impedance can be assumed to be purely resistive. During final "fine tuning" of a filter design, resonances partially due to source reactance may need to be addressed, but the resistive first-cut approximation is valid for the purpose specified. To put the source impedance into proper scale, the nominal 40 Ω impedance at 1 MHz is representative of only 6 μH of inductance, which is small compared to often-used filter inductors. Additionally, phase relationships are usually of no concern with power line filters.

7.3.3.2 Load Impedance

A first-cut approximation of filter load impedance can be made using Ohm's Law, at the power frequency:

$$Z_{load} = \frac{E_{applied}}{I_{load}}$$

The simplifying first assumption can again be made that the filter's load is resistive, although there is more danger of error in dealing with the load than was the case on the power line source impedance side. The rule of thumb, then, would be to use the Ohm's Law load resistance approximation at all frequencies, unless enough was known about the actual load (in all relevant modes and levels of operation) to determine more realistic impedances.

Ofttimes, a switched load may resonate with the reactance of a power line filter, necessitating a redesign of filter or load circuitry, or both.

7.3.4 Stopband Insertion Loss

The insertion loss of a lowpass EMI power line filter in the stop bank (i.e., above the cutoff frequency) is the primary performance aspect of the filter. The amount of filtering to be expected can be described as follows:

"Filtering above the cutoff frequency increases at a rate of 20 dB per frequency decade per effective component, limited by inductor parasitic capacitances, capacitor parasitic inductances and input to output cable crosstalk."

The preceding statement needs to be analyzed. First of all, the cutoff frequency, which is the dividing line between the lower-frequency passband and the higher-frequency stopband, is the frequency at which the filter gives 3 dB of insertion loss. Above that frequency, each element of the filter contributes 20 dB/decade (or, equivalently, 6 dB/octave) to increasing insertion loss, if each component is effective. By "effective" it is meant that each succeeding element must present an impedance mismatch with the preceding and following elements, including the source and load impedance. If source and load impedances were very low, for example, a pi-section filter (i.e., shunt capacitor, series inductor, shunt capacitor configuration) would have two ineffective elements: the two capacitors. If source and load impedances were high, a tee-section filter (i.e., series inductor, shunt capacitor, series inductor configuration) would also have two ineffective elements: the two inductors. In each case, the filter input and output elements do not represent impedance mismatch to the termination impedances.

The impedance mismatch concept has very real practical applications. To provide a filter which needs to work into a 10 μF source impedance such as traditionally prescribed by U.S. Air Force and Navy MIL-STD-461 EMI tests, a filter should generally have an inductor facing the 10 μF test setup capacitor (exception: at higher frequencies where the standard 1 m power cable length looks like a high impedance due to wire inductance, a small-value, high RF quality capacitor can present an impedance mismatch and thus increased insertion loss).

Extending the preceding element impedance mismatch concept, it is clear that simply paralleling shunt capacitors or adding inductors in series should not give 20 dB per frequency decade per component increased insertion loss, as all of those components are not effectively separate filter components. Paralleling and series combining of components can lead, however, to somewhat better high-frequency response of components. Such improved response is due to reduced magnitude and effect of inductor parasitic capacitances and capacitor body and lead inductances.

Input-to-output, cable-to-cable crosstalk can be minimized by routing of cables remotely from each other to minimize capacitive and inductive coupling factors (refer to Section 7.4 for installation guidance).

7.3.5 Power Frequency Effects

Ideally, a power line EMI filter should have no effects at the power frequency. Any potential effects, then, are prone to be adverse and undesirable, such as power line voltage drop, voltage rise and waveform or harmonic distortion of the power frequency.

Voltage drop in an EMI filter can be caused by excessive inductor winding dc resistance, excessive inductor core loss (which appears as an additional resistance at the power frequency), or by a filter cutoff frequency too close to the power frequency. Voltage rise can be caused by insertion loss "ripple" in the passband, which includes the power frequency. Voltage rise is very common with heavily capacitive power line filters when lightly loaded.

Harmonic distortion of the power frequency (i.e., generation of harmonics of the power frequency by the filter) is commonly due to saturated large value inductors, which function as nonlinear impedances over the current sinusoidal waveform. Such harmonic generation can be avoided by limiting the saturation of series filter inductors to a conservative 20 percent, or 50 percent as an absolute maximum, at peak load current. Another way of stating this is that each series inductance at full rated power line load current should be not less than 50 to 80 percent of the no load inductance. Also, the total series inductive reactance at the power frequency should be small compared to the power source and load series impedance. Keeping the ratio small (≈ 1 to 10 percent maximum) will minimize both voltage drop and harmonic frequency generation.

7.3.6 Filter Schematic Determination

The rules for effective power line filter design and schematic determination are simple and few, and are based upon the premises of:

1. Negligible impedance change of the previously existing power circuit
2. Maximum impedance mismatch at interference frequencies above the cutoff frequency
3. Utilization of realizable component values

Classical filter design techniques and modern network analysis can also be used, but with rather disappointing results, and perhaps time consuming iterations, due to the somewhat ill-behaved complex power line source and load impedances seen by power line filters. Classical design methods are well covered in existing literature and will not be re-presented here.

To minimize disturbance of existing power line impedances, it is suggested that the initial value of total series filter inductance be limited to produce a maximum total X_L magnitude at the power frequency of 1 percent of the load impedance. Likewise, initial shunt capacitance should be limited to produce a minimum total capacitive reactance at the power frequency of 100 times the load impedance. For example, if the power frequency is 60 Hz, and if R_{load} = 10 Ω, then:

$$X_L = \frac{R_{load}}{100} = \frac{10}{100} = 0.1 \ \Omega \text{ maximum at 60 Hz}$$

and maximum $X_L = 2\pi fL = 2\pi(60)L$, so:

$$L_{maximum} = \frac{X_L}{2\pi(60)} = \frac{0.1}{2\pi(60)} = 265 \ \mu H$$

This maximum total of 265 μH can be one inductor or the total inductance of all series inductors in the filter. Likewise, X_c = $100R_L$ = 100(10) = 1,000 Ω = $1/(2\pi fC)$, and:

$$C_{maximum} = \frac{1}{2\pi(60) \ (1,000)} = 2.65 \ \mu F$$

This capacitance can be one capacitor or the total of all shunt capacitors in a filter.

To achieve maximum impedance mismatch, and thus maximum filtering effect at higher frequencies, a filter series inductor should face a low-impedance source or load, and a filter shunt capacitor should face a high-impedance source or load. Since almost all power lines can be considered as low impedances at low to mid frequencies, it would seem that almost all power line filters should have inductive inputs. As will be seen later (see Section 7.3.7 herein), it is best to use an inductive input in most cases. Impedance mismatching is summarized in Fig. 7.12.

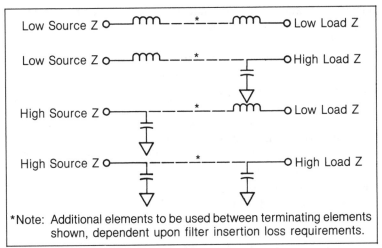

*Note: Additional elements to be used between terminating elements shown, dependent upon filter insertion loss requirements.

Figure 7.12—Proper Filter Terminations for Maximum Effectiveness

Realizable component values for power line filters are limited by power frequency voltage for capacitors and power current for inductors.

Capacitor size increases due to the dielectric withstanding voltage requirements. Higher voltages require thicker dielectric material and perhaps multiple layers of dielectric. A filter capacitor often comprises many windings of dielectric and metal foil, so the dielectric material thickness is multiplied many times. Maximum achievable total capacitance (i.e., total of all shunt capacitors) for a 100 A, 120 Vac (line-to-case) EMI filter would be on the order of 100 to 200 μF. The limitation is primarily one of available volume and weight.

Filter inductor ferrous core sizes increase as the current level increases. The core material effective permeability (and effective inductance) decrease with increasing ampere-turns. To decrease saturation, either the current or the number of coil turns must be reduced. The filter designer usually has no control over the current, so he must either decrease the coil turns (which reduces inductance and filter insertion loss) or use a larger core. Incidentally, air-core inductors are of very limited utility in power line filters due to the very large number of turns required (with associated high parasitic winding capacitance, low self-resonant frequency and limited operating frequency range) to achieve even a minimal inductance. Maximum practical inductance in a 100 A power line filter is on the order or 200 to 300 μH, again limited by reasonable volume and weight constraints.

The maximum inductances and capacitances acceptable for a 100 A/120 Vac filter would change for higher-voltage or higher-current filters. As higher voltages would tend to produce physically larger capacitors, a 100 A filter rated at more than 120 Vac (such as a 277 Vac line-to-ground rating) would tend to be designed with more inductance and less capacitance. Contrarily, filters with current ratings greater than 100 A would tend to have lower inductance values and greater capacitance. A further restriction on total capacitor value is the amount of allowed capacitive leakage current to ground, which is a simple matter of capacitive reactance, power frequency and power line voltage.

In summary, the following specific recommendations are in order for successful power line EMI filter design:

1. Start with X_L of total series inductance equal to $R_{load}/100$ at the power frequency.
2. Start with X_C of total shunt capacitance equal to R_{load} x 100 at the power frequency.
3. Use an inductor on the power line input end of the filter.
4. Use an inductor on the load end of the filter if the load is "low" impedance at the intended cutoff frequency (i.e., lower than total X_L of total filter inductance).
5. Use a capacitor on the load end of the filter if the load is "high" impedance at the intended cutoff frequency (i.e., higher than total X_L of total filter inductance).
6. Determine the filter cutoff frequency by circuit analysis (manual or by computer) or by testing a prototype filter.
7. Determine the adequacy of attenuation in the stopband by analysis or measurement of a prototype filter facing realistic source and load impedances.
8. Increase the number of filter elements as needed to increase the slope of the filter insertion loss curve above the cutoff frequency. This can be done without increasing the total inductance or capacitance.
9. Increase the total capacitance and/or inductance to lower the cutoff frequency (this will violate rules 1 and/or 2, so power frequency effects will need to be monitored).
10. Iterate steps 7 through 9 until a filter design is reached which satisfies both power frequency and stopband requirements.

11. If an acceptable performance design is reached which is too large or heavy, experiment with increasing capacitance and decreasing inductance for a relatively high-current filter, or increasing inductance and decreasing capacitance for a relatively high-voltage filter.

7.3.7 Transient Protection

Transients on a facility power distribution bus can often have short rise and fall times. Fourier analysis of such transients reveal the amount of high-frequency energy content, which EMI filters themselves tend to suppress. Depending upon the duration and magnitude of those transients, the filter may offer inadequate protection for the load. Indeed, the filter itself (especially the capacitors) may need protection from high-energy events such as lightning-induced waveforms, inductive field collapse transients or nuclear electromagnetic pulse (EMP).

The mechanism of protection is to limit the incoming line-to-line and line-to-ground (case) voltages to protect both filter and load. The various voltage-limiting devices available (ionizable spark gaps, varistors, Zener diodes) should be selected after consideration of rated "firing" voltage, speed of operation, effects on power circuit and power dissipation capability. Hybrid or mixed-device suppression schemes should be considered, to advantageously utilize both high-power/slow-response and low-power/fast-response devices. Additionally, the first capacitor in a filter should be isolated from the transient-affected source with a series inductor. Without the inductor, a high-voltage transient will tend to drive a large current through the first capacitor to case ground.

The author is aware of one incident in which a capacitor physically exploded due to high transient inrush current. If a hybrid protection scheme is used, the higher-power/slower-response and lower-power/quicker-response devices should be placed on either side of the source-facing inductor. Figure 7.13 depicts such a protection scheme. Note that the 5 to 30 μH minimum inductor provides EMI filtering as well as serving as part of the transient protection circuit. The transient protection circuit may be built into the EMI filter case.

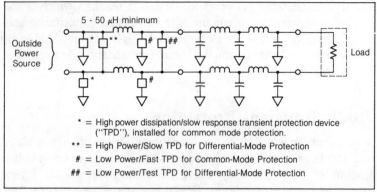

Figure 7.13—Hybrid Transient Protection Scheme

7.3.8 Mechanical Considerations

A facility power line filter is normally encased in a tin-plated fabricated sheet steel housing of sufficient gauge metal to provide adequate rigidity and strength. The case is usually filled with a potting compound after wiring all filter circuitry to prevent motion or damage to the components. The potting process and potting material must not cause mechanical or electrical degradation of the filter components.

Each individual filter case (for one line of a power distribution system) is often itself mounted within a filter cabinet. For example, a typical filter cabinet would contain four filters for a three-phase, four-wire, 120 Vac, 100 A service. At one end, the individual filters are typically mounted to a shielded box, which serves to avoid any coupling from "line" leads to "load" leads.

7.3.9 Environmental Considerations

MIL-F-15733 and MIL-STD-202 describe the electrical and environmental test requirements for EMI filters. The tests are intended to ensure that safe, reliable, durable and mechanically sound electrical hardware is procured. Pertinent included tests are:

Visual and mechanical examination
Seal
Capacitance and inductance
Temperature rise
Dielectric withstanding voltage (high potential or "hipot" test)
Barometric pressure (reduced pressure)
Insulation resistance
Voltage drop
Insertion loss
Overload
Terminal strength
Resistance to soldering heat (soldered terminals only)
Salt spray (corrosion)
Temperature and immersion cycling
Shock (mechanical)
Vibration
Moisture resistance
Life

Many of the above tests are called out per MIL-F-15733 and specific contractual requirements for military hardware. The test methods can also be very useful for commercial products, but the test costs should be evaluated prior to automatic imposition.

7.3.10 Grounding

Facility power line filtering relies on inductance (high series impedance elements) and capacitance (low shunt impedance to local ground through the filter case). To achieve full filter performance, the metallic case of the filters must have a low-impedance path to local ground. Considering that a total filter capacitance of 100 μF or more represents a mere 15.9 mΩ at 100 kHz, for example, it is obvious that any substantial ground path impedance in series will quickly start detracting from full filter RF performance.

From a safety standpoint, if the filter cases are not securely bonded to local ground, a severe safety (shock) hazard will exist for personnel who may contact such ungrounded cases.

7.3.11 Filter Aging Effects

Like professionally built transformers, facility power line filters can be considered semipermanent electrical fixtures. Probably the three most common failure mechanisms of filters are (1) component insulation degradation due to high-voltage partial discharge or corona effects (due to voids or bubbles existing in the potting compound because of improper potting techniques), (2) capacitor dielectric failure (due to inadequate dielectric voltage rating, excessive line transient voltages and/or lack of use of transient protection devices) and (3) simple terminal failure (due to mechanical over-torquing of filter terminals). Gross damage to series conductors, including inductors, is possible if the filter load is shorted, but such occurrences are infrequent. All in all, power line filters have been seen to last 20 years or more.

As was the case with transformers, however, power line filters previously used polychlorinated biphenyl products (PCBs) for impregnation (of capacitors). PCBs were determined to be carcinogenic, and older power line filters are being removed from service to remove that perceived environmental hazard. The handling and disposal of such materials must be in accordance with mandated procedure, by qualified personnel.

7.4 Filter Installation Considerations

7.4.1 Bulkhead Mounting

One of the few absolutes in the field of facility power line filters is that to achieve maximum performance from a high insertion loss filter, it absolutely **must** be bulkhead mounted, with the line end of the filter separated from the load end by a solid metal barrier. Such mounting removes any real possibility of "crosstalk" or near-field cable-to-cable coupling around the filter.

7.4.2 Filter Panels

Most facility filters are grouped in assemblies, each handling a complete power service. For instance, a three-phase, four-wire, 120/208 Vac service would require four power line filters, one each for phase A, B, C and neutral. For convenience of wire routing, labeling and for prevention of potential input to output crosstalk due to inconsistent installation, all four filters would be mounted in a single metal box, or "filter panel." Such a panel is shown in Fig. 7.14.

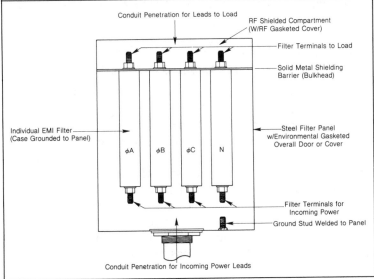

Figure 7.14—Typical Facility Power Line Filter Panel (3 Phase, 4 Wire)

7.4.3 Grounding Considerations

As was true for individual filters, the filter panel must have a low-impedance path to local ground reference. The individual filter cases are bolted to the filter panel, with the filter panel's ground stud in turn being attached to a local ground point with a low RF impedance conductor.

7.4.4 Shielded Enclosure Filters

Shielded enclosure filters are simply high-performance facility power line filters, with the ultimate in protection against radiated coupling from power source leads to load leads. That is, the metal barrier used for the isolation of line from load is extended to completely enclose the load. A filter so installed can display its true and full RF isolation capability. A common traditional requirement for shielded enclosure filters has been insertion loss of 100 dB from

14 kHz to 10 GHz. High-performance shielded enclosure manufacturers and users are now extending the frequency range to 18 GHz and above and calling for 120 dB filters. Such filters are feasible, given adequate allowances for increased size, weight and cost.

7.5 Synopsis: Filter Specification and Acquisition Considerations

For some years now (decades, actually) facility EMI power line filters have been typically acquired by specifying, primarily, voltage rating, current rating and "100 dB insertion loss from 14 kHz through 10 GHz." The intent, of course, is to acquire a filter with 100 dB or RF isolation as installed. With the 50 Ω source/50 Ω load filter insertion loss measurement system of MIL-STD-220, however, and a non-50 Ω actual power system, the actual system performance of the filter is completely unspecified. Obviously, then, the 50 Ω performance is not the proper design goal for a filter. The following procedures present a summary of this chapter and a more appropriate set of guidelines than has been used heretofore.

7.5.1 Insertion Loss Requirements

Determine or approximate the actual in-circuit RF isolation requirements. This can be done by comparing the measured or predicted RF conducted emissions level on the noise source end of the intended filter (which can be on either the electrical power source or load side) to the permitted or desired noise level on the opposite end of the filter. The difference in those two levels versus frequency is the bare minimum insertion loss requirement for the filter.

Establish a reasonable safety margin of excess filtering, so the resultant filtered level will be somewhat below the allowed level. Safety margins normally achievable without undue filter volume increase are:

Frequency Range	Target Safety Margin
10 kHz − 100 kHz	3 dB
100 kHz − 1 MHz	6 dB
1 MHz − 10 MHz	12 dB
> 10 MHz	12 to 20 dB

7.38

Use the sum of the minimum insertion loss requirement and the safety margin in decibels as the required *in situ* insertion loss for the filter. At this point, the MIL-STD-220 50 Ω/50 Ω insertion loss is of no valid concern.

7.5.2 Power Frequency Effects

Evaluate the expected power source voltage maximum variations and the minimum/maximum voltage limits of the intended loads. Use those source variations and user limits to establish a maximum voltage drop and maximum voltage rise for the EMI filter.

Approximate or measure the power frequency harmonic distortion existing on the power line prior to filter insertion. Determine the maximum harmonic distortion acceptable to load equipment and the maximum allowed distortion to be produced by the EMI filter.

Determine the maximum power frequency surge voltages and currents likely to be experienced by the filter as well as the expected nature and repetitiveness of short duration transients.

7.5.3 Installation Methods

If maximum required filter insertion loss is on the order of 40 to 60 dB, plan to at least separate filter input and output cables to minimize crosstalk. If more than 60 dB is required, and certainly for best performance always, plan on bulkhead mounting the filter. Proper low RF impedance of filter case to local ground reference is mandatory. For safety, the power frequency ground path must **never** be broken.

7.5.4 Schematic Considerations

Always use an inductive input (power source side of the filter). The extra input inductor protects the input capacitor from high-energy transients and provides additional filtering facing the low-impedance (at low frequencies) source. The extra inductor will contribute little to increased insertion loss in the 50 Ω/MIL-STD-220 test setup; by the time a high enough frequency is reached for the typical-valued inductor to look large compared to the 50 Ω test source, the inductor will have passed self-resonance and will begin to perform as a decreasing (capacitive) reactance.

Determine the power system source impedance versus frequency. If unknown, use the suggested design source impedances of Paragraph 7.3.3.1 herein.

Determine the anticipated power load impedance versus frequency. If unknown or impractical to compute, use the Ohm's Law resistive approximation at the power frequency as a first approximation.

Using the power frequency load impedance, initially set total filter $L_{maximum}$ as:

$$L_{maximum} = \frac{Z_{load}/100}{2\pi f} = \frac{Z_{load}}{200\pi f}$$

where,
   f = ac power frequency

and total filter $C_{maximum}$ as:

$$C_{maximum} = \frac{1}{2\pi f(100Z_{load})} = \frac{1}{200\pi f Z_{load}}$$

If these total values of inductance and capacitance or less are used, voltage rise or drop should not occur.

For a relatively low-impedance load, use an inductor as the last filter element on the load end. For a relatively high-impedance load, use a capacitor. For general applications, the load end of the filter is often a high RF quality feedthrough capacitor.

For best performance, divide the initial maximum inductance and maximum capacitance into two more or less equal values, respectively, resulting in a four-element filter (L-C-L-C), or divide the inductance into three similar values (L-C-L-C-L) if there is a low-impedance load.

Modify the number of alternating L-C filter sections upward or downward to adjust the stopband insertion loss slope. Increase or decrease the total L-C values from the initial values as necessary for cutoff frequency adjustment, remembering that voltage rise or drop will tend to occur as those initial maximum values are exceeded.

For safety purposes, bleeder resistors should be inserted to discharge large filter capacitors for personnel handling safety.

Transient protection devices, if needed, should be placed, as a minimum, on the power input side of the first filter inductor, per Paragraph 7.3.7 herein.

Iterate component values, number of filter stages and individual component designs until all power frequency and stopband requirements are met. By computer analysis or actual prototype exercises, demonstrate that all electrical requirements are met.

Now test the successful prototype filter to determine performance per the 50 Ω test method of MIL-STD-220. Use this prototype data as a basis for specifying filter quality assurance insertion loss requirements, with allowances for manufacturing tolerances (i.e., perhaps 2 dB relaxation from 10 kHz to 100 kHz, 4 dB relaxation from 100 kHz to 1 MHz, and 6 dB above 1 MHz). Do not waste the time and efforts of everyone "downstream," however, with unnecessarily demanding testing; if the prototype filter has 80 dB of insertion loss at 1 MHz, but only 60 dB is actually needed, use 60 dB as the minimum "pass" requirement.

7.5.5 Quality Assurance Testing

Quality assurance testing should be performed to ensure that manufactured filters are electrically and mechanically sound, safe and meet all pertinent electrical, mechanical, performance and environmental durability requirements. The level of testing will depend upon contract requirements and how critical the given application is, as well as any historical problems the filter buyer has had with filters. As discussed previously herein, MIL-F-15733, MIL-STD-202 and MIL-STD-220 prescribe appropriate quality control tests.

7.5.6 Sources

Facility power line EMI filters are supplied by many U.S. manufacturers. A partial alphabetical listing of those manufacturers follows. No credit for inclusion on this list nor discredit for exclusion is intended, and none should be inferred. Manufacturers can serve as an important source of filter design and application assistance.

Axel Electronics, Inc.
134-20 Jamaica Avenue
Jamaica, NY 11418
(718) 291-3900

Capcon, Inc.
147 West 25th Street
New York, NY 10001
(212) 243-6275

Captor Corporation
5040 S. County Road
Tipp City, Ohio 45371

Fil-Coil Co., Inc.
800 Axinn Avenue
Garden City, NY 11530
(516) 228-9445

Filtron Co., Inc.
148 Sweet Hollow Road
Old Bethpage, NY 11804
(516) 752-1144

Genisco Technology Corp.
14930 E. Alondra
La Mirada, CA 90638-5754
(714) 523-7001

Lectromagnetics, Inc.
6056 W. Jefferson Blvd.
Los Angeles, CA 90016
(213) 870-9383

RFI Corporation
100 Pine Aire Drive
Bay Shore, NY 11706
(516) 231-6400

7.6 Bibliography

Interference Control Technologies, Inc., "Grounding and Shielding" (Seminar Notebook), Gainesville, VA, 1988.
Interference Control Technologies, Inc., "EMI Practical Fixes" (Seminar Notebook), Gainesville, VA, 1988.

MIL-F-15733G, "Filters and Capacitors Radio Interference, General Specification for," 1984.

MIL-STD-202E, "Test Methods for Electronic and Electrical Component Parts," 1973.

MIL-STD-220A, "Method of Insertion-Loss Measurement," 1959.

MIL-STD-462, "Electromagnetic Interference Characteristics, Measurement of," Notice 3(EL), 1971.

*SAE ARP 4244 (Proposed), "Recommended Insertion Loss Test Methods for Electromagnetic Interference Powerline Filters" (Warrendale, PA: Society of Automotive Engineers, Committee AE-4P, 1988).

White, Donald R. J., *A Handbook on ELECTRICAL FILTERS Synthesis, Design and Applications* (Gainesville, VA: Interference Control Technologies, Inc., 1963).

---

*Note: The interested reader is strongly encouraged to procure ARP 4244 from the SAE; the final version of the document is anticipated to be published and available for sale by the SAE in early to mid 1989. The content of the published version may differ significantly from the preliminary test descriptions herein.

Chapter 8

Power Line Conditioning

by Warren H. Lewis
Lewis Consulting and Engineering
San Juan Capistrano, CA 92675

8.1 Overview of Power Line Conditioning

When the best operational reliability of electronic load equipment is required, it is generally recommended that the equipment not be directly connected to the building's electrical supply system. Instead, the equipment is interfaced to the ac power source via an externally installed power line conditioner (PLC). The PLC is then used to improve the "quality," reliability or both of the power being provided to the electronic load equipment. This chapter explores some of the basics of power line conditioning in overview fashion.

8.1.1 What is Power Line Conditioning?

Power line conditioning is the installation of any components, devices or equipment to the ac supply system or its circuits (**typically externally** to the subject load equipment) whereby a **beneficial effect** is produced upon the quality and reliability of the ac being used by the load equipment.

A PLC may be a simple device such as a metal-oxide varistor (MOV^{TM}) which is applied to the ac supply wiring, or it may be as complex as a full **uninterruptible power supply (UPS)** system. Combinations of available items produce an almost limitless range of PLC designs and possibilities. Therefore, a "power line conditioner" may or may not be considered to be a complete and manufactured product of some complexity since it may also be a simple electrical component applied to the electrical wiring in the field.

However, manufacturers of power line conditioning equipment tend to favor a definition of a PLC which excludes anything which doesn't meet the criteria for their products. For example, a product containing an isolation transformer, voltage regulation and possibly some filtering is widely agreed to be a PLC. However, manufacturers of products containing only a simple isolation transformer or some type of filter generally disagree with this view and also want their products included in the definition. There is, therefore, no formal agreement on the definition of a PLC.

8.1.2 When Is a Power Line Conditioner Needed?

A PLC is generally needed anytime an ac power source has factually been shown by proper testing to be unsuitable for the support of the intended load. Evidence of such unsuitability is provided anytime the load equipment can be shown to have malfunctioned in some manner which may be directly related to the occurrence of any specific perturbation(s) in the ac supply source serving the load.

Several landmark studies of the quality of ac power in the U.S.A. have been conducted.[1,2] In each case, the conclusions were similar: the ac power is not 100 percent reliable and may be unsuitable for the support of electronic load equipment, especially **electronic computer/data processing equipment (EC/DPE)**.

These studies have typically pinpointed the major problem to be momentarily low line voltages (sags). High voltages (surges) and impulses of all types (transients), as well as losses of power ($\geqslant 1$ cycle) are also encountered, but not as frequently. The general findings from these tests are listed in Table 8.1.

Typically, a PLC is required to "protect" the electronic load equipment from the unwanted effects of ac power perturbations if the best in reliability and if continuous operation is required.

	Goldstein-Speranza Study* (Bell)	Allen-Segall Study (IBM)
Date of Study:	1977-1979	1969-1972
Length of Study:	270 monitor months	147 monitor months
Number of Sites:	24	29

* Sites confined to Bell System sites only.

TYPE OF DISTURBANCE	PERCENT PER Goldstein-Speranza	PERCENT PER Allen-Segall
Oscillatory, Decaying:	* *	48.79%
Impulses (Sub-Cyclic):	7.4%	39.52%
Sags (RMS):	87.0%	11.23%
Surges (RMS):	0.7%	* *
Outages (RMS Loss):	4.7%	0.47%

** Not Specifically Identified By The Study.

TABLE 9-1
IBM AND BELL SYSTEM POWER QUALITY STUDIES RESULTS

This table is based on data extracted from a paper by Mayo Tabb, Jr. (Liebert Corporation) which was presented at the University of Wisconsin in a short-course on UPS and power quality at the October 1986 session. Its title is: "Conducting and Understanding a Power Line Study."

Tabb reported that the apparent discrepancies between the results could be easily explained by noting that the sensing thresholds for the two Power Line Analyzers (PLAs, and of differing design); were set at different points. For example, the Bell study used a "Sag" threshold of ±4% of nominal, while IBM used a ±10% threshold. Therefore, all "Sags" deeper than -4% but not less than -10% would not be reported as "Sags" by the IBM study. Instead, they would be classified as "Impulses." This one specific example underlines the absolute importance of being intimately familiar with the actual test conditons involved with any power study before comitting to an interpretation of it, or a comparison of it to some other study. Certainly, a lack of familiarity could result in the selection of improper or non cost-effective power conditoning equipment on a given site.

The foregoing also underscores the problems in relying upon a power conditioning equipment vendor's "interpretation" of these (and other) studies. There is a surprizing tendency for these vendors to "interprete" the data in a way most favorable to whatever product they market, etc.

8.1.3 What are Some General Concerns Relating to Testing and Test Equipment for AC Power Lines?

Since the evidence of unsuitable ac power is typically gathered via the use of a special recording instrument called a **power line analyzer (PLA)**, the selection of the PLA must then play a critical part in determining the validity of the evidence to be gathered.*

The foregoing is a very important consideration because several vendors of PLAs exist, and not all of the available products are suitable for the intended tests; i.e., they may not produce accurate (or adequate) output indications based upon the input conditions. Also, PLAs of different design and manufacture do not generally produce the same indications when provided with identical input conditions.

8.1.3.1 Advice on Selecting the Power Line Analyzer

It is always recommended that the PLA chosen must be acceptable to both the supplier and maintainer of the load equipment and to the party responsible for the testing. If this concurrence is not established, the party not favored by the test results may later question the test's validity and become uncooperative until equipment of his own choosing is brought in and used. This may reverse the direction of disagreement or resolve it, although the former is more likely.

The worst scenario is easy to predict and is the case where two different types of PLAs are used for the testing and where their output indications do not "agree" in the area(s) of dispute. Unfortunately, this is the probable case, as there are no industry-wide or recognized test or performance standards to which PLAs are manufactured and calibrated.

It is generally conceded that two vendors of PLAs represent what may be called the *de facto* standard for these devices in the industry at this time. The two vendors are **Basic Measuring Instruments, Inc. (BMI)** and **Dranetz, Inc**. However, even in the case of these two principal vendors of PLAs, one should not necessarily expect the output indications between the brands to be in agreement when both are subjected to the same input conditions.

---

*It is assumed that the operator of the PLA possesses the requisite skill to properly apply it for testing and to interpret the results of such testing.

8.4

8.1.4 Proper AC Power Wiring and Grounding Is Important

To improve the performance and reliability of the served electronic load equipment to acceptable levels, it is often sufficient to (1) follow the legally required National Electrical Code (NEC)[3] safety requirements and **nationally recognized** engineering practices* and guidelines,† and (2) correct obvious deficiencies in the ac power wiring and grounding configurations and fix other poor wiring installation methods. Under these conditions the installation of a PLC would normally be unnecessary from a technical standpoint, and it would also not make financial sense.

Therefore, even when testing is done using a PLA, it must be carefully determined whether the indicated ac power perturbations being recorded are the result of such things as inadequate ac supply wiring or grounding as opposed to being externally originated, line conducted ac power disturbances. Failure to make this determination typically results in the installation of a power conditioning device which does not correct the problem or may even intensify it.

Some examples of basic ac distribution and some grounding techniques (good and bad) are shown in Fig. 8.1. In addition, three typical and specific methods of interfacing the electronic load equipment to the ac supply in the building are shown in Fig. 8.2. It is important to note that the insets in both of the figures are labeled: **Poor!**, **Better!** and **Best!** It is also important to note that in each case where the figure is labeled **Better!** or **Best!** an isolation transformer‡ has been used to effect the basic interface, and a **zero signal reference structure (ZSRS)** [4,5] has been installed for proper **high-frequency (HF)** and common-mode "noise" current control.

---

*Typically, these are ANSI/IEEE standards for field wiring and construction and UL standards for safety for manufactured equipment. Manufacturer's recommendations are also followed except when they conflict with the NEC or UL requirements (if the product is listed, and normally it must be listed to meet the NEC).

†The Federal Information Processing Standard (FIPS) 94, "Guideline on Electrical Power for EDP Installations," is one such document.[4]

‡In the subject figures, any power conditioning device could be substituted for the isolation transformer so long as it performed an isolation function and allowed the creation of a new, separately derived ac source at its output which could be locally grounded and bonded as shown. As such, a **line voltage regulator (LVR), motor alternator (MA)** set or an **uninterruptible power supply (UPS)** could be used.

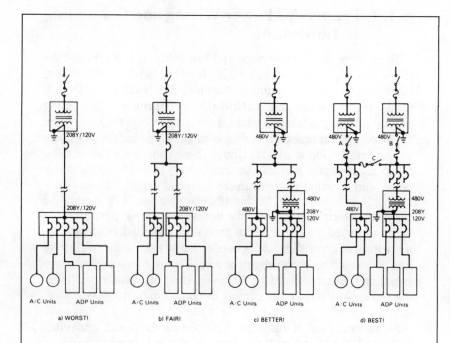

This is Figure 11 as taken from FIPS-94. This figure shows the typical non-recommended and recommended ways of providing ac power and related grounding to sensitive electronic load equipment via the use of feeders.

As shown, method "A" is worst as it causes all current to be shared on the same set of conductors and ac power source. This allows for common IZ drops and Et = L di/dt problems to be experienced by the electronic loads as a function of the non-electronic loads. The remote ac system ground is also highly undesirable.

Method "B" is an improvement, but still has a shared ac supply and a lower voltage feeder which will have significant losses, etc. due to high amperes/kVA conditons. The remote ac system ground is also highly undesirable. Operation of the ac supply at the load's utilization voltage level also encourages remote location of the ac supply and a lengthy feeder (and neutral conductor) run. All are undesirable conditons.

Method "C" is highly preferred in all cases. The electronics loads are now on a dedicated ac supply and also have a local grounding point provided by the isolation transformer or CPC (preferred). Also, the feeders are of a higher, and more efficient voltage level with a reasonable amperes/kVA conditon.

On very large sites, method "D" is best, if such an arrangement can be installed. In some cases, "A" and "B" may be two separate services, but only under terms of a special arrangement with the serving utility. For safety reasons, tie-Breaker "C" is never closed while breakers "A" and "B" are also still closed. Services are not to be paralleled.

Figure 8.1—Common Feeders and Shared AC Supplies

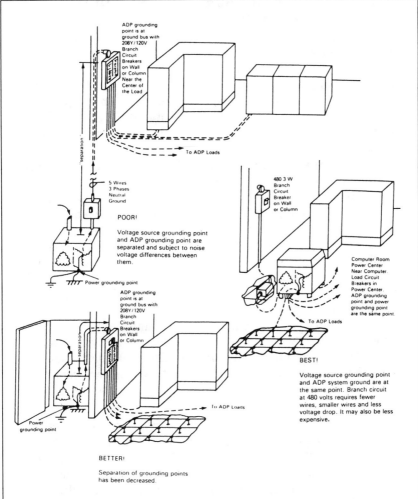

The normal method of interfacing shown in "A" is not desirable, but is commonplace. There are significant common-mode "noise" problems with this design.

Method "A"may be modified into method "B" for a significant improvement in performance, especially in the area of common-mode "noise" and High-Frequency grounding/bonding.

Method "C" is the recommended practice in all cases. Either method "A" or "B" may be easily upgraded to "C" by the addition of a Computer Power Center (CPC) as shown. Many computer OEMs manufacture such items and highly recommend their use as a direct means of increasing the electronic system's reliability.

In both "B" and in "C" the use of a Zero Signal Reference Structure is mandatory for best operation.

Figure 8.2—Three Methods of Interfacing the Loads

8.7

8.1.4.1 Electrical Isolation and Solid Grounding

Ungrounded ac supply sources are not generally permitted by the NEC **except** where the voltage from line to ground would exceed 150 V rms.* Therefore, in this context no ac supply source which is external to the load equipment and is used on typical 1 ϕ systems with nominal voltages of 120 V rms or 240 × 120 V rms may be grounded except by **solid means**. The same NEC sections also require the common 3 ϕ, 208Y/120 V rms system to be solidly grounded.

The term **solid grounding** is used above to indicate that it is not permissible to install ac supply circuits with ungrounded (i.e., **floating**), resistance or impedance grounded supply windings (i.e., secondary or output). Solid grounding is therefore the requirement where the neutral/midpoint/common terminal of the supply source's output winding is directly connected (i.e., grounded and bonded) to the metal frame or enclosure containing the ac supply, and then **also** to an ac system grounding electrode.

In relation to the foregoing, the nearest available structural building steel is both the required and preferred electrode according to the NEC. Others are permitted in addition to the structural steel connection, but they may be used in lieu of it only if the structural steel is ungrounded, **completely** electrically discontinuous, nonexistent or **truly** inaccessible.† The NEC's fallback choice for the electrode in these cases is effectively and continuously grounded and bonded metal cold water piping.

For example, an ac supply source such as an **isolation transformer** (see Fig. 8.3) that is installed in accordance with the NEC is not an "isolation transformer" in the sense that it isolates either the primary or secondary circuits from the metal conduit or raceway, the **equipment safety grounding conductors (ESGCs; i.e., green wires)** and other general building safety

---

*See NEC Section 250-26, "Grounding Separately Derived Alternating-Current Systems," Paragraph (c), "Grounding Electrode."

†This is not an applicable exception if the supply is a 480Y/277 V rms system and the neutral is used to supply any current to any loads.

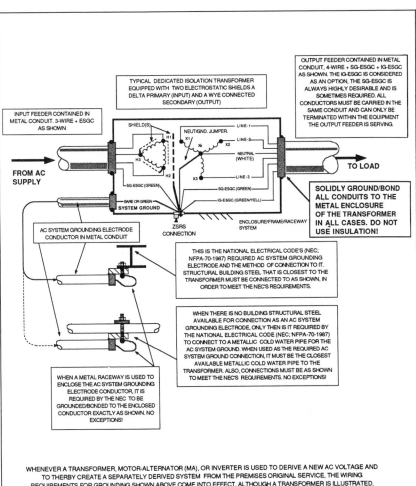

Figure 8.3—Properly Wiring an Isoltion Transformer

grounding systems such as building steel, etc. These are all metallic items that are required by the NEC to be effectively grounded and bonded together into a single electrically continuous mass, all of which is ultimately connected back to the required ac system grounding electrode for the service. Additional (i.e., **supplementary**) grounding electrodes are also required to be connected (grounded and bonded) together and to the site's principal grounding electrode(s) to produce a single, solidly interconnected set of electrodes (Fig. 8.4a). Isolated, separated and individual or dedicated grounding electrodes in any form thus are also not permitted (Fig. 8.4b).

Electrical isolation of an ac supply serving electronic load equipment is in fact not generally advisable in any case as ungrounded secondaries do not permit filter and fault currents to be circulated between the "isolated" supply and the load or faulted point (see Fig. 8.5). Subsequent degradation of the filter's performance in some modes and a general failure to operate overcurrent protective devices on line-to-ground faults results from the use of such ungrounded designs. Many forms of surge protective devices will similarly become ineffective if they do not have a proper "ground current" return path to work against.

Therefore, the connection of the isolation transformer or other form of ac supply into any form of an independent, separate, isolated or otherwise dedicated earth grounding electrode is expressly forbidden by the NEC and is otherwise not recommended* as it will pose both electrical safety and common-mode noise problems for the equipment served by the ac supply.

---

*By several IEEE recommended practices, FIPS 94, UL and **knowledgeable** OEMs of product safety listed electronic computer/data processing equipment.

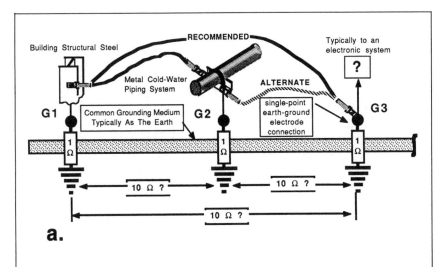

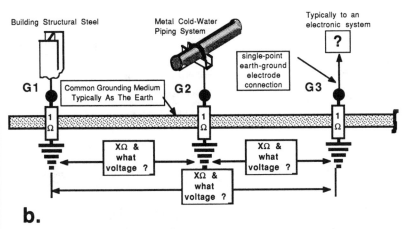

The NEC requires that all grounding electrodes on the premises be grounded/bonded together into a single mass so as to prevent the development of high and unsafe potentials between them during lightning and/or ac system ground-fault conditions (a). When electrodes are connected together per the NEC, then potential between them is limited. If low impedance bonding is used between them the "noise" potential between the grounds will be similarly reduced (highly desirable!). Simple ohm's law dictates that for every ampere that flows through 1-ohm there will be a 1-volt drop across the the 1-ohm. In the above case a 1-ohm grounding electrode connection is meaningless when one considers the number of ohms possible to exist between the electrodes as the source of the unwanted "noise" potential which results from the IZ drop through the earth as shown. Systems as shown in (b) are also highly dangerous to personnel working with equipment connected into them as they are directly exposed to unsafe potentials between "grounded" items that they believe (erroneously) to be at a "safe" potential (i.e., "ground," but which one?). Electronics connected across the different grounds in (b) also suffer a lot of common-mode "noise," which is what isolated grounding is said to reduce!

Figure 8.4—(a) NEC Correct Electrodes Are Interconnected (b) NEC Violation Electrodes Not Interconnected

Power Line Conditioning

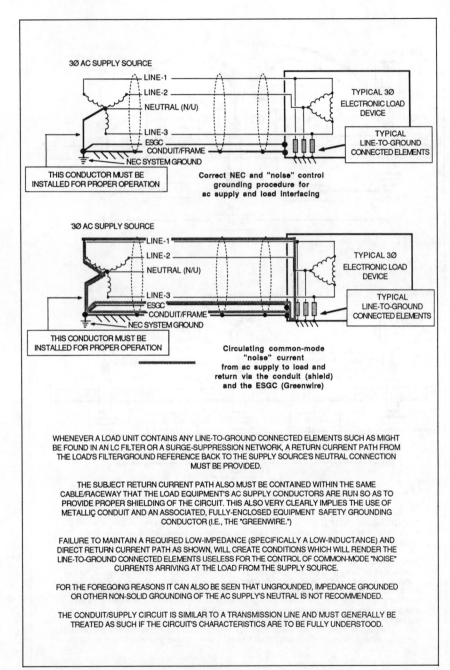

WHENEVER A LOAD UNIT CONTAINS ANY LINE-TO-GROUND CONNECTED ELEMENTS SUCH AS MIGHT BE FOUND IN AN LC FILTER OR A SURGE-SUPPRESSION NETWORK, A RETURN CURRENT PATH FROM THE LOAD'S FILTER/GROUND REFERENCE BACK TO THE SUPPLY SOURCE'S NEUTRAL CONNECTION MUST BE PROVIDED.

THE SUBJECT RETURN CURRENT PATH ALSO MUST BE CONTAINED WITHIN THE SAME CABLE/RACEWAY THAT THE LOAD EQUIPMENT'S AC SUPPLY CONDUCTORS ARE RUN SO AS TO PROVIDE PROPER SHIELDING OF THE CIRCUIT. THIS ALSO VERY CLEARLY IMPLIES THE USE OF METALLIC CONDUIT AND AN ASSOCIATED, FULLY-ENCLOSED EQUIPMENT SAFETY GROUNDING CONDUCTOR (I.E., THE "GREENWIRE.")

FAILURE TO MAINTAIN A REQUIRED LOW-IMPEDANCE (SPECIFICALLY A LOW-INDUCTANCE) AND DIRECT RETURN CURRENT PATH AS SHOWN, WILL CREATE CONDITIONS WHICH WILL RENDER THE LINE-TO-GROUND CONNECTED ELEMENTS USELESS FOR THE CONTROL OF COMMON-MODE "NOISE" CURRENTS ARRIVING AT THE LOAD FROM THE SUPPLY SOURCE.

FOR THE FOREGOING REASONS IT CAN ALSO BE SEEN THAT UNGROUNDED, IMPEDANCE GROUNDED OR OTHER NON-SOLID GROUNDING OF THE AC SUPPLY'S NEUTRAL IS NOT RECOMMENDED.

THE CONDUIT/SUPPLY CIRCUIT IS SIMILAR TO A TRANSMISSION LINE AND MUST GENERALLY BE TREATED AS SUCH IF THE CIRCUIT'S CHARACTERISTICS ARE TO BE FULLY UNDERSTOOD.

Figure 8.5—AC Supply to Load Ground-Loop and Filter Return Paths (Proper)

8.1.4.2 Some Typical Electrical Wiring Problems and Solutions

Shared electrical wiring by different classes of load equipment is a known contributor to ac power problems. The most common form of this is where building mechanical equipment is served from the same electrical **panel board (PB)** which in turn is supplied via a long feeder run. This is shown in Fig. 8.1a. Under the conditions thus produced, unwanted voltage drops/losses are typically produced on the shared circuit and are manifested in the form of poor voltage regulation on the circuit. These poor voltage regulation conditions are then "seen" by all loads connected to the shared circuit. Also, mechanical equipment typically may produce significant and unwanted harmonic currents and transient voltages (possessing fast rise times) on shared wiring of this type. The connected electronic load equipment is very often seriously affected by these latter disturbances.

The general solution to the foregoing and the preferred approach is one where the electronic load equipment is placed upon **dedicated** electrical circuits and PBs which are supplied from larger sources of bulk ac power and which possess a low bus impedance. Therefore, connection into the building's **service entry** for ac power that is to serve electronic load equipment is a recommended approach as opposed to obtaining ac power from smaller sources of power downstream from the service entry such as local, **general purpose** PBs and transformers which are used for other loads as well.

8.1.4.3 Some Typical Grounding Problems and Solutions

Poor and improper ac system equipment (i.e., safety) grounding ranks very high as a source of creating unreliability on electronic load equipment. Unfortunately, the related symptoms are often misread as an ac power problem. Applying a PLC to this form of problem most often produces no practical improvement in the situation, but it may go a long way toward showing that the problem is **not** related to ac power quality, so it must be "something else." This is a very expensive and unnecessary form of diagnostic testing, especially where the applied PLC is a large UPS or MA set, for example.

The typical "grounding" problem is one where the electronic load equipment or its ac supply have been installed in an **ungrounded**, or **floating ground** manner, or have been connected into some form of **quiet, isolated, dedicated, insulated, separate**, or other form of "special computer ground." These grounds are typically designs which have **not** been effectively and solidly grounded and bonded into the building's NEC required safety grounding electrode system, and they therefore do not conform to the NEC's safety requirements.* They also do not then conform to the requirements of the National Lightning Protection Code, ANSI/NFPA-78-1983.[6] In addition, connection of UL-listed equipment into them typically invalidates the listing of the product being so miswired, and this in itself is also an NEC violation.†

Included in the foregoing list of typical "grounding" problems are instances where the electronic load equipment or any of the serving electrical system components have been "isolated" or "insulated" in some fashion, from the NEC required equipment safety grounding system. This system consists of the metal conduit/raceway system‡ and any related Equipment Safety Grounding Conductors (ESGCs; i.e., green wires) for the ac system serving the load equipment.

These foregoing forms of unwanted grounding are legally considered to be unsafe and also pose significant risk to the connected equipment in the event of a lightning strike or ac system ground fault condition. Under either of the indicated conditions, destructive arcing and hazardous potentials may develop between electrically or electronically interconnected elements of the subject equipment. These potentials are also likely to appear between any

---

*See NEC Sections 250-54, "Common Grounding Electrode;" 250-75, "Bonding Other Enclosures;" 259-81, "Grounding Electrode System;" and 250-91, "Materials," Paragraph (c), "Supplementary Grounding."

†See NEC Section 110-3, "Examination, Identification, Installation and Use of Equipment," Paragraph (b), "Installation and Use."

‡See NEC Sections 300-10, "Electrical Continuity of Metal Raceways and Enclosures;" 250-50, "Equipment Grounding Conductor Connections;" and 250-51, "Effective Grounding Path."

of the equipment and any other grounded metal in the building.* Also, and most important, overcurrent protective devices may not open under ground-fault conditions if these methods of "grounding" are employed.

Severe common-mode noise currents may be caused to flow between equipment of all types which are connected to grounding systems of the foregoing described type and they (along with their associated common-mode potentials) may cause dielectric breakdown of insulation systems and of solid-state components within equipment. The return current path and hence the performance for line-to-ground connected filter and surge protective elements will also be seriously degraded or rendered ineffective by the foregoing, non-recommended grounding practices. They are, therefore to be avoided.

In summary, the application of a PLC should not be expected to solve the foregoing problems, each of which will require its own solution. If successfully implemented, these solutions may eliminate the often perceived need for a PLC.

8.1.5 Power Source Impedance

The concept of power source impedance is very important in the proper application of a PLC and is generally illustrated in Fig. 8.6. Power source impedance creates a voltage drop at the load as load current is increased. During step load changes such as when starting some types of equipment, the line voltage drop is immediate. The **line voltage regulator (LVR)** cannot anticipate this voltage drop and can only begin a corrective action after it has occurred and been detected by the LVR. A low internal power source impedance will limit this load-related and resultant voltage drop which occurs before any LVR can respond to it.

Power line conditioners that have not operated successfully are often found to have an incompatibility with their connected loads which is directly related to the internal impedance of the PLC. To

---

*Per ANSI/NFPA-78, "Lightning Protection Code 1983 (see Ref. 6), a lightning side-flash condition of at least 6 ft (1.8 m), resulting from a direct strike on the building, is to be expected between equipment and any building structural steel, piping, etc. This is a large arc, and it is very dangerous. It will penetrate concrete walls, etc., to complete its path to ground.

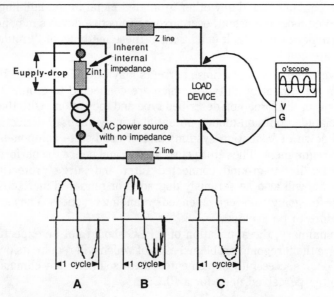

The typical ac supply source is often erroneously viewed as being a "perfect" source with no internal impedance so that instantaneous load current demands will not affect the output voltage waveform and it will always look as shown in (A).

However, there is always some internal impedance in the supply. This manifests itself as an internal voltage-drop which is produced in proportion to the instantaneous current demands from the load. Example (B) shows what might be the result of a high instantaneous current demand on the ac supply as produced by a switch-mode power supply "firing" in the last quadrant of each half-cycle in response to load demand on its output. Some SCR-based equipment also produces similar waveshapes.

Example (C) illustrates what is commonly referred to as "flat-topping" of the ac voltage waveform. This is generally produced from linear-regulated or unregulated ac-dc power supplys when the output filter capacitor requires recharging current. The less recharging current the less flat-topping.

The shown unwanted effects are further exacerbated if the ac supply wiring between the ac supply and the load has appreciable impedance as it will simply appear in series with the ac supply's internal impedance. This can be checked for by comparing the distortion seen at the input terminals to the load device to that seen at the output terminals of the ac supply. If conditions are significantly worse at the load than at the ac source, then line impedance is a problem.

Simple isolation transformers may possess surprising amounts of internal impedance, especially in some of the high-isolation types. Electronic or ferro-magnetic voltage regulators also possess internal impedance as shown, and in addition have a voltage correction response time factor to be concerned with. This is also true for inverters in UPSs and for Motor-Alternator sets.

Figure 8.6—Internal Supply Impedance Effects on Voltage Wave

be effective, a PLC must possess a reasonably low impedance to currents flowing within its output circuits at the supply line's fundamental and some harmonically related frequencies. If the impedance is too high, there will be ac voltage waveform distortion or poor voltage regulation on the output. Unfortunately, both of these latter conditions are typical conditions that a PLC is often installed to reduce or eliminate. In addition, the impedance may be too high to allow for proper fault clearing.

Compared to the serving public utility's bus impedance, smaller ac supply sources such as isolation transformers, **motor-alternator (MA)** sets and electronic inverters (as are commonly seen in solid-state UPS equipment) are all of a higher source impedance. In some cases, this impedance increase may be nearly negligible (such as with a large isolation transformer), and in others it may be very significant (as in a typical ferroresonant transformer).

8.1.5.1 Percent Impedance

When dealing with ac supply sources, the **percent impedance (%Z)** of the ac supply is an important specification that must not be overlooked as it has a bearing upon the maximum fault current that the ac supply can provide and upon the supply's ability to support high peak current demands from the load(s) without poor voltage regulation becoming troublesome. A low %Z indicates a "stiff" ac supply, and a high %Z indicates a "soft" one which will possess poor voltage regulation as a function of load current demand. Percent impedance is mainly calculated in the following manner:

$$\%Z = 100 \ (I_{fla}/I_{max \ sc}) \tag{8.1}$$

where,

$\%Z$ = percent impedance
I_{fla} = output current in amperes of the advice at full (100 percent) rated load
$I_{max \ sc}$ = maximum short-circuit current available from the supply in amperes

As can be seen from the foregoing, an ac supply with a 5 %Z can provide 5 times the fault current than one of the same design except having a 25 %Z. This relationship also implies that the voltage regulation (**discounting automatic feedback and correction**) would be 5 times better on the 5 %Z supply as compared to the 25 %Z supply, and that load current induced voltage "transients" would be 5 times less on the 5 %Z supply per unit of load current change than for the 25 %Z supply.

Good ac power system isolation transformers should typically fall into the 3 to 5 %Z range, electronic tap-changing LVRs into the 4 to 6 %Z range, typical MA sets into the 15 to 30 %Z range and typical ferroresonant transformers into the 25 to 50 %Z range, with the magnetic synthesizer version exhibiting about 33 %Z.*

8.1.6 Voltage Waveform Harmonic Distortion

When the ac power voltage waveform is not a "pure" sinusoid (usually the case), the resultant distortion often has unwanted effects upon both the ac power system and the loads being served. The unwanted effects range from heating in magnetic (iron) devices such as transformers, motors and chokes, to additional ripple in the output of ac-dc power supplies and the varying of threshold limits in peak and averaging sensing circuits.† These are all causes of serious concern to the designers of the electrical system, the suppliers of the connected electronic load equipment and those attempting to perform maintenance on either.

Typical manufacturers of electronic load equipment specify limits on the amount of voltage waveform harmonic distortion that can be permitted without creating unwanted reactions in the equipment. This limit is generally specified as the amount of allowable **total harmonic distortion (THD),** expressed as a percentage

---

*One manufacturer claims a limit of about 300 percent of the full load amperage (i.e., $3 \times I_{fla} = I_{max\ sc}$) is achieved, at which point inherent "current limiting" begins as a function of reduced output voltage. Using Eq. (8.1), this works out to about a 33 %Z.

†This is of special concern where peak or averaging (rms "calibrated") voltmeters and ammeters are in use to measure quantities on the electrical system. When used on harmonically distorted ac systems, these instruments generally read **less** than the true rms value, which is the desired value. An error factor of $2 \times$ is possible on the low side. This allows electrical equipment to be placed into an area of overload without the instruments reflecting the danger. As a result, what appears to be a partially loaded PB, wiring or an ac supply may actually be **overloaded.**

(THD%) of deviation from the perfect sinusoidal wave.

A high power source impedance will interact with a nonlinear load which requires a high peak current demand from the ac supply, and this will produce unwanted harmonics. The **switch-mode power supply (SMPS)** and phase-controlled motor speed control are two good examples of a harmonic-producing load which, when connected to an ac supply having a high internal source impedance, will generate a voltage waveform with very high THD%. Another such load is a simple rectifier load.

A common limit imposed by many manufacturers for harmonics which originate from the ac supply is about 5 percent THD and 3 percent for any **one** harmonic. Some electronic load equipment manufacturers specify the THD% limit on the ac supply as being measured **after** the installation of their equipment. This is of interest as their equipment may be the principal cause for the added distortion appearing on an otherwise "good" ac supply which has a low THD% without the equipment being connected to it.

Other manufacturers are more tolerant of their own equipment's ability to produce harmonics, and they are primarily interested in the THD% existing on the ac supply prior to the connection of their equipment. As a result of this confusing situation, it is wise to make the determination of which way the specification is to be applied and what the "real" limits on THD% will be, well in advance of the installation of either the power conditioning or the electronic load equipment.

Since the typical power conditioning device has a higher internal source impedance than the typical ac supply from a public utility would have, the installation of the power conditioning device may be expected to increase the amount of THD% in many cases rather than reducing it. This means that a power conditioning device is not always a recommended way to reduce the THD% on an ac supply serving electronic load equipment, even though the harmonic distortion may be viewed as a "power problem" which needs "conditioning" to resolve.

8.2 The Power Susceptibility Curve

The power susceptibility curve shown in (Fig. 8.7) originated within the **Computer and Business Machines Manufacturers Association (CBEMA)**, with Subcommittee 3 (SC-3),

Power Line Conditioning

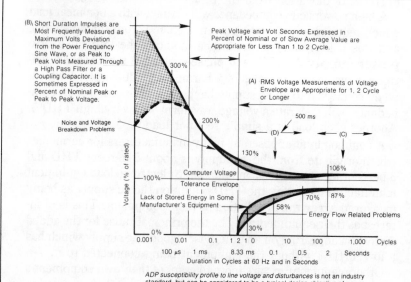

ADP susceptibility profile to line voltage and disturbances is not an industry standard, but can be considered to be a typical design objective of power conscious computer hardware designers.

1. This curve is from FIPS-94 and is the Computer and Business Equipment Manufacturers Association (CBEMA) curve on ac power disturbance susceptibility as estimated by the Power Interface Subcommittee (SC-3). It is not an adopted standard nor is it a requirement that any equipment actually meet the conditions implied by the curve.

2. However, because of widespread use and popularity of the curve, it has virtually become a *de facto* standard in the industry. It is often written into purchase agreements.

3. The curve should be carefully used in conjunction with a power line analyzer (PLA) so that the conditions found on the ac circuit being examined may be correlated with the conditions of operation and non-operation implied by this curve.

4. Test results falling outside of the curve's envelope should be marked in red. Those falling within it should be marked in green. Events falling within the curve, but which are also associated with an electronic system or unit malfunction, should also be marked in red.

5. Red marked areas should be examined to see what class of problem that they represent (i.e., impulse, low rms or high rms voltage, voltage loss, etc.). According to the type and duration of the event, a power conditioning approach may be knowledgeably decided upon, while others not suitable may be discarded.

6. A true UPS is generally not needed unless ac power is actuallly lost for longer than about 500 ms. Below this time, a motor alternator may be most "cost-effective". In areas where ac power is not lost but where other problems exist, line voltage regulators (LVRs) or impulse filtering devices may be more "cost-effective".

7. Voltage clamping devices are ineffective in the area below the 100% line in all cases.

Figure 8.7—"CBEMA" Power Tolerance Curve

8.20

the Power Interface Subcommittee. It later was promulgated through the IEEE "Orange Book"[7] and then through the NBS FIPS-94 guideline.[4] It is not yet an official standard of any kind, but it is rapidly becoming something of an industry-wide *de facto* standard. However, no principal manufacturers of electronic load equipment are presently known to be guaranteeing or warranting that their equipment will necessarily meet all of the requirements of the curve.

This curve, however, is highly suggestive of a useful way in which the relationship between time, ac power quality and its reliability may all be related to the operational performance of the connected electronic load equipment. As an important side benefit, it also provides a strong indication of what kind of power conditioning equipment would or would not be suitable for a given set of problems. It is therefore a highly useful tool to use in relation to ac power and power conditioning problems and decisions.

For example, in reference to Fig. 8.7, it can be seen that if the electronic load equipment were responding to power perturbations in the area represented by (A), a simple isolation transformer would be of no value because it does not automatically correct for variations in ac line voltage. However, it might be very useful in area (B) where short-term impulses are indicated as being the problem.

Also in reference to the figure, unwanted power loss events occurring at point (C) would be easily corrected by a full UPS but would not be correctable by a simple MA set because the amount of required **ride-through** would exceed that for which the MA set is normally able to provide. The MA set, however, would be quite effective in area (D) and would be a less costly solution to the problem than would be the complete UPS.

Using the output of a PLA in conjunction with the curve and with a written log of the electronic load equipment's performance, one can derive a visual record of power perturbation events which are and **are not** associated with equipment malfunctions being placed on the curve. At a later time, the **clustering** of "failure" events can be used to indicate the kind of power conditioning equipment which will be needed to correct the bulk of the problems. Individual events may be ignored as isolated cases or may be considered as requiring attention.

Additionally, the curve may be used to indicate what type of equipment to avoid. For example, a voltage-clamping device (i.e., an MOV) will be of no help whatsoever if the problem is an impulse which is less than the peak line voltage plus the needed **headroom** for the clamping device. A capacitor might be a better choice in this case as it both acts as a low-impedance to an impulse placed across its terminals and stores energy which may be released to fill in a voltage **notch**. Such a notch is one which could be produced by an impulse of opposite polarity to the supply's polarity at the instant of occurrence.

The curve's original authors are presently contemplating a revision of the curve to indicate increased susceptibility to short-duration, fast rise time impulses which are not properly suggested by the original rendering of the curve. The suggested revision is tentatively described by the shaded area in the left-hand portion of the curve.

8.3 What are Some of the Principal Types of Power Line Conditioners?

Several forms of commonly used power line conditioning devices will be generally discussed in the following paragraphs, but not all available types are included. The ones discussed herein are from the family of mainstream technologies which are most often encountered.

8.3.1 Isolation Transformers

Isolation transformers (i.e, ones with separate primary and secondary windings which are not connected as an auto-transformer) are recommended as a basic means of interfacing the electronic load equipment to the ac supply source (see Figs. 8.2b and 8.2c) and for significantly reducing the unwanted effects of common-mode noise currents. Such a transformer may also have a beneficial effect on the reduction of some normal-mode noise as well, depending upon its normal-mode HF bandpass characteristics.*

---

*It's not easy to design an audio output transformer that has a good, flat bandpass from 20 Hz to 20 kHz, let alone a power transformer that could go into the higher frequency ranges without significant attenuation occurring. Therefore, unwanted leakage paths resulting from stray, reactive coupling are the predominant paths for the transfer of higher frequencies between windings. In practice these are often discovered in the form of field-installed metal conduit/raceway systems which are coupled to the primary and secondary supply wiring (which is also sometimes intertwined). They are often found not to be functions of the transformer's inherent design.

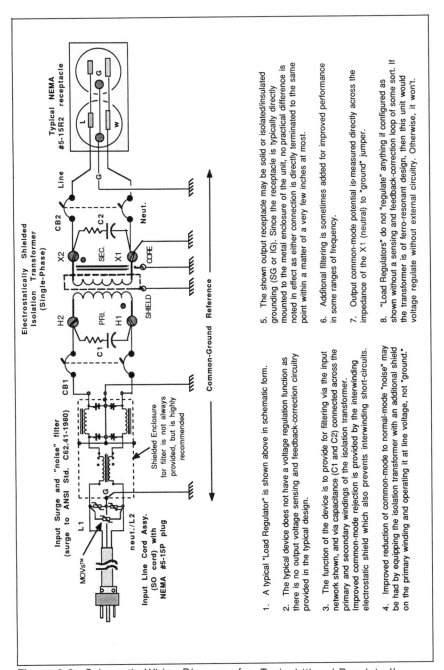

Figure 8.8—Schematic Wiring Diagram of a Typical "Load Regulator"

Isolation transformers, by their very nature, are intimately associated with the acts of grounding and bonding. Therefore, a general review of this topic as presented in Section 8.1.4.1, "Electrical Isolation and Solid Grounding," is recommended before reading the following paragraphs.

8.3.1.1 The Basic Isolation Transformer

A basic isolation transformer is shown in Fig. 8.3 and is configured in accordance with the requirements of the NEC. A simple isolation transformer used to support electronic load equipment should be specified with a percent impedance (%Z) of between 3 and 5 percent if unwanted interaction between the transformer and its served loads is to be avoided.

Efficiencies of the typical isolation transformer may be as high as 97 to 98 percent under conditions of full or near-full loading. Excessive harmonic currents flowing through the transformer for any reason will increase losses significantly, and otherwise partially loaded transformers may then appear to be (or actually become) overloaded based upon the increased heat dissipated as a result of the unwanted harmonic currents.

Delta-wye connected isolation transformers are highly recommended to be used as a principal means of reducing the amount of triplen harmonics from the load(s) which are transmitted back onto the main ac supply system. The action of the delta-connected primary is beneficial in this regard.

With the exception of the following optional but recommended enhancements, the isolation transformer has no special design characteristics of significant practical importance. Therefore, typical **dry-type transformers** used in building electrical systems often qualify for the role of an isolation transformer and generally work well in the application.

8.3.1.2 Recommended Enhancements

Isolation transformer enhancement is generally recommended via the addition of electrostatic shielding (see Fig. 8.3). It should at least be equipped with a good single-layer, interwinding shield which is also properly connected (i.e., grounded and bonded) to the metal frame or enclosure of the transformer using low-inductance means. This shield is used for the reduction of common-mode noise and to prevent interwinding short-circuits from occurring.

A related recommendation exists for one additional insulated interwinding shield to be installed and operated above ground at line voltage. This shield is used to reduce the conversion of common-mode noise current to normal-mode noise current across the windings.

In general, additional shields are not required in the practical world, and claimed common-mode noise attenuation values much in excess of -50 to -60 dB are not generally realizable on installed transformers, nor are they needed. OEM tests in special test stands which produce significantly greater attenuation claims are not generally valid as a means of predicting the common-mode noise rejection performance of installed and operating isolation transformers. The real world tends to provide numerous leakage paths from primary to secondary in the common mode, all of which have been carefully reduced in the OEM's test stand. This allows the production of impressive sales specifications, but little more is accomplished of practical interest.

Additional enhancements are recommended to be in the form of supplemental impulse and surge current diverters, such as an MOV, which are internally installed by the transformer's OEM in line-to-line and line-to-neutral/chassis (i.e., ground) configurations. Typically, these are recommended to be applied to both the primary and secondary windings.

The addition of small ac **bypass capacitors** (approx. $0.01\ \mu\mathrm{F}$) within the transformer by its OEM is another enhancement which is highly recommended. These capacitors are connected in line-to-line and in line-to-neutral/chassis configurations. Typically, these are recommended to be applied to both the primary and secondary windings and are useful for the reduction of HF noise which is below the voltage threshold of the supplemental impulse and surge current diverter elements.

In addition, larger ac capacitors (approx. 1 to 2 $\mu\mathrm{F}$ per ampere of line current on the connected circuit) may be applied in a fashion similar to the above bypass capacitors for the purpose of creating a fairly effective low-pass filter arrangement using the transformer's leakage inductance. These capacitors may also have some beneficial effect on the circuit's **power factor**. In addition, if carefully applied, they may be effective in reducing the magnitude of unwanted harmonic currents which would otherwise flow in the transformer's winding's and cause voltage waveform distortion and reduced transformer capacity from related heating and losses.

Finally, the isolation transformer becomes much more useful if it is equipped with a set of voltage adjusting taps (manual) on its primary winding. This allows for compensation of chronically high or low line voltages and permits the output of the transformer to hit or approach the actual ac system's nominal design voltage. Tapping ranges of +10 percent **full capacity above nominal (FCAN)** and –15 percent **full capacity below nominal (FCBN)** are typically recommended.

8.3.1.3 Location and Grounding of the Isolation Transformer

When used as recommended for the reduction of common-mode noise currents, the isolation transformer must be placed in very close proximity to the served load equipment on its secondary and it must also be effectively grounded and bonded in accordance with the National Electrical Code.* For best results at HF it must also be placed onto and effectively grounded and bonded to the same zero signal reference structure (ZSRS)[4, 5] that its served loads share.

8.3.1.4 Isolation and the Isolation Transformer

As previously discussed in Section 8.1.4.1, "Electrical Isolation and Solid Grounding," the term **isolation** cannot always be taken to mean that the secondary winding of the isolation transformer may be installed in an ungrounded, floating or insulated form in relation to either the building's structural steel and metal interior piping systems, the primary or secondary side's metallic frame/enclosure/raceway/conduit system, nor from any installed **equipment safety grounding conductors (ESGCs; i.e., green wires)** associated with **any** of the isolation transformer's circuits. Also, as noted previously, the only NEC **exceptions** allowed for this are when the ac supply would exhibit more than

---

*See NEC Sections 250-5, "Alternating-Current Circuits and Systems to be Grounded," and 250-26, "Grounding Separately Derived Alternating-Current Systems."

150 V rms to ground,* in which case the supply may be ungrounded, resistance or impedance grounded.† Otherwise, the NEC rule is to provide solid grounding.

The term **isolation** as used in relation to the isolation transformer should principally be taken to mean only that no primary current will appear in the secondary winding and vice-versa. It should not be taken to mean that the input and output sides are not solidly connected (i.e., grounded and bonded) to one another for referencing and fault current purposes via the NEC required safety grounding paths.

Additionally, and in relation to the isolation transformer, **isolation** should also be taken to mean that a **new electrical system has been derived from the originating ac supply** and that this new, **separately derived ac system (SDS)** must now be connected to an immediately adjacent and local ac grounding electrode system. It must also be connected to local grounding and bonding reference points which are near the served loads, but still solidly interconnected to the overall safety grounding and bonding and ac grounding electrode system for the building.

8.3.1.5 Load Regulators

The term **load regulator** is sometimes used to describe some available non-voltage regulating, isolation transformer-based power conditioning equipment. The descriptive term **load regulator** appears to be a generally misleading and confusing term which was apparently derived from vendor efforts to more effectively market a simple isolation transformer in an enclosure, along with some ac line voltage clamping (via MOVs) and other filtering.‡ A general form of wiring diagram for a typically observed load regulator is provided in Fig. 8.8.

The product called a load regulator also appears to generally include a basic single-point connection to its frame/enclosure/chassis (see Fig. 8.9) for most internal circuitry requiring grounding and bonding. This grounding and bonding connection is sometimes

---

*See NEC Section 250-5, "Alternating-Current Circuits and Systems to be Grounded."

†As previously noted, this exception does not include the 3 φ, 480Y/277 V rms system if the neutral is used to supply any current to any type of load.

‡Both low-pass filtering and input line lightning surge protection have been observed in the product.

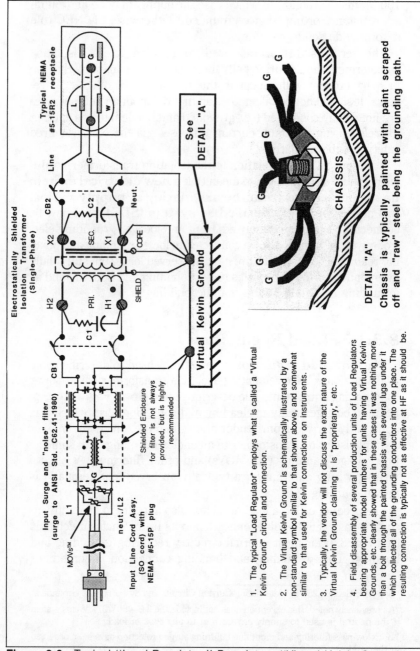

Figure 8.9—Typical "Load Regulator," Proprietary "Virtual Kelvin Ground" Detailed

referred to as a **Virtual Kelvin Ground**. This oft encountered but actually unexplained grounding term appears to be essentially meaningless in the context of the equipment's actual design.

Both the terms **load regulator** and **Virtual Kelvin Ground** are apparently important to the product's associated marketing effort which seems to enjoy the use of such undefinable terms as a means of increasing sales and confounding competitors. The terms are not otherwise helpful in accurately describing the equipment from a technical standpoint and in trying to understand its application to the needs of the power conditioning effort.

The load regulator is a popular and effective power conditioning device if it is used and recognized for what it is: an isolation transformer with some surge protection and filtering plus a common grounding and bonding point for the internal circuits of the unit. It is a generally recommended form of power conditioning device.

8.3.2 Automatic Line Voltage Regulators

An automatic LVR is a possible solution to line voltage variations which exceed the ability of the electronic load equipment's internal regulating power supplies to compensate for. They are also useful to provide correct voltage for non-self-regulating load devices such as drive motors and fans which are also frequently found within the electronic load equipment.*

The basic concept of voltage regulation in any circuit, expressed in percentage (Reg%), is:

$$\text{Reg\%} = \frac{100\ (V_{\text{no load}} - V_{\text{full load}})}{V_{\text{no load}}} \qquad (8.2)$$

Since each manufacturer of electronic load equipment has its own specification relating to the variation in nominal line voltage allowable at the input terminals of the subject device, the foregoing equation may be useful in determining the compatibility of the

---

*Some switched-mode power supplies can operate over a range of input voltages from about 90 to over 250 V rms, and the line voltage regulator is of minimal importance in these cases. However, these same power supplies may be installed in a rack or equipment cooled by simple impedance-protected, motor-driven fans and may be equipped with other drive motors, linear power supplies, relays, contactors and lights, all of which will not operate over such a wide range of voltages without either reduced air flow, speed problems or overheating and burnout problems.

electronic load equipment's requirements vs. the available or expected voltage regulation on the electrical circuit to be connected to.

Critical electronic load equipment which is sensitive to changes in the rms value of the ac voltage being supplied will require rms line voltage regulation in the range of about ±3 percent from nominal. Most electronic load equipment will accept input voltage in the range of +5 percent to −10 percent without significant problems.[4, 8] However, an unregulated ac supply in a building might normally be expected to experience rms voltage variations in the range of +5 percent to +6 percent and −13.3 percent from nominal as a result of permissible public utility operating ranges and user/premises distribution losses.[4, 9] Therefore, an additional effort at providing for line voltage regulation is usually necessary if the best operation of the electronic load equipment is to be realized.

8.3.2.1 Line Voltage Regulators and Isolation

Unless the LVR is designed around or combined with a transformer possessing separate primary and secondary windings, it will not be able to provide needed electrical isolation between the input and output sides. As a result, no new local, separately derived ac system* and connected load grounding reference point may be created, and it is highly desirable to be able to do this in almost all cases.

8.3.2.2 Line Voltage Regulator Correction Response Time

Line voltage regulators which are chosen on their ability to swiftly correct for voltage variations (i.e., they have a short response time) may create serious problems if the served load has a similar response time in its regulating circuits. In cases where these conditions have been observed to exist, a virtual **flip-flop** condition may be created where each regulator attempts to compensate for the actions of the other in a feed-back mode.† This is illustrated in Fig. 8.10.

---

*A **separately derived ac system** as defined in the NEC per Section 250-5, "Alternating-Current Circuits and Systems to be Grounded," Paragraph (d), "Separately Derived Systems."

†The worst combination appears to be with two similarly rated ferroresonant transformers working one-on-one with each other. An example is where one is internal to an electronic load unit and an external one is attached to and dedicated to that unit to "improve" power quality (see Ref. 4).

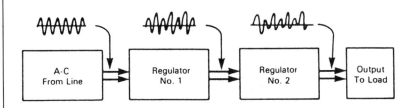

1. This is taken from FIPS-94 and shows a typical problem of interactive instability as commonly exhibited by two similar Line Voltage Regulating (LVR) transformers that are effectively in series with one another.

2. The problem is most pronounced if the two LVRs are of ferro-resonant design. Other factors included in determining the instability of the configuration are the relative sizes (i.e., kVA) of the LVRs and the time-constant of the regulation response time.

3. When the two LVRs are of equal kVA and when both have nearly identical regulation response times, the indicated instability will be most pronounced and can result in virtual "flip-flopping" of the outputs. This can actually be heard by the ear as a loud, rising and falling "humming" sound.

4. At other times the indicated configuration may not be so unstable as to constantly interact in oscillatory fashion, but will intermittently (randomly) experience an instability excursion under certain conditons of line, load and response. These are difficult problems to identify if one is not alert to the foregoing possibility. Most often such conditons are misread to be ac power source problems in the building and are not readily identified as LVR instability problems.

5. The most common circumstances encountered relating to this instability problem are where a well-meaning person has "dedicated" a small LVR to one unit of load equipment in an attempt to provide it "better ac power." Oftentimes, this also occurs because the LVR salesperson does not have available, or does not think that a single, large LVR can be sold at the site. As a result, the small, individual LVR is installed on a unit level with its associated high probability of interaction.

6. LVRs of dissimilar regulating technology are least afffected when placed in series as a general rule. Hence, a ferro-resonant unit and an electronic tap-changing LVR are generally compatible and don't cause these problems.

7. One must therefore, always check to see what kind of voltage regulation is in use within the electronic load unit before dedicating any external LVR to that unit.

Figure 8.10—Voltage Regulator Instability Due to Interaction

Slower LVRs are therefore often better choices than fast ones so long as they can complete the task of correction within a few cycles. During the period of correction, the load's internal power supplies will bridge the gap, and the fans and other motors will not noticeably react in an undesirable manner. Speed is therefore not that important and may actually be a problem.

8.3.2.3 Line Voltage Regulator Internal Impedance

Since the LVR is a smaller ac supply source than the serving public utility, it may be expected to possess a higher output bus impedance and will therefore be susceptible to load-source interaction problems and may also not be able to effectively clear faults. The specification of this parameter is therefore of some real importance.

8.3.2.4 Common Types of Line Voltage Regulators

Some commonly encountered forms of LVRs are discussed in the following paragraphs.

8.3.2.4.1 Ferroresonant Types

The typical ferroresonant transformer in use today is configured around an isolation transformer form and by itself can provide the recommended electrical isolation needed to create the needed **separately derived ac system (SDS)**.

The ferroresonant transformer does provide a high degree of noise reduction in both the normal and common modes. In some cases, the reduction is exceptional. However, there are disadvantages to the ferroresonant transformer which are related to this performance benefit. Two of the principal disadvantages are low efficiency (especially at partial load) and an inherent inability to provide large amounts of peak or fault current to the connected load.*

---

*Manufacturers of the ferroresonant transformer often portray this as an advantage in that the transformer may have its output short circuited, and all that will happen is that the voltage will go down and the transformer will hum a little louder. This is not an advantage, however, it is a serious disadvantage in almost all applications that require a high peak current or need to operate overcurrent devices so as to clear faults and remove hazardous potentials from the faulted circuits (see Ref. 4).

Typical **current limiting** points where the ferroresonant transformer cannot continue to supply current into the load are in the range of 125 to 150 percent of its full (100 percent) output rating. This is often too little current to support some electronic load equipment's peak current demands without the ac voltage waveform becoming severely distorted (**flat-topping** or even collapsing) due to the inherent current limiting characteristics of the device. Unwanted load-source interaction is the result of this condition due to the normally high internal impedance of the ferroresonant transformer.

Unless the design of the ferroresonant transformer is such that it has a compensating winding, it will produce a quasi-square wave output. This is not suitable for many forms of loads, and they may overheat. Compensated units produce a quasi-sine wave output which is generally suited for almost all loads.

Three-phase ferroresonant transformer designs which consist of banked 1 ϕ units are generally not well suited for application on 3 ϕ, wye-connected circuits using the neutral as a current-carrying conductor and where there is any appreciable unbalanced load. Under these conditions, the line voltage regulation is often unstable, and the output voltage unacceptably varies as a result of the instability. Direct current on the neutral line from direct connected rectifier loads may also contribute to core saturation in the transformer bank with attendant problems from overheating and improper output voltage.

The ferroresonant transformer is very reliable as it contains no parts which wear out with the exception of an ac capacitor and the internal insulation systems. Proper selection of the capacitor and good cooling of the transformer will allow long-term reliable operation.

8.3.2.4.2 Magnetic Synthesizer Types

Magnetic synthesizers are significantly improved ferroresonant transformers and are specifically noted for their ability to properly support most balanced and unbalanced wye-connected 1 ϕ and 3 ϕ loads. However, the term **magnetic synthesizer** appears to be primarily a marketing-derived term and therefore may not be indicative of a truly new technology.

The magnetic synthesizer is capable of supplying overload and fault current in the range of up to 300 percent of the unit's full-load

(100 percent) rating. This is about 2 to 2.5 times better than for the standard ferroresonant transformer. Although this appears to be a dramatic improvement in output current capability, it is often still not enough to properly clear some fault conditions or to supply the required peak or starting surge current required by some electronic load equipment.

The magnetic synthesizer generally contains a large number of ac capacitors which are required by its design. These capacitors may be prone to failure due to the waveforms imposed upon them, and this may reduce the reliability of the design over the long term. This could be a problem in some cases unless continuing preventive maintenance is carried out to locate and replace marginal and failed capacitors prior to overall unit failure.

In other respects, the magnetic synthesizer may be viewed as being much the same as the previously described standard ferroresonant transformer.

8.3.2.4.3 Electronic Tap-Changing Transformers

The electronic tap-changing transformer is an LVR based upon a transformer* which is equipped with a number of primary or secondary winding taps, each of which may be selected in no-break fashion by means of an electronic switch. In general, tapped-primary designs are preferred over the tapped-secondary designs when the transformer is used in a **voltage step-down** application because this reduces the amount of current that the switching elements are called upon to handle. This becomes very important in designs above a few tens of volt amps. Switching designs based upon SCRs, triacs or transistors are available.

The employed switch is synchronized to the zero-crossing point of either the voltage or current waveform.† A feedback loop pro-

---

*Both auto-transformer and isolating transformer designs are available with the isolating types being recommended design so that a separately derived ac system (SDS) may be created on the output of the unit.

†Current-crossing synchronization is strongly recommended over voltage crossing as switching transients are often produced by the voltage crossing designs when working into some types of loads, particularly those with a poor **power factor** (see Ref. 4).

vides for switching on the next zero-crossing point in either tap direction, based upon the error signal.* Full regulation is generally achieved in one to three cycles with steps on the order of 2 to 3 percent of the nominally rated voltage being common. During correction, the internal voltage regulating power supplies within the electronic load equipment normally compensate for the variation which is basically sinusoidal and of an rms nature. Other internal loads such as motors and fans are not generally affected by the short-term rms variation in line voltage during the correction period.

The electronic tap-changing transformer offers a low output impedance of 4 to 6 %Z or so, which is comparable to a typical isolation transformer. This is a feature which makes it very suitable for the support of switched mode power supply based loads, or loads which require large amounts of starting surge or peak current. Most all faults are quickly cleared, and overcurrent devices are promptly opened as a result of this benefit. It is also one of the most efficient forms of power conditioning equipment with efficiencies near 96 to 97 percent (25 percent to full-load) being available from some vendors.

Support of all forms of combined 1 ϕ and 3 ϕ loads by the electronic tap-changing transformer is possible when it is based upon a three-legged core design† as opposed to non-recommended banked 1 ϕ units. Independent regulation of each output phase is normal with the design, and some tolerance to dc being returned on the neutral line is achieved as well.‡

Electronic tap-changing transformers are somewhat susceptible to damage to the active switching elements from ac line-conducted switching or lightning transient voltages. As a result of this, the better-designed units include effective lightning and transient voltage protection in the form of filtering and supplemental impulse and surge current diverters. These are typically installed within the tap-changing LVR and are performance matched to the units by

---

*Hysteresis** is now commonly used to avoid the past problem on some designs where the switches would oscillate between two taps because of a sensing condition where the error voltage was just between setting points (often called **tap dancing**).

†This is the only recommended transformer configuration for 3 ϕ designs (see Ref. 4).

‡This is a problem when the load consists of several 1 ϕ power supplies which have rectifiers connected from line to neutral. Return current on the neutral under these conditions typically contains a dc component which can easily saturate a single core in a banked transformer based design (see Ref. 4).

their OEMs. With this internal protection the electronic tap-changing transformer becomes very reliable, and the supported loads also receive the same benefit from the internal filtering and supplemental impulse and surge current diverters as does the tap-changer itself.

8.3.2.5 Motor-Alternator Sets and Uninterruptible Power Supply Systems Acting as Line Voltage Regulators

These devices also contain the inherent ability to provide an LVR function to their connected loads due to the presence of an internal voltage regulator and control-feedback system. This beneficial function is best realized if they are placed close to their served loads. However, if they are remotely located from their served loads and there is significant impedance in the intervening supply line conductor system (i.e., a branch circuit or a feeder), an additional **downstream** and load-end placed LVR may be required to achieve proper voltage regulation at the load.

8.3.3 Motor-Alternator Sets

The **motor-alternator (MA)** set consists of a motor and an alternator which are mechanically coupled by a shaft, gear or drive belt and pulley arrangement. The mechanical coupling ensures that total electrical isolation exists between the input and the output circuits except through the required ac system safety grounding connections which are required by the NEC.* The output of the MA set is generally configured as a separately derived ac system per the NEC's definition.

The MA set provides for the electromechanical equivalent of an electronic or electromagnetic-based LVR. However, with the MA set there is also the valuable addition of a **ride-through** period which becomes available upon loss of input power to the drive motor.

---

*The metallic systems in the building such as conduit, raceways, wireways, ESGCs (green wires), structural steel, etc. are all **shared** by each electrical system and all of the load equipment in the building. This is required by the NEC for electrical safety and does not normally pose any **real** problems to the reduction and control of common-mode noise currents which may be effectively dealt with by other means (so long as the means are within NEC guidelines).

It is the result of releasing stored, inertial energy in the MA set's rotating masses. In this design, short-term uninterruptible power is made available by converting **kinetic energy (KE)** contained in a rotating mass to electric energy:

$$KE = \frac{(WK^2)\ (r/min)^2}{(3.23 \times 10^6)} \tag{8.3}$$

where,

W = weight in pounds
K = radius of gyration in feet
(r/min) = revolutions per minute

Some designs employ flywheels to increase this available stored energy (WK^2) and can provide a longer **ride-through** than would otherwise be possible. Other designs increase the rotational speed of the rotating mass to accomplish the same thing. Typical useful ride-through periods are from 100 to 500 ms (6 to 30 cycles at 60 Hz), depending upon the design.

The MA set is a small and independent ac power source compared to the serving utility on the building. As a result, it often cannot supply large amounts of peak, inrush or fault current to loads or to short circuits.

The output current available from the MA set is generally limited as a function of the internal impedance of the alternator. In most designs, this amounts to an internal impedance for a single unit in the range of from 15 %Z to 30 %Z as seen by its effect on load-induced transient voltages on the output.* This is about 3 to 6 times the internal percent impedance available from an isolation or electronic tap-changing transformer, which typically may have about a 5 %Z.† As a result, there may be load-source induced transients produced, typically ranging from 3 to 6 times the magnitude available from the transformer. Also, typically available fault current may be from 3 to 6 times less as compared to the same transformer.

---

*MA sets may be paralleled for increased output and a lower bus impedance. Therefore, paralleled units may be capable of providing significant peak, surge and fault current to the connected loads. This is a two-edged sword, however, as the removal of one or more **redundant** MA sets from the bus may then increase the impedance of the bus to the point that load-source interaction may be a problem and available fault current may be too low to promptly clear short-circuits.

†Which will produce available fault current no more than 20 times the full-load current rating of the transformer.

The voltage regulator and exciter characteristics affect the stability of the output from the alternator. Stability of the nominal output voltage level is therefore highly dependent upon the application of a properly applied regulator and exciter which will respond rapidly to transient effects and which will furnish a high degree of field-forcing for the alternator.[10] Generally, the modern solid-state voltage regulator and static exciter are highly recommended as being suitable for this type of service as compared to the older types. Care must be used to ensure that compatibility exists between the voltage regulator and the exciter, however, as a mismatch between these items can produce nominal voltage instability and create serious problems between the ac source and the load(s).[10]

8.3.3.1 Commonly Available Drive Motor Types

Two ac drive motor types are commonly available: induction and synchronous. Of the two, the induction motor is less costly, is easier to start and restart and is more readily available (if it is a separate motor from the alternator). However, the synchronous motor provides a better **power factor** to the line and is slightly more efficient than the induction motor.

Induction motor based designs using 1:1 ratio mechanical coupling between the motor and the alternator will produce an output frequency which is less than the input. This is because of the **slip** that induction motors inherently possess. As a result, an input of 60 Hz generally produces an output from around 59.5 to 59.7 Hz, depending upon the motor's design, the input voltage and the output loading on the unit. This may not be a satisfactory range of frequencies for some electronic load equipment, especially if the MA set goes on **ride-through** and the rotational speed's decay further reduces the output frequency.

Synchronous motor based designs typically use 1:1 ratio mechanical coupling between the motor and the alternator and will produce an output frequency that is the same as the input frequency. However, there will also be a percent-load-related output phase shift and this means that input and output voltage waveform zero-crossings will not coincide. On ride-through, this 1:1 drive ratio permits a slightly higher starting point from which to decay than in the case of an induction motor based design.

8.3.3.2 Effects of Driving Ratios Other Than 1:1

The alternate use of drive coupling methods which are not of a 1:1 ratio allows the alternator to be spun at a higher rpm than the drive motor. This may be used to create a 60 Hz output from an induction motor based MA set.

Another very useful configuration is where the motor is allowed to rotate at a much higher rpm than the alternator, and the motor is equipped with a flywheel. In this configuration, three important benefits are realized:

1. The output frequency may be set a little higher than 60 Hz (to about 60.5 Hz), and this allows more rotational decay to occur before the frequency goes out of the acceptable range.
2. More stored mechanical energy may be obtained from a smaller flywheel spinning at the higher rpm, so that more useful ride-through time is made available.
3. An induction motor may be used instead of a more expensive and difficult to start/restart synchronous motor.

8.3.3.3 Slew Rate and Frequency Decay

The rate of frequency change (the **slew rate**) for an MA set operating on ride-through or being restarted during the ride-through period is very important as some electronic load equipment is sensitive to this parameter. A slew rate in excess of about 1 Hz/s is generally considered to be in the trouble area. Some frequency-sensitive equipment may require a slew rate not in excess of about 0.5 Hz/s, and this worst-case load requirement will then dictate the design of the whole system.[4] Some representative frequency-decay and slew-rate curves are shown in Fig. 8.11.

Lightly loaded MA sets will frequency decay (slew) more slowly than heavily loaded ones, but will reaccelerate (slew) faster during a restart. This latter condition could be a problem on a lightly loaded unit. Those MA sets equipped with flywheels generally have better overall slew-rate characteristics than those without flywheels.

When using an MA set, the ability of the unit to restart after a momentary loss of input power is critical in maintaining uninter-

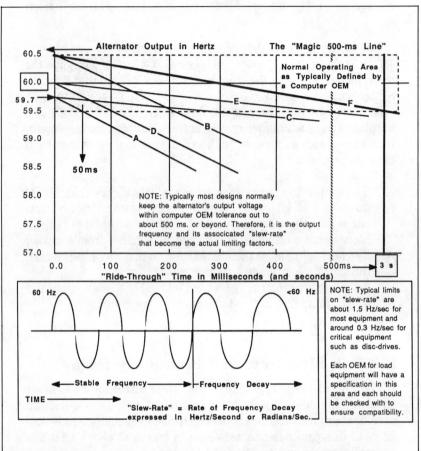

A. Straight shaft-driven by induction motor, no flywheel and 100% loading.

B. Step-up RPM belt-driven by induction motor, no flywheel, and 100% loading.

C. Straight shaft-driven by induction motor, with flywheel and 100% loading.

D. Straight shaft-driven by synchronous motor, with no flywheel and 100% loading.

E. Straight shaft-driven by synchronous motor, with flywheel and 100% loading

F. Step-up RPM belt-driven by induction or synchronous motor, with flywheel and 100% loading.

NOTES: The 500 ms line is the typical OEM specification desired by the computer manufacturer and which the MA set OEM must try to meet for "ride-through" purposes.

With partial loading the available "ride-through" time is extended dramatically in both the frequency decay and voltage output areas. With partial loading, motor restart operations are also more "forgiving" and also more dependable.

These curves are approximate and have been obtained from a variety of OEM sources, each with a competitive posture in relation to some of the others. No definitive tests of various units is known to have been published to date. Therefore, the performance available from individual vendors may be seen to vary from what is shown.

Figure 8.11—Typical MA Set Slew Rates and Ride-Through

rupted output. Therefore, the starting/restarting inrush current requirements for the MA set must be carefully matched to the design of the ac system used to supply it under all conditions of operation. If this is not done, the MA set may simply be disconnected from the line by operation of an overcurrent device in the motor circuit, and the unit will simply spin down to a full stop.

8.3.3.4 Typical Efficiencies

The electrical efficiency of a typical MA set is on a curve with percent load dictating the efficiency range (assuming a nominal input voltage). Some typical efficiencies for different ratings of units are shown in Fig. 8.12.

8.3.3.5 Input-Output Phase Synchronization

The MA set's output normally cannot be **continually** phase synchronized with its input because of an inherent difference in phasing between input and output. This may be also be because of the slippage caused by an induction motor drive or increased alternator rpm from a gear or belt drive. However, designs (principally induction motor based) are available where zero-crossing synchronism may be obtained several times per minute between the input and output. It is during these times that a synchronous, **no-break transfer** may be made for the load between the output of the alternator and the input power source to the motor. Several cycles may elapse over the period of switching, so it is not instantaneous. Such a transfer is generally for maintenance bypassing purposes and typically is manually initiated.

8.3.3.6 General Comments on Reliability

The modern MA set is extremely reliable and, if packaged in an acoustic enclosure, will not produce significant audible noise. Modern bearing and rotor designs have also reduced vibration to virtually unnoticeable levels. Such well packaged designs are now typically installed within the room housing the electronic load equipment and are not required to be located in separate mechanical rooms (Fig. 8.13).

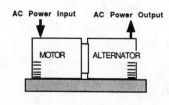

kVA RATING	% of Full-Load		
	50%	75%	100%
12.5 - 18.75	75	77	80
23 - 37.5	76	78	82
50 - 75	80	82	87
94 - 156	85	88	90
219 and Higher	87	90	92

Typically Expected Relative Efficiency of Synchronous-Motor Drive and No Flywheel

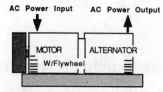

kVA RATING	% of Full-Load		
	50%	75%	100%
30	80	83	82
125	85	88	87

Typically Expected Relative Efficiency of Induction-Motor Drive With Matched Flywheel

AC Power Input

MOTOR W/Flywheel

AC Power Output ALTERNATOR Belt-Drive Typical is Step-Up RPM

kVA RATING	% of Full-Load		
	50%	75%	100%
18.7	81.6	82.3	83.1
30	82.3	83	83.7
50	85.2	86	86.7
75	86.1	86.9	87.6
125	87.8	88.6	89.3
187	87.3	88	88.8
237	88	88.8	89.5
312	89	89.8	90.5

Typically Expected Relative Efficiency of Step-Up Belt Drive With Matched Flywheel

1. These are typical operating efficiencies as have been taken from a variety of OEM sources. Actual performance may vary between manufacturers of similar items.

2. No definitive curves of loading vs. efficiency are known to have been published so all data is representative of particular OEMs and products. Therefore, actual efficiencies may even vary if the equipment is tested under "neutral" conditions and to a standard means of evaluation. Not all vendors respond to inquiries.

3. There are several variations on the belt-driven design which are not shown. Each will possess unique characteristics.

Figure 8.12—Typical Motor Alternator Efficiency

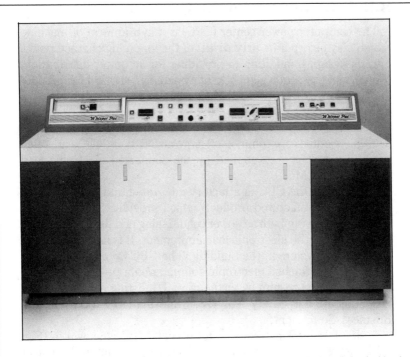

1. This is a photo of a large MA set that has been specially packaged for installation inside of a computer room as opposed to being installed in a mechanical equipment room, etc.

2. New packaging techniques and mechanical design improvements on the MA set itself, have enabled the current crop of designs to be installed within the computer room without adding significantly to audible noise and vibration levels. Some are so "quiet" that they cannot be heard in operátion while standing within about a foot of them in a normal computer room.

3. Being able to position the MA set in the computer room is an important performance advantage over remotely located units. For example, the MA set may be fed from a higher voltage feeder .(i.e., 480 v) for better efficiency and lower losses, etc. It may also be located directly on the sar..e Zero Signal Reference Strucure (ZSRS) used for the electronic system and will thereby provide superior common-mode "noise" rejection without the need for an interfacing isolation transformer between a remoted MA set and the electronic loads. Also, the length of the ac wiring between the MA set and the ac distribution panelboards may be significantly reduced by not having a remotely located MA set.

4. Placing the ac power conditoning equipment in the computer room also enhances site security as the power conditoning equipment itself is in the most secure area and is not exposed to tampering.

5. An MA set such as the one shown may be obtained for the purpose of interfacing to a CPC which in turn, is used to effect the actual ac power and grounding interface to the computer load equipment. This keeps the MA set and CPC functions separate (sometimes advantageous).

Figure 8.13—Typical Large MA Set in Computer Room Package

8.3.4 Computer Power Centers

The computer power center (CPC) is a hybrid form of machine which may incorporate **any or all** of the foregoing characteristics into its design in addition to providing for ac power distribution, overcurrent protection and both safety and many critical HF grounding functions. A representative example of a CPC in the range of about 75 to 150 kVA, is shown in Fig. 8.14. Sizes range from a little less than 1 kVA (see Fig. 8.15) to about 300 kVA per module. Multiple modules are common on large installations. CPCs are often recommended or are supplied by the connected electronic load equipment OEM.

Specifically, the CPC is a factory-integrated and preassembled system (a manufactured product) which provides for a UL-listed means of achieving both ac power conditioning and flexible ac power distribution to the electronic load equipment. It is not a part of the fixed wiring system in the building. The CPC is considered to be a part of the attached electronic computer/data processing equipment (EC/DPE) system by virtue of its UL listing category under UL Standard for Safety No. 478, "Information Processing and Business Equipment."

A simplified wiring diagram for a basic CPC is shown in (Fig. 8.16). More complex versions are frequently encountered, some of which contain very sophisticated but optional **control packages**. The optional features in these packages provide for electrical metering functions of all types, malfunction and warning alarm reporting and may even involve sophisticated electronic local and remote control systems. Some designs provide for electronic monitoring systems which are the full (but proprietary) equivalent of a **power line analyzer (PLA)**.

The CPC is highly recommended as the **basic** means for interfacing electronic load equipment to the intended ac supply and the associated HF grounding structure (a ZSRS) in the building.[4] Its use is heavily supported by several mainframe OEMs in the EC/DPE business, and there are several independent vendors.

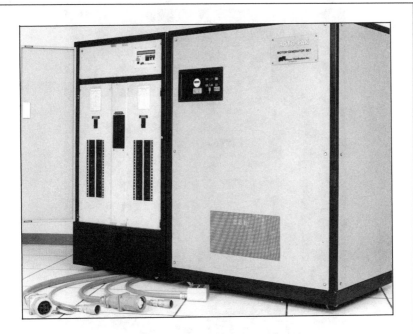

1.   This is an oblique frontal view of a large Computer Power Center (CPC) which is listed by U.L. to Standard for Safety No. 478 (i.e., for Computer Equipment).

2.   This CPC is additionally equipped with a Motor-Alternator (MA) set in the right-hand enclosure. It is of the belt-driven, flywheel, high-speed variety. The left-hand enclosure contains an isolation transformer and overcurrent devices as shown. Instrumentation is provided in the upper panel and can become very extensive.

3.   The input to the isolation transformer is protected by the large circuit breaker in the center of the panel in the left-hand enclosure. The other circuit breakers protect the output circuits which are shown in representative form just below the the unit.

4.   Each output circuit is constructed in a water-resistant fashion using plastic covered liquid-tight flexible metal conduit for the cable portion of the circuit. These are classed as interconnecting cables by the NEC and are not branch circuits. Therefore, they may be installed in the same manner as any computer interconnecting cable may be on a given site. They are not required to be secured in place or otherwise anchored. Large numbers of these cables are available on a single unit and they may be of lengths in excess of 100 ft.

5.   Some CPCs of this general form may be equipped with synchronized transfer switching circuits that allow the output to be transferred between the MA set and "raw" utility power interfaced via the isolation transformer. The isolation transformer is not normally on-line to the load(s) while the MA set is providing the load(s) with power.

6.   Single-bay CPCs are available if an MA set is not required. Automatic voltage regulation is available on transformer-only based designs. The most popular appears to be electronic synchronous tap switching in nature.

Figure 8.14—Typical Large Computer Power Center (75 to >200 kVA)

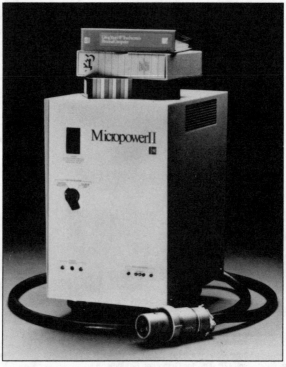

1. This is a frontal view of a small Computer Power Center (CPC) which is listed by U.L. to Standard for Safety No. 478 (i.e., for Computer Equipment).

2. The rear apron (not shown) of the unit is equipped with numerous electrical receptacles for the connection of ac supply cordsets from the equipment to be powered from this unit.

3. Each of the above receptacles is locally equipped with a matching overcurrent device (i.e., a circuit breaker) for protection of each output circuit.

4. Standard NEMA receptacle patterns and electrical configurations are provided as required to mate with the plug on the load equipment's cordset. Non-standard configurations are available on special order, providing that no conflicts arise with the NEC or with U.L.

5. The model shown is a synchronous tap-switching voltage regulating CPC using an isolation transformer equipped with SCR-controlled primary taps for voltage correction. The controls are micro-processor controlled in models from some vendors. Preferred switching is at zero-current crossing and not zero-voltage crossing for reasons of reliability and for elimination of switching "noise."

6. In the shown model, the switch on the front panel is used to bypass the switching elements so that the unit may be operated without automatic voltage regulation.

7. Units are typically equipped with low-pass filters and surge-suppression circuits.

Figure 8.15—Typical Small CPC (1 to 15 kVA)

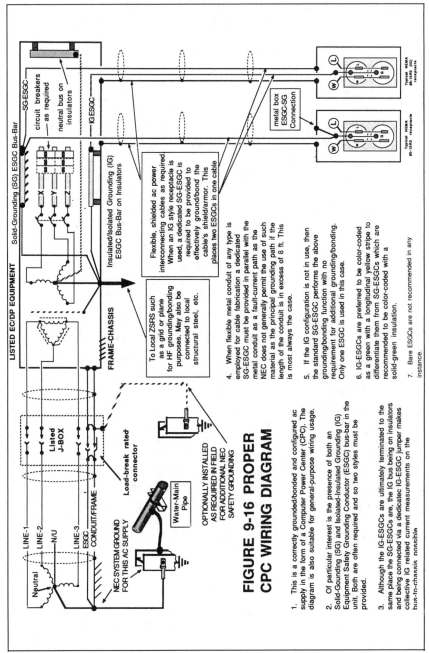

FIGURE 9-16 PROPER
CPC WIRING DIAGRAM

1. This is a correctly grounded/bonded and configured ac supply in the form of a Computer Power Center (CPC). The diagram is also suitable for general-purpose wiring usage.

2. Of particular interest is the presence of both an Solid-Gounding (SG) and Isolated-Insulated Grounding (IG) Equipment Safety Grounding Conductor (ESGC) bus-bar in the unit. Both are often required and so two styles must be provided.

3. Although the IG-ESGCs are ultimately terminated to the same place the SG-ESGCs are, the IG bus being on insulators and being connected via a dedicated IG-ESGC jumper makes collective IG related current measurements on the bus-to-chassis possible.

4. When flexible metal conduit of any type is employed for cable fabrication a dedicated SG-ESGC must be provided in parallel with the metal conduit as a fault-current path as the NEC does not generally permit the use of such material as the principal grounding path if the length of the conduit is in excess of 6 ft. This is most always the case.

5. If the IG configuration is not in use, then the standard SG-ESGC performs the above grounding/bonding function with no requirement for additional grounding/bonding. Only one ESGC is used in this case.

6. IG-ESGCs are preferred to be color-coded as a green with a longitudinal yellow stripe to differentiate them from SG-ESGCs which are recommended to be color-coded with a solid-green insulation.

7. Bare ESGCs are not recommended in any instance.

Figure 8.16—Proper CPC Wiring Diagram

8.47

8.3.4.1 Upgrading the CPC to an Uninterruptible Power Supply System

Some versions of the CPC may be initially obtained or may be **field upgraded** to full UPS status by one of two principal paths:

1. The CPC is initially ordered with UPS capability in the form of an **internal** battery and dc-to-ac static inverter operated MA set (see next paragraph). Battery power is either provided externally or via an adjacent cabinet containing **maintenance free** sealed batteries.
2. The CPC is initially ordered with an internal MA set to which an **external** battery-rectifier, dc-to-ac static inverter and transfer switching arrangement are field connected.

Typically, in either of the foregoing cases, the inverter is offline and only drives the motor when ac power fails. This is discussed further in the next section on UPS units.

Other configurations are possible and practical, but the foregoing are the most likely to be encountered.

8.4 Uninterruptible Power Supplies

A block diagram of a typical UPS is shown in Fig. 8.17. It is shown in simplified form and is therefore generally applicable.

A UPS is a system where there is no interruption of the ac power from its output in the event of a loss of input power, and where this output is maintainable over an extended period of time while the UPS draws operating power from an alternate, backup source.

The typical and generally preferred short-term* backup source for a UPS is a battery. This provides dc to the UPS, which converts it to ac of the proper type. A long-term backup source, generally in the form of an automatically started engine-alternator (EA) set, may be brought on line before the battery is exhausted. The battery is sometimes internal to the UPS† or may be external in a separate battery room. In some cases, a **second backup** utility service may be available, but this is uncommon.

---

*Five min. is about the practical minimum, 15 min. is very common and 30 minutes is preferred. Beyond 30 min., the cost per kVA/min. may become very high, especially in the larger UPS sizes.

†Using the new sealed, maintenance-free battery types which are enclosed either within the UPS cabinet or are placed in a matching one adjacent to it.

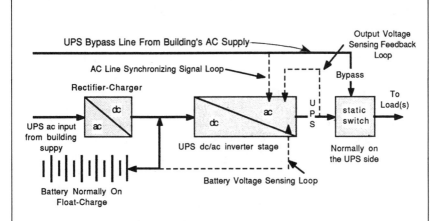

1. A typical and basic Uninterruptible Power Supply (UPS) configuration is shown above.

2. The use of a synchronized ac bypass circuit and a static transfer switch is an important feature of this configuration as it allows no-break switching to occur between the bypass ac supply and the UPS' output at any time.

3. Without the output sensing and feedback loop shown, the UPS' output voltage would decline as a function of declining battery voltage. This problem is eliminated as a practical concern by the shown circuitry.

4. Several designs are available for the inverter and its output. The best ones are those that have along with high efficiency, a low output impedance. A low output impedance permits the support of loads that have high inrush-starting or high-peak current demands.

5. The most modern designs are employing Pulse-Width Modulation (PWM) at a high frequency. The oldest designs employ some form of ferro-resonant transformer as an output stage. The PWM design is generally preferrable in all cases.

6. In the event that the inverter stage is inoperative or cannot support the current demand of the load for any reason, the static bypass switch will operate and connect the load directly to the bypass line. This is generally a direct connection to a utility source of ac and is therefore a "stiff" source (i.e., one of lower impedance) which can generally support such current demands.

7. If the inverter cannot handle the load's current demands under all conditions of operation, and the bypass line is frequently in use for these temporary conditions, then overall system reliability may be suffering for if the bypass line is unavailable for whatever reason, the load will not be properly powered and may fail.

8. If the bypass line is supported by on-site engine-alternator (EA) sets, then the output bus from these EA sets must also be able to support the types of current demands that the utility supported bypass line furnished for normal operation.

Figure 8.17—A Typical Basic UPS Configuration

A UPS is commonly available in two forms: electromechanical (MA set based) or static (in this case, meaning "no moving parts, all electronic").

The electromechanical MA sets generally employ an ac motor for normal operation. They either have a battery-supported dc motor on the same shaft which may be energized upon failure of the ac motor's input supply, or they employ an external, battery supported dc to ac inverter* to which the ac motor may be transferred to during a brief period of inertial ride-through. Restoration of normal operation occurs in reverse to the foregoing procedure once the alternator's output is allowed to **slowly** "walk back" into synchronism with the main ac supply's frequency. The ac supply then normally sees only an ac motor as a load with the battery charger on **float**. After a period of operation on the battery, the ac supply sees only the required charging current which may also be limited by design in some styles of equipment.

Static UPS designs generally employ an online battery rectifier/charger which supplies dc to both the battery (for charging) and to the dc-to-ac solid-state inverter on the output. The battery rectifier/charger must continuously pass the full kVA (including losses and battery recharging current) through itself. At times, this places a heavy demand upon the ac input circuit to the battery rectifier/charger.

As a result of the foregoing conditions, harmonic distortion is often seen on the battery rectifier/charger ac supply circuit (and sometimes the entire ac supply system itself), and this may be a problem to other equipment connected directly to those circuits. This situation is most often encountered on UPS installations of medium (several tens of kilovolt amps) to large sizes (100 kVA and up). Special (and expensive) harmonic filters are often required to correct this problem, although dedicated electrical circuits often can be used to advantage. Sometimes, placing an isolation transformer between the battery rectifier/charger and its ac supply is helpful in reducing the problem.

There are several successful competing designs for the output inverter in the static UPS. Some are better than others in some

---

*This inverter is typically de-energized (i.e., offline), but with its clock kept in synch with the ac line, during normal operation. It is started upon receipt of an ac power failure signal from the MA set and is automatically connected to the ac motor. This decreases operating efficiency losses and may contribute to greater reliability as the inverter is not always running.

ways, and worse in others. The first designs employed a ferror-esonant transformer in the inverter's output. These types are still with us and are successful, especially in the smaller and fractional kilovolt amp ranges. However, the most modern approach is to employ an inverter based upon a high-frequency **pulse-width modulation (PWM)** scheme.

The PWM design appears to provide a greater number of advantages than disadvantages. One of the significant advantages to the PWM process is its ability to provide a usefully lower output impedance and better voltage regulation from the inverter (compared to other designs). This is a very important feature as it permits a greater output current capability under conditions of instantaneous, peak, surge or inrush current demand from the load. It is also of critical importance when fault clearance is required.

All static UPS inverters employ some system of output current limiting. It is either inherent (i.e., using a ferroresonant transformer based design) or achieved by means of electronic feedback circuits. The current-limiting characteristic is required to prevent the solid-state elements in the circuit from being destroyed under conditions of excessive current. This is therefore also a disadvantage when it comes to the UPS's ability to provide large amounts of instantaneous, peak, surge, inrush or fault current to the loads or to clear a short circuit. When these higher currents are required, the static UPS often has no choice but to provide them via its synchronous bypass line, which is discussed in the next paragraph.

Some static UPS designs are equipped with an automatic bypass capability (Fig. 8.18) which allows an instantaneous, synchronous, no-break transfer (sub-cycle) of the load from the UPS output to a zero-crossing synchronized backup source of ac power.* The public utility itself is the typical bypass source most often used. The transfer is initiated manually or automatically at any time it is required. Automatic transfer is used when the UPS itself fails or more peak, surge or inrush current is demanded by the load or a fault than the UPS's inverter output can provide. In this situation, the utility form of bypass can supply all the needed current, provided it is available and has not failed.

---

*The UPS itself is synchronized to the ac line by internal feedback and a backup clocking circuit. It is kept in perfect zero-crossing synchronism with its bypass line at all times except when the utility power returns after being lost. At this time, the UPS must be slowly **walked back in** to synchronism with it and then locked back into it. The frequency **slew rate** during this time is kept low by the design of the feedback circuit.

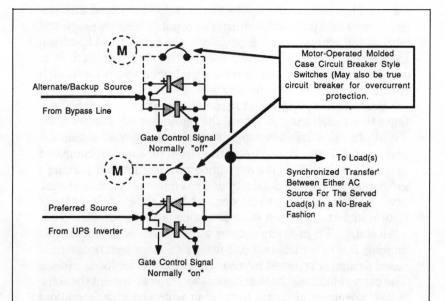

1. The typical static transfer switch is configured as shown using back-to-back pairs of SCRs which are alternately and synchronously switched according to which ac supply is to be connected to the load(s).

2. Typically, both pairs of SCRs are not on at the same time and the two ac supplys are not placed in parallel. In some cases however, a brief paralleling condition may occur on a sub-cycle basis with some designs.

3. If the shown SCRs are capable of handling the full rms current for the load(s) on a continuous basis, then they are the only switching elements used. However, in many designs smaller, less costly SCRs are used which can handle the rms current only for brief periods.

4. When the SCRs are rated as above for "intermittent" duty, then a motor-operated switch is placed in parallel with the SCR pair and the SCRs only need to carry the rms current until this switch is closed at which time the SCRs are gated-off.

5. On a transfer operation, the motor-operated switch is generally "shunt-tripped" into an off/open conditon as a fast way of removing it from the circuit.

6. Designs employing the motor-operated switches almost always have a brief period of paralleling between the two input ac supply sources.

7. This is only one of several possible designs. For example, some UPS inverters are configured in such a way that only one SCR pair is needed (on the bypass line) as they can be electronically switched-off.

Figure 8.18—Typical UPS Static Transfer Switch

UPS equipment may be connected into paralleled configurations (Fig. 8.19) for greater kilovolt amp capability. UPS modules may also be placed into a parallel redundant mode (Fig. 8.20) by adding more modules to the shared bus than are required to support the load, and for providing for automatic removal from the bus of any malfunctioning modules. Isolated redundant configurations are also sometimes required and can be constructed (see Fig. 8.21).

When UPS modules are paralleled onto a common bus, the output impedance of the ac supply thus created is decreased, and the available fault current increases. Under these conditions, there may be no unwanted load-source interaction as the paralleling bus can supply all of the current needed for required peak, surge, inrush and fault clearing. However, if one or more redundant UPS modules are taken offline for whatever reason, this may not remain the case as the bus impedance will have increased, and the available instantaneous current from it will have been decreased. Therefore, interaction problems may not become apparent under conditions of normal operation, and the design may become unreliable under some abnormal (but to be expected) operating conditions.

8.4.1 Special Transfer Switching Grounding Requirements

The UPS is a special form of ac supply system in that it may employ a no-break transfer switching system to allow the connected loads to be operated from either the UPS output or from an alternate, backup source of ac. When the UPS output is ungrounded or is configured so as to not require the use of a neutral/midpoint/common terminal, the required transfer switching does not involve significant grounding/bonding considerations. An example of this latter condition would be the transfer between two delta-connected ac systems which are ungrounded as they exhibit more than 150 V rms to ground and are excepted from grounding by NEC Section 250-5, "Alternating-Current Circuits and Systems to be Grounded." A typical transfer and grounding system for this configuration is shown in (Fig. 8.22).

On the other hand, if the **ac supply pair** is configured as a neutral grounded 3 ϕ wye, or it is a 1 ϕ source with one end or a neutral/midpoint/common terminal connected (i.e., grounded/bonded) to ground, then the situation becomes much more complex, and

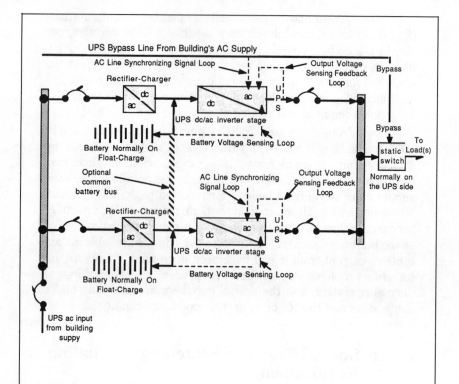

1. The parallel operation of UPS modules is a common practice to achieve a higher kVA or KW rating than would otherwise be available from a single module. Sizes of modules up to about 750 kVA are common and are paralleled as shown.

2. Parallel operation often requires the addition of an external paralleling bus and control unit on the common output of the modules to be paralleled. This takes additional floor space and rewiring of the equipment if the add-on was not pre-planned for.

3. In some cases, UPS modules of different characteristics may be paralleled, but this is a very risky situation which takes significant engineering skill to accomplish in a proper fashion. The general practice is to parallel only compatible UPS modules from the same vendor and product line. This is a very conservative and safe practice.

4. Simple parallel operation may result in some excess UPS output capacity, but less than would be required for redundant operation where either module could support the full connected load. In a simple parallel connection, loss of one module typically means loss of power for the connected loads in general.

Figure 8.19—A Typical Basic UPS Parallel Configuration

8.54

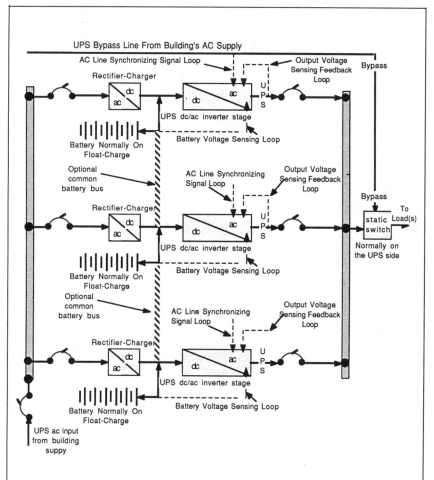

Figure 8.20—A Typical Basic UPS Parallel Configuration

1. Several UPS modules may be paralleled for a redundant configuration where in this case, any two of three modules can support the full load and the third module may be either on-line, or in a "hot-standby" conditon. Some designs feature fast start-up and are in "cold-standby." However, the most common configuration is with all modules on-line and load-sharing.

2. A common dc bus may be employed or dedicated ones may be used. The advantage to the common bus is longer operating time on the battery if one (or more) modules are down. The advantage to isolated/dedicated dc supplys is that a failure on one battery will not affect the other modules on separate batterys.

3. There are other possible configurations.

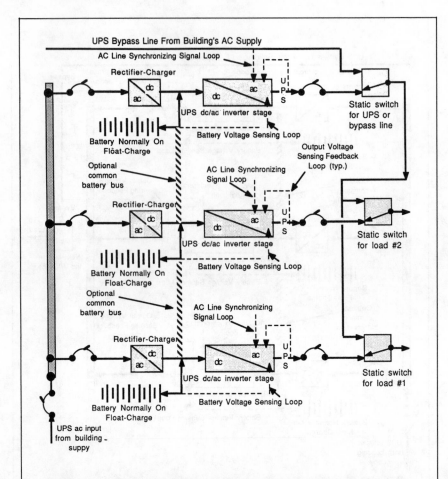

1.   This configuration allows each load to be both "isolated" from the other load while being supported by a UPS backed-up bypass line which will automatically connect if either dedicated UPS "fails" for any reason.

2.   Unless the back-up UPS module is capable of handling the combined loads of #1 and #2, the utility supplied ac bypass line will be the sole back-up in the event that both isolated UPS modules "fail" or are taken off-line for whatever reason.

3.   Many variations on this configuration are possible including making the whole system redundant by the addition of UPS modules cofigured as in previous figure 9-19.

4.   This form of UPS is generally used for loads requiring the utmost in reliability and where short-circuits, etc. on one load are not permitted to affect the other load.

Figure 8.21—A Typical Basic UPS Isoalted Parallel-Redundant Configuration

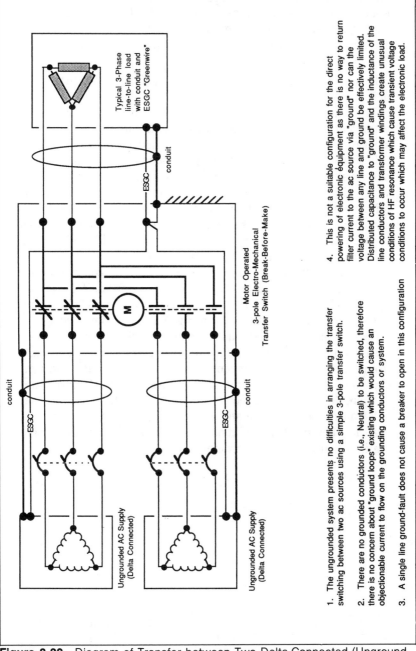

1. The ungrounded system presents no difficulties in arranging the transfer switching between two ac sources using a simple 3-pole transfer switch.

2. There are no grounded conductors (i.e., Neutral) to be switched, therefore there is no concern about "ground loops" existing which would cause an objectionable current to flow on the grounding conductors or system.

3. A single line ground-fault does not cause a breaker to open in this configuration

4. This is not a suitable configuration for the direct powering of electronic equipment as there is no way to return filter current to the ac source via "ground" nor can the voltage between any line and ground be effectively limited. Distributed capacitance to "ground" and the inductance of the line conductors and transformer windings create unusual conditions of HF resonance which cause transient voltage conditions to occur which may affect the electronic load.

Figure 8.22—Diagram of Transfer between Two Delta-Connected (Ungrounded) Systems

8.57

an NEC safety violation may occur if the grounding/bonding is not done properly.* Performance problems with the served electronic load equipment may also accompany the safety problems. A typical transfer and **incorrect** grounding system for this configuration is shown in Fig. 8.23.

In the foregoing "incorrect" example, the existence of more than one grounding/bonding point for the interconnected neutral/midpoint/common terminal pair can be clearly seen along with the unwanted and unsafe flow of **normal operating current** into the safety grounding system that the configuration will produce.

For **no-break** transfer switching between grounded ac systems, one must use a multi-pole, ganged transfer switch (per Fig. 8.24) which simultaneously transfers the neutral/midpoint/common terminal conductor along with the line current carrying conductor switching, otherwise the switching will need to be done using an isolation technique such as the one illustrated in Fig. 8.25. Such an isolation technique is not generally possible with a 1ϕ system operating at 120 V rms and where only two line conductors are available, one of which is the grounded conductor for each ac system. Under the latter condition, the transfer switching and bypassing arrangement shown in Fig. 8.26 is recommended.

Because most electronic load equipment requires clean, sub-cycle, no-break transfer switching for proper operation, the use of electromechanical switching means is typically inadequate, and synchronous, no-break electronic switches are required. Unfortunately, there do not appear to be any electronic switches available that will transfer both the line and neutral/midpoint/common terminal together. This creates conditions where the use of one of the foregoing isolation techniques becomes mandatory.

---

*See NEC Section 250-21, "Objectionable Current Over Grounding Conductors" and Ref. 7, Fig. 64, pp 177, for further information.

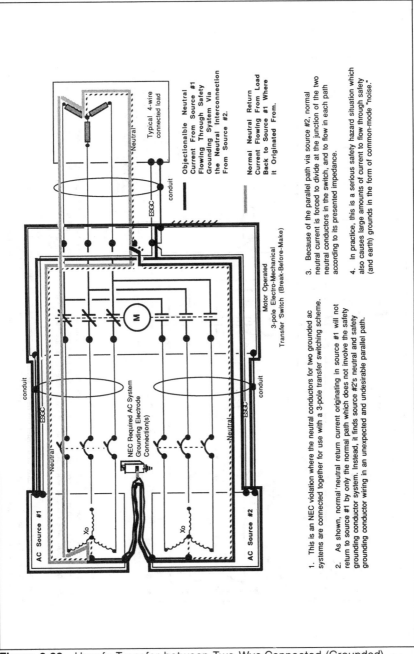

Figure 8.23—Unsafe Transfer between Two Wye-Connected (Grounded) Systems

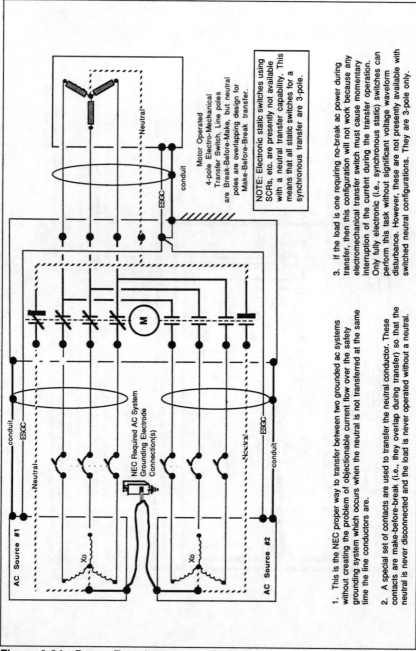

Figure 8.24—Proper Transfer between Two Wye-Connected (Grounded) Systems

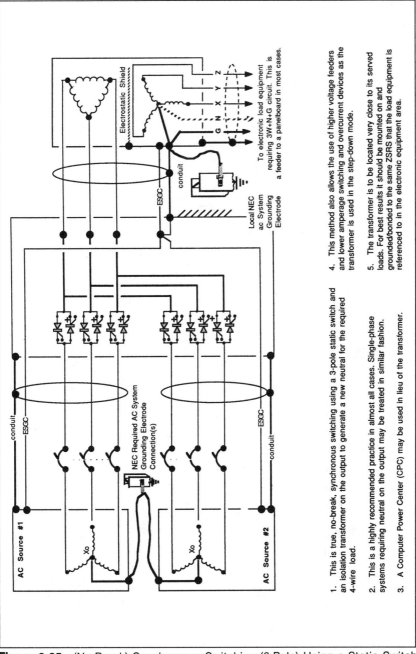

Figure 8.25—(No-Break) Synchronous Switching (3-Pole) Using a Static Switch (4-Wire Out)

8.61

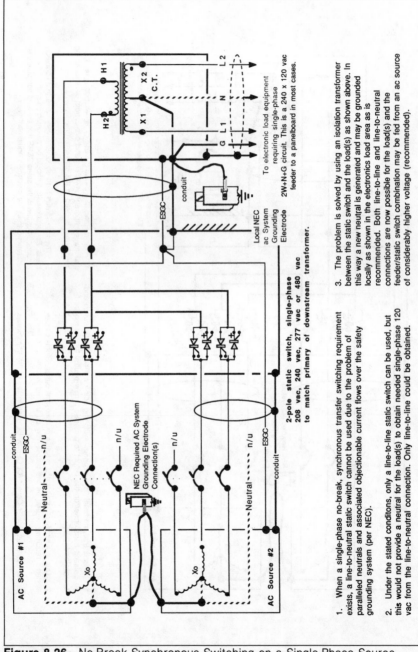

The following text appears around the figure:

2-pole static switch, single-phase 208 vac, 240 vac, 277 vac or 480 vac to match primary of downstream transformer.

To electronic load equipment requiring single-phase 2W+N+G circuit. This is a 240 x 120 vac feeder to a panelboard in most cases.

1. When a single-phase no-break, synchronous transfer switching requirement exists, a line-to-neutral static switch cannot be used due to the problem of paralleled neutrals and associated objectionable current flows over the safety grounding system (per NEC).

2. Under the stated conditions, only a line-to-line static switch can be used, but this would not provide a neutral for the load(s) to obtain needed single-phase 120 vac from the line-to-neutral connection. Only line-to-line could be obtained.

3. The problem is solved by using an isolation transformer between the static switch and the load(s) as shown above. In this way a new neutral is generated and may be grounded locally as shown in the electronics load area as is recommended. Both line-to-line and line-to-neutral connections are now possible for the load(s) and the feeder/static switch combination may be fed from an ac source of considerably higher voltage (recommended).

Figure 8.26—No-Break Synchronous Switching on a Single-Phase Source

8.62

8.5 Summary

The definition of the power line conditioner (PLC) has been seen to be very broad and to include both manufactured products and field-installed components of an individual nature. The true test of a PLC, however is whether or not it is effective in resolving the problem being experienced on the affected electronic load equipment.

A PLC should not be applied to any given situation blindly. Some checking and research should be undertaken prior to committing to the application of any PLC. Competent testing of the ac supply by a good PLA is required to help determine the condition of the ac supply and its effect on the connected electronic load equipment. It is also used to help select the type of PLC (if any) which will be needed.

Selection of the PLA itself is of vital importance. If the test equipment is not proper or if it is not acceptable to all of the principal parties involved in the problem, then it should not be used. Obtain mutually agreed to test equipment of high quality in all cases.

Poor and improper ac supply wiring and grounding plays a major part in causing malfunctions in electronic load equipment. Efforts to verify the correctness of these items and to resolve deficiencies is worth while and may eliminate the need for an expensive PLC. In all cases, the electrical wiring and grounding of all equipment and systems must conform to the actual requirements of the NEC (see Ref. 3) at a minimum.

Electrical isolation of ac supplies and equipment metal frames and enclosures generally is an unsafe practice for most electronic load equipment and is typically not allowed by the NEC.[3] The general rule is to provide solidly grounded and bonded ac supply systems, conduit/raceway/enclosure systems, and for all of the ESGCs (green wires). Connections into any forms of isolated, insulated or dedicated earth grounding electrodes is expressly forbidden by the NEC and is otherwise detrimental to the reliability of the connected electronic load equipment.

High-frequency grounding and bonding requirements for modern electronic load equipment dictate avoidance of the low-frequency and dc only single-point or radial form of grounding/bonding in favor of true, HF multipoint grounding means which generally employ a zero signal reference structure[5] (ZSRS) of a suitable form for system referencing.

Realistically, one should not expect that the application of a PLC will resolve an HF grounding related problem of any kind all by itself. However, if it does **seem** to do so, it may indicate that general or specific problems exist with the grounding system. Even if masked by the PLC, these underlying and now hidden problems must be addressed.

Whatever PLC is chosen to be applied, it generally must possess a sufficiently low internal source impedance (expressed as %Z) to provide for good voltage regulation in response to any load-related step, instantaneous, peak or surge current demands. A low internal power source impedance is also required for proper fault and short-circuit clearing.

The PLC itself may be a source of increased and unwanted harmonic distortion to its own ac input supply's voltage waveform. Alternately, it may have excessive harmonic distortion on its output as a function of its interaction with its connected loads. In both cases it is the high source impedance of the supply circuit interacting with the connected loads that is the general problem.

Excessive harmonic distortion of the ac voltage waveform is generally unwanted and should be minimized so as to avoid the detrimental effects associated with such distortion.

The electronic load equipment itself is susceptible to perturbations on its incoming ac supply. These effects may be generally predicted or actually charted by reference to the **power susceptibility curve** provided in Fig. 8.7. This curve is highly useful in determining what is affecting the electronic load equipment and what type of PLC is or is not required to resolve the problem.

There are several principal forms of PLC. Chief among these are the isolation transformer (along with its recommended enhancements), various forms of LVRs, and full UPS systems. Each has its strong and weak points, and no one item seems to be both fully cost and performance effective as a **general** defense against ac power problems. However, if taken on a case-by-case basis and applied in response to the data plotted on the power susceptibility curve, a PLC may be chosen which is both cost and performance effective in almost any specific cases.

It has been noted that the application of a PLC should not be undertaken lightly and in a manner that does not consider the compatibility of the PLC with its intended loads. This is particulary a problem with the line voltage regulator (LVR). It is sometimes a problem with a motor-alternator (MA) set and with some forms of uninterruptible power supply (UPS), either static or electromechanical.

The use of a computer power center (CPC) is generally recommended as the basic means of interfacing electronic load equipment with its building ac supply and grounding system. The CPC is a replacement for most of the fixed portion of the premises wiring system and may be equipped with internal LVR, MA set or even full UPS capability in addition to its normal function as an isolation transformer based PLC. It is also useful as it provides a flexible wiring method between itself and its connected load equipment. Furthermore, it is a recommended means of interface between the electronic load equipment and any provided HF ZSRS.

The application of full UPS technology is only cost and performance effective if there is the real possibility of a loss of ac supply power to the electronic load equipment and if such a loss and a subsequent system restart and recovery cannot be tolerated. Under these conditions, the UPS is a virtual requirement. Both static and electromechanical based designs are available, and there is apparently no clear-cut performance advantage to either. Both are effective and about equally reliable.

Many otherwise effective UPS installations are rendered less effective or unsafe by improper grounding and bonding of the UPS output to the bypass supply's neutral/midpoint/common terminal and to a subsequent grounding electrode or other common point of reference. Special attention is required to the NEC (Ref. 3) and to other recommended practices in order to avoid this type of problem (Ref. 7).

The subject of power conditioning has been discussed in overview fashion and is much more complex and detailed than a simple examination of this chapter might imply. The following reference and bibliography sections are a recommended place to begin further research into the subject matter.

In all cases, it is not considered to be acceptable in any sense to create or to maintain an electrical safety hazard as a means of attempting to increase the reliability or performance of any connected load equipment. It is mandatory to first meet the legally required safety codes and to then make the equipment work as desired, even if the equipment must be modified to do so.

8.6 References

1. Allen and Segal, IBM Corporation, "Monitoring of Computer Installations for Power Line Disturbances." IEEE Conference Paper C74-199-6. This is a classic informative summary of the magnitudes and frequencies of occurrence on normal mode power source disturbances and outages observed at numerous EDP sites. More recent and more detailed studies have been started by others, with results hopefully to be published in the near future.

2. Goldstein and Speranza, Bell Laboratories, Whippany, NJ, "The Quality of U.S. Commercial AC Power," IEEE International Communications Energy Conference Proceedings, Oct. 3-6, 1982. This provides statistical results of 270 months of data gathering at 24 EDP sites. Data are arranged in tables to show the number of disturbances of various types predicted per year and the improvements expected from several types of power conditioning equipment. As with other surveys, no distinction is made between normal-mode and common-mode disturbances, but data are more recent and in a more useful form for general use. This is a significant piece of work.

3. NFPA-70-1987 (ANSI/NFPA-70), "National Electrical Code," (Boston, MA: National Fire Protection Association). This is the basic code used throughout the United States for wiring commercial and domestic buildings, and with which EDP on-site wiring and grounding must comply. It contains Article 645, "Electronic Computer/Data Processing Equipment," in addition to general requirements for power, grounding conductor wiring and wiring devices and materials. See also ANSI C2-1981.

4. Kalbach and Lewis, Federal Information Processing Standard No. 94 (FIPS-94), "Guideline on Electrical Power for ADP Installations" (Boulder, CO: U.S. Department of Commerce, National Bureau of Standards, 1983). Available from the National Technical Information Service, U.S. Department of Commerce, Springfield, VA 22161. When ordering, refer to: "Federal Information Processing Standard No. 94 (FIPS-PUB-94)." Microfiche is available. Payment may be made by check, money order or NTIS deposit account. it is a landmark document covering many phases of electrical power, grounding (safety and high-frequency), static electricity and site life-safety

considerations. FIPS-94 has become *de facto* standard in the industry.

5. Ziegler, R.M., "Electrical Common Reference for Computer Systems," A Technology and Application Guide (Malvern, PA: Burroughs [UNISYS] Corporation, 1980). The guide contains practical details and a list of electrical hardware suitable for constructing signal reference grids for EDP sites, either by separate conductors or by the use of a typical cellular raised floor's grid structure.

6. NFPA-78-1983, "National Lightning Protection Code," (Boston, MA: National Fire Protection Association). NFPA-78 contains important information relating to the required and recommended means of providing lightning protection for ordinary buildings, miscellaneous structures and special occupancies, heavy-duty stacks and structures containing flammable liquids and gases. This code covers the installation of typical electronic load equipment such as EC/DPE.

7. IEEE Std. 446-1980, "Recommended Practice for Emergency and Standby Power Systems for Industrial and Commercial Applications," (New York: IEEE), known as the "Orange Book". This covers uninterruptible power systems, with pp 57-74 devoted to data processing. It has an important chapter on grounding relating to transfer switching between ac systems (i.e., alternate, backup and bypass circuits).

8. ANSI X4.11-1973, American National Standard, "Operating Supply Voltage and Frequency for Office Machines" (New York: American National Standards Institute). This standard lists the frequency range and one or more voltage ranges for which office machines should be designed, and which installers should verify so the electricity supplied to such machines will comply.

9. ANSI C84.1, American National Standard, "Voltage Ratings for Power Systems and Equipment (60 Hz)" (New York: American National Standards Institute). This lists nominal voltage ratings together with operating tolerances for electric supply and utilization systems, including principal transformer connections and grounding.

10. ANSI/IEEE Std. 399-1980, "IEEE Recommended Practice for Power System Analysis" (New York: IEEE), known as the "Brown Book." This publication contains much useful information on the electrical characteristics of the ac supply and distribution system.

8.7 Bibliography

IEEE Std. 141-1976, "Recommended Practice for Electric Power Distribution for Industrial Plants (New York: IEEE), known as the "Red Book". This publication applies to design of power conditioning equipment and wiring techniques to isolate and protect loads from excessive disturbances and fault conditions.

Ott, Henry W., *Noise Reduction Techniques in Electronic Systems* (New York: John Wiley & Sons, Inc., 1976). This book contains a very good chapter on grounding as it applies to communications and EDP circuits and their interface with power circuits, and is written from a background of Bell Laboratories experience.

Soares, P.E. and Eustace, C., *Grounding Electrical Distribution Systems for Safety*, (Mayne, NJ: March Publishing Company). This 181 page textbook is devoted to the details of grounding in building wiring, with particular emphasis on the return path for ground fault currents. It is well illustrated with diagrams and fully NEC compatible.

UL Standard for Safety No. 478, "Information Processing and Business Equipment" (Underwriters Laboratories: Santa Clara, CA, revised 1986). This standard contains requirements and test specifications for safety of electrically operated units that, separately or assembled in systems, electronically accumulate, process and store data. It applies to listed manufactured products and the conditions for their intended installation and use. It includes ac and dc power conditioning and distribution equipment which is a part of the EC/DPE system, but does not affect such equipment if it is installed as a part of the building wiring system itself.

Index

1

2

3

4

I.4

5

6

8

9

10

Other Books Published by ICT

1. Carstensen, Russell V., *EMI Control in Boats and Ships*, 1979.
2. Denny, Hugh W., *Grounding for Control of EMI*, 1983.
3. Duff, Dr. William G., *A Handbook on Mobile Communications*, 1980.
4. Duff, Dr. William G. and White, Donald R.J., Volume 5, *Electromagnetic Interference Prediction & Analysis Techniques*, 1972.
5. Feher, Dr. Kamilo, *Digital Modulation Techniques in an Interference Environment*, 1977.
6. Gabrielson, Bruce C., *The Aerospace Engineer's Handbook of Lightning Protection*, 1987.
7. Gard, Michael F., *Electromagnetic Interference Control in Medical Electronics*, 1979.
8. Georgopoulos, Dr. Chris J., *Fiber Optics and Optical Isolators*, 1982.
9. Georgopoulos, Dr. Chris J., *Interference Control in Cable and Device Interfaces*, 1987.
10. Ghose, Rabindra N., *EMP Environment and System Hardness Design*, 1983.
11. Hart, William C. and Malone, Edgar W., *Lightning and Lightning Protection*, 1979.
12. Herman, John R., *Electromagnetic Ambients and Man-Made Noise*, 1979.
13. Hill, James S. and White, Donald R.J., Volume 6, *Electromagnetic Interference Specifications, Standards & Regulations*, 1975.
14. Jansky, Donald M., *Spectrum Management Techniques*, 1977.
15. Mardiguian, Michel, *Interference Control in Computers and Microprocessor-Based Equipment*, 1984.
16. Mardiguian, Michel, *Electrostatic Discharge—Understand, Simulate and Fix ESD Problems*, 1985.
17. Mardiguian, Michel, *How to Control Electrical Noise*, 1983.
18. Smith, Albert A., *Coupling of External Electromagnetic Fields to Transmission Lines*, 1986.
19. White, Donald R.J., *A Handbook on Electromagnetic Shielding Materials and Performance*, 1980.
20. White, Donald R.J., *Electrical Filters—Synthesis, Design & Applications*, 1980.
21. White, Donald R.J., *EMI Control in the Design of Printed Circuit Boards and Backplanes*, 1982. (Also available in French.)
22. White, Donald R.J. and Mardiguian, Michel, *EMI Control Methodology & Procedures*, 1985.
23. White, Donald R.J., Volume 1, *Electrical Noise and EMI Specifications*, 1971.
24. White, Donald R.J., Volume 2, *Electromagnetic Interference Test Methods and Procedures*, 1980.
25. White, Donald, R.J., Volume 3, *Electromagnetic Interference Control Methods & Techniques*, 1973.
26. White, Donald R.J., Volume 4, *Electromagnetic Interference Test Instrumentation Systems*, 1980.
27. Duff, William G., and White, Donald R.J., Volume 5, *Prediction and Analysis Techniques*, 1970.
28. White, Donald R.J., Volume 6, *EMI Specifications, Standards and Regulations*, 1973.
29. White, Donald R.J., *Shielding Design Methodology and Procedures*, 1986.
30. *EMC Technology 1982 Anthology*
31. *EMC EXPO Records 1986, 1987, 1988*

All of the books listed above are available for purchase from Interference Control Technologies, Inc., Don White Consultants, Subsidiary, State Route 625, P.O. Box D, Gainesville, Virginia 22065 USA. Telephone: (703) 347-0030; Telex: 89-9165 DWCI GAIV.

EMC Training

Interference Control Technologies, Inc. (ICT) is the premier EMI/EMC and TEMPEST training organization in the world. Founded in 1970 as Don White Consultants, Inc., ICT has educated over 45,000 degreed electronic engineers, technicians, scientists and managers from over 49 countries, representing over 1300 organizations.

All ICT seminars are designed to provide the latest pragmatic insight and methodology to *real-world* interference control and noise suppression issues. Our goal is to equip each student not only with the appropriate theory but with field-tested, proven solutions.

ICT achieves this objective in two ways. First, by providing an instructor who is both a seasoned communicator and a practicing expert in his field. Collectively our staff brings over 600 years of international work experience from diverse industrial, commercial, military and regulatory backgrounds.

Secondly, ICT updates its extensive student handout materials regularly to ensure clarity and relevancy. All students receive a notebook with a copy of every transparency presented, as well as, hardbound handbooks, computer software, an *EMC Technology* magazine subscription and other related materials.

Seminars can be taught in one of seven different languages and are regularly scheduled throughout the Unites States, Europe, the Middle and Far East, South America and Austrailia.

ICT also offers any one of its more than 25 standard seminars as is, or we can tailor any class to meet the clients specific need. These seminars can then be taught at the client's facility and at a time most conducive to the client's schedule.

Course Titles Inclide:

Grounding & Shielding
Practical EMI Fixes
EMC Design & Measurement
Intro to EMI/RFI/EMC
TEMPEST: Design & Measurement
TEMPEST: Facilities Design
Plus 15 other EMI control courses!

—ICT—

EMC Testing

THE MEASURE OF SUCCESS

Electro Service Corporation has assembled a staff of the *Right People*. People with the *need-to-know* to get your product to the marketplace quickly.

Years of work and millions of dollars in development money can go to waste when regulatory delays occur, often because of a simple problem: not knowing the correct regulations and procedures to obtain approvals in the shortest time. ESC can prevent those regulatory delays because we understand the system, inside and out, and guide you through the maze to compliance accecptance.

FULL SERVICE CAPABILITY

ESC will ensure your product gets the careful consideration it deserves. We specilaize in obtaining product approvals from these regulatory agencies:

Canadian Standards Association
Electrical Testing Labs
Canadian Dept. of Communicatons
Dept. of Health & Human Services
Federal Communictions Commission
TUV Rheinland USA
Underwriters Laboratories
Verband Deutscher Elektrotechniker

MEETING YOUR TESTING NEEDS

ESC uses sophisticated testing equipment and procedures, RF screen rooms, test sites, and ground planes to provde RFI/EMI test capabilities from 10 kHz to 60 GHz. ESC can meet your testing needs if you manufacture or market any of the following similar devices:

* Business/Industrial Equipment
* Computers/Computer Peripherials
* Home Appliances
* Industrial Radio Systems
* Multi-Band Receivers
* Office Equipment
* Public Broadcast Receivers
* Radio-Controlled Devices
* Satellite Receivers
* Security Systems
* Telephones/ Auto Dialers
* Transformers
* Transmitters/ Receivers
* Video Games

---

for more information ...

**Electro Service
Corporation
2 Davis Drive
Belmont, CA 94002
415-592-5111**

—ICT—

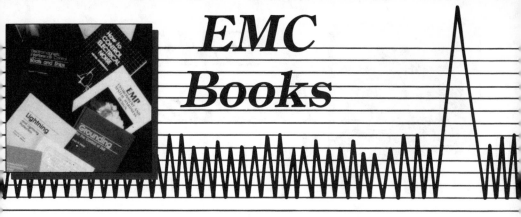

EMC Books

HANDBOOKS

ICT provides over 30 technical handbooks on EMI/EMC and related disciplines. Written by practicing experts in their field each book is designed to go beyond the tutorial by providing the reader with practical applications, illustrative examples as well as tested and proven methodologies. Each book is packed with illustrations, graphs, tables and math models, and is writen in a clear, consise format to assure the reader understanding and immediate use of the material.

GENERAL TITLES AND APPLICATIONS

Electromagnetic Shielding
Electrical Filters
ESD - Understand, Simulate and Fix
EMC Pocket Primer
EMP Environment and System
  Hardness Design
EXPO Symposium Records
How to Contol Electrical Noise
Grounding for the Control of EMI
Lightning and Lightning Protection

SPECIFIC TITLES AND APPLICATIONS

Aerospace Engineers Handbook of Lightning Protection, Coupling of External Electromagnetic Fields to Transmition Lines, EMI Control in Computers and Microprocessor-Based Equipment, EMI Control in the Design of PCBs and Backplanes, Fiber Optics and Optical Isolators.

THE MUST EMI/EMC LIBRARY

(1) EMI Control Methodology and Procedures *and* (2) Shielding Design Methodology and Procedures.

THE EMC SOURCE
(A 12-Volume EMI/EMC Series)

Vol 1 Fundamentals of EMC
Vol 2 Grounding and Bonding
Vol 3 Electromagnetic Shielding
Vol 4 Filters & Power Conditioning
Vol 5 EMC in Components & Devices
Vol 6 EMI Test Methods/Procedures
Vol 7 EMC in Telecommunications
Vol 8 EMI Control Methodology
Vol 9 USA Commercial Standards
Vol 10 Int'l Commercial Standards
Vol 11 USA MIL-STDs Part 1
Vol 12 USA MIL-STDs Part 2

ICT

EMC TECHNOLOGY MAGAZINE

EMC Technology magazine meets the need for up-to-date information and addresses critical noise suppression issues facing the design engineer and his management. Each issue is developed around a central theme covering either new design technology or applications, product and component development, or test and measurement procedures, techniques and equipment.

Each article is written with a pragmatic slant not only to define the problem but also eliminate it. The *must* objective is that each article not only inform but instruct.

Each issue contains a number of supporting *Departments* giving the reader the latest news on *Meetings and Conferences, People, Places and Events, Products and Service, and Standards and Regulations.*

Many issues also include *Hands-on Reports* and product evaluations. Rounding out each issue are thought provoking editorials and *Letters to the Editor*, Special Products, brochure and catalog listings, and an advertising matrix and index created for easy cross referencing of product and service advertisements.

In addition to the six bi-montly issues

EMC Technology also provides two special issues each year. Its annual *Buyers Guide and Sales Directory* provides the reader with alphabetical listings of vendors complete with product description, sales contact, locations and telephone numbers, and a listing of vendors by Product or Service provided. The second special issue is set aside for unique topics requiring in-depth coverage and emphasis.

EMC EXPO

EMC EXPO is an annual international symposium designed solely for the issues of EMI/EMC, Electrical Noise suppression and other relative disciplines. Over 50 papers are presented in 20 technical workshops.

Exhibitors provide hands-on demonstrations as well as free information and literature.

—*ICT*—

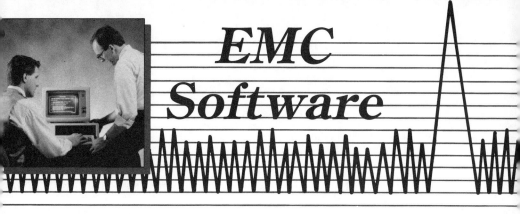

CAE SOFTWARE

These programs will predict and eliminate interference problems during product conceptualization rather than at the more costly prototype or retrofit stages. Tedious calculations now take only minutes displaying with accuracy effects of design criteria supplied by the user.

PROGRAM 5220:
TWO BOX RADIATED EMI SUSCEPTABILITY CONTROL

This program will enable the user to detect and measure radiation susceptability levels from interconnected equipment, ground loops and radiation to/from cables, and common and differential mode sources.

The user is provided with comparative data predicting interference levels with both analog and logic victum sensitivities. Prompters will provide various fix options to help achieve maximim cost savings.

PROGRAM 5300:
BOX RADIATED EMISSION AND CONTROL

This program will enable you to detect and measure applicable radiated emission levels from, printed curcuits, backplanes, chips, and internal cabling.

A composite of radiation levels emanating from the input design are compared against specification limits. Prompters will provide various fix options to help achieve the most economical solution.

PROGRAM 5500:
EMC DESIGN OF BOXES, CASES, CABINETS AND ENCLOSURES

This program enables the user to design shielding housings against specified or synthesized shielding requirements. Selection criteria include type of material used (metals or composites), surface impedance and thickness. Aperature designs are defined and tested, with failures indicated and fix options provided.

All design criteria are combined and overall shielding performance is determined.

ICT–